30p
KT-145-378

PRINCIPLES OF MAGNETIC RESONANCE

PRINCIPLES OF MAGNETIC RESONANCE

WITH EXAMPLES FROM SOLID STATE PHYSICS

Charles P. Slichter

PROFESSOR OF PHYSICS

UNIVERSITY OF ILLINOIS

A HARPER INTERNATIONAL STUDENT REPRINT
jointly published by
HARPER & ROW, New York, Evanston & London
and JOHN WEATHERHILL, INC., Tokyo

This Harper International Student Reprint is an unabridged, photo-offset reproduction of the American edition. It is for sale in Japan by JOHN WEATHERHILL, INC., *50 Ryudo-cho, Azabu, Minato-ku, Tokyo, and in other designated countries by* HARPER & ROW, PUBLISHERS, INCORPORATED, *49 East 33rd Street, New York 16, New York. /* *Copyright © 1963 by Charles P. Slichter. / All rights reserved; no part of this book may be used or reproduced in any manner whatsoever without written permission except in the case of brief quotations embodied in critical articles and reviews. For information write Harper & Row at the address given above. /* *Library of Congress catalog card number 63-11293. / Printed in Japan. / First printing, March, 1964.*

CONTENTS

PREFACE

THE FIELD OF MAGNETIC RESONANCE has grown at a prodigious rate since the first successful experiments were performed in 1946 by Purcell, Pound, and Torrey at Harvard and by Bloch, Hansen, and Packard at Stanford. The problem faced by a beginner today is enormous. If he attempts to read a current article, he often finds that the first paragraph refers to an earlier paper on which the whole article is based, and with which the author naturally assumes familiarity. That reference in turn is based on another, so the hapless student finds himself in a seemingly endless retreat.

I have felt that graduate students or others beginning research in magnetic resonance needed a book which really went into the details of calculations, yet was aimed at the beginner rather than the expert.

As background, I have assumed a standard one year graduate course in quantum mechanics from a text such as those by Schiff, Bohm, or Pauling and Wilson, and knowledge of elements of statistical mechanics, principally familiarity with distribution functions. No real background in solids is needed, though it would probably be useful at one or two places.

I have included a group of problems of widely varying difficulty. Perhaps they will be of interest to people giving a course in quantum mechanics. I have also tried to provide a useful bibliography, the main objective being to keep the length short. The philosophy of selection is explained at greater length in the introduction to the bibliography.

The book is based on a course titled "Magnetic Resonance in Solids," the Morris Loeb Lectures, which I delivered at Harvard in the spring semester of 1961. I wrote the first draft in Cambridge, and the second draft in Urbana during the summer and fall of 1961, when I repeated the lectures at the University of Illinois. The classes at both institutions consisted of physicists and chemists, as well as people working in applied physics. I have made reference to solids in the titles of the book and of the lectures to indicate that I had in mind the application of resonance to the study of various physical problems as an ultimate goal. The book does not attempt to show how to apply resonance. Rather, it is concerned with principles of resonance. But the field of resonance is so vast that it is helpful in selecting topics and examples to keep the applications in mind.

The subject matter of magnetic resonance has been developed by many workers. I did much of the reworking of it presented here in contact with my own graduate students. I presented certain portions in preliminary form at the Summer School on Solid State Physics at the Ècole Normale Superieure in Paris in 1958, but I did the major work of organization, development, and writing in Cambridge, in connection with the Loeb Lectures. In fact, the invitation to give the lectures provided not only the opportunity to do the work but also the impetus to do something which would be a tangible reminder to me of my visit.

I am indebted to various of my colleagues for reading the manuscript and making helpful suggestions for revisions in the first and second drafts. In particular, George Benedek, David Pines, Alfred Redfield, Robert Schumacher, Ronald Tucker, Robert Silsbee, and Edward Purcell have made valuable suggestions. My own graduate students provided great assistance at catching errors in the manuscript since they took the trouble to carry through the details of many of the calculations in the text. The first draft was typed in Cambridge by Mrs. Sally Rand who added this major chore to her other activities with the greatest good grace. The second and third drafts were typed by Mrs. Ann Wells, Mrs. Barbara Fiorillo, Mrs. Deanne Sande, and Miss Joyce Pershing. I am indebted to them for the speed and accuracy with which they turned out the manuscript to be distributed to my class.

C.P.S.

CHAPTER 1

ELEMENTS OF RESONANCE

1·1 INTRODUCTION

Magnetic resonance is a phenomenon found in magnetic systems that possess both magnetic moments and angular momentum. As we shall see, the term *resonance* implies that we are in tune with a natural frequency of the magnetic system, in this case corresponding to the frequency of gyroscopic precession of the magnetic moment in an external static magnetic field. Because of the analogy between the characteristic frequencies of atomic spectra, and because the magnetic resonance frequencies fall typically in the radio frequency region (for nuclear spins) or microwave frequency (for electron spins), we often use the terms *radio frequency* or *microwave spectroscopy*.

The advantage of the resonance method is that it enables one to select out of the total magnetic susceptibility, a particular contribution of interest—one that may, for example, be relatively very weak. The most spectacular example is, no doubt, the observation of the feeble nuclear paramagnetism of iron against a background of the electronic ferromagnetism. Resonance also permits the gathering of precise, highly detailed magnetic information of a type not obtainable in other ways.

One of the reasons for the impact of magnetic resonance on physics is its ability to give information about processes at the atomic level. In this book we seek to give some of the background necessary or useful to the application of magnetic resonance to the study of solids. Most of the book will be concerned with nuclear resonance, but the final chapters will focus on certain problems particularly important for electron spin resonance. Many of the principles developed in the earlier portions are, of course, equally applicable to nuclear or electron magnetic resonance. Our object is not to tell how to apply magnetic resonance to the study of solids. However, the activity in magnetic resonance has proceeded at such a vigorous pace, pouring out so many new concepts and results, that an author or lecturer faces an enormous task in the selection of material. In this book, we shall use the study of solids as a sort of ultimate goal that will help to delineate the topics for discussion and from which we shall attempt to draw most of the concrete examples of the more formal techniques.

As we remarked above, we are concerned with magnetic systems that possess angular momentum. As examples, we have electron spins, or the nuclei of atoms.

A system such as a nucleus may consist of many particles coupled together so that in any given state, the nucleus possesses a total magnetic moment $\boldsymbol{\mu}$ and a total angular momentum $\mathbf{J}$. In fact the two vectors may be taken as parallel, so that we can write

$$\boldsymbol{\mu} = \gamma \mathbf{J} \tag{1}$$

where γ is a scalar called the "gyromagnetic ratio." For any given state of a nucleus, knowledge of the wave function would in principle enable us to compute both $\boldsymbol{\mu}$ and $\mathbf{J}$. Hence we should find that the quantity γ would vary with the state. Such calculations are beyond the scope of this book.

Of course, in the quantum theory, $\boldsymbol{\mu}$ and $\mathbf{J}$ are treated as (vector) operators. The meaning of the concept of two operators being "parallel" is found by considering the matrix elements of the operators. Suppose we define a dimensionless angular momentum operator, $\mathbf{I}$, by the equation:

$$\mathbf{J} = \hbar \mathbf{I} \tag{2}$$

$\mathbf{I}^2$ then has eigenvalues I which are either integer or half-integer. Any component of $\mathbf{I}$ (for example, I_z) commutes with $\mathbf{I}^2$, so that we may specify simultaneously eigenvalues of both $\mathbf{I}^2$ and I_z. Let us call the eigenvalues I and m, respectively. Of course m may be any of the $2I + 1$ values $I, I - 1, \cdots, -I$. The meaning of Eq. (1) is then that

$$(Im|\mu_{x'}|Im') = \gamma\hbar(Im|I_{x'}|Im') \tag{3}$$

where $\mu_{x'}$ and $I_{x'}$ are components of the operators $\boldsymbol{\mu}$ and $\mathbf{I}$ along the (arbitrary) x'-direction. The validity of this equation is based on the Wigner-Eckart theorem, which we shall discuss in Chapter 6.

We shall, for the remainder of this chapter, give a very brief introduction to some of the basic facts of magnetic resonance, introducing most of the major concepts or questions that we shall explore in later chapters.

1·2 SIMPLE RESONANCE THEORY

We shall wish, in later chapters, to consider both quantum mechanical and classical descriptions of magnetic resonance. The classical viewpoint is particularly helpful in discussing dynamic or transient effects. For an introduction to resonance phenomena, however, we consider a simple quantum mechanical description.

The application of a magnetic field $\mathbf{H}$ produces an interaction energy of the nucleus of amount $-\boldsymbol{\mu} \cdot \mathbf{H}$. We have, therefore, a very simple Hamiltonian:

$$\mathcal{H} = -\boldsymbol{\mu} \cdot \mathbf{H} \tag{1}$$

Taking the field to be H_0 along the z-direction, we find

$$\mathcal{H} = -\gamma\hbar H_0 I_z \tag{2}$$

The eigenvalues of this Hamiltonian are simple, being only multiples $(\gamma\hbar H_0)$ of the eigenvalues of I_z. Therefore the allowed energies are

$$E = -\gamma\hbar H_0 m \qquad m = I, I - 1, \cdots, -I \tag{3}$$

They are illustrated in Fig. 1.1 for the case $I = 3/2$, as is the case for the nuclei of Na or Cu. The levels are equally spaced, the distance between adjacent ones being $\gamma\hbar H_0$.

m	
$-3/2$	———
$-1/2$	———
$1/2$	———
$3/2$	———

FIG. 1.1. Energy levels of Eq. (3).

One should hope to be able to detect the presence of such a set of energy levels by some form of spectral absorption. What is needed is to have an interaction that can cause transitions between levels. To satisfy the conservation of energy, the interaction must be time dependent and of such an angular frequency ω that

$$\hbar\omega = \Delta E \tag{4}$$

where ΔE is the energy difference between the initial and final nuclear Zeeman energies. Moreover, the interaction must have a non-vanishing matrix element joining the initial and final states.

The coupling most commonly used to produce magnetic rèsonances is an alternating magnetic field applied perpendicular to the static field. If we write the alternating field in terms of an amplitude H_x^0, we get a perturbing term in the Hamiltonian of

$$\mathcal{H}_{\text{pert}} = -\gamma\hbar H_x^0 I_x \cos \omega t \tag{5}$$

The operator I_x has matrix elements between states m and m', $(m'|I_x|m)$, which vanish unless $m' = m \pm 1$. Consequently the allowed transitions are between levels adjacent in energy, giving

$$\hbar\omega = \Delta E = \gamma\hbar H_0 \tag{6}$$

or

$$\omega = \gamma H_0 \tag{6a}$$

Note that Planck's constant has disappeared from the resonance equation. This fact suggests that the result is closely related to a classical picture. We shall see, in fact, that a classical description also gives Eq. (6a). By studying the two formulations (classical and quantum mechanical), one gains a great deal of added insight.

From Eq. (6a) we can compute the frequency needed to observe a resonance if we know the properties that determine γ. Although such calculations are of basic interest in the theory of nuclear structures, they would take us rather far afield. However, a simple classical picture will enable us to make a correct order-of-magnitude estimate of γ.

Let us compute the magnetic moment and angular momentum of a particle of mass m and charge e moving in a circular path of radius r with period T. The angular momentum is then

$$J = mvr = m\frac{2\pi r^2}{T} \tag{7}$$

while the magnetic moment (treating the system as a current loop of area A carrying current i) is

$$\mu = iA \tag{8}$$

Since $i = (e/c)(1/T)$, we get

$$\mu = \frac{e}{c}\frac{\pi r^2}{T} \tag{9}$$

Comparison of the expressions for μ and J therefore gives us $\gamma = e/2mc$. Besides enabling us to make an order of magnitude estimate of the expected size of γ, for our purposes the important result of this formula is that large masses have low γ's. We expect about a factor of 1,000 lower γ for nuclei than for electrons. In fact, for magnetic fields of 3,000 to 10,000 gauss, electronic systems have a resonance at $\omega/2\pi = 10{,}000$ Mc (the 3 cm microwave region), whereas nuclear systems are typically 10 Mc (a radio frequency). Of course one can always change ω by changing H_0, but in most cases it is advantageous to use as large a magnetic field as possible, since the quanta absorbed are then larger and the resonance is correspondingly stronger.

In later sections, we shall comment somewhat more on typical experimental arrangements.

1·3 ABSORPTION OF ENERGY AND SPIN-LATTICE RELAXATION

We now wish to go a step further to consider what happens if we have a macroscopic sample in which we observe a resonance. For simplicity we consider a system whose nuclei possess spin 1/2 (Fig. 1–2). Since there are many nuclei in our macroscopic sample, we shall specify the number in the two m states $+1/2$ and $-1/2$ by N_+ and N_-, respectively.

$$\begin{array}{ll} -1/2 \;\underline{\hspace{3cm}} & N_- \\ \quad\quad\quad\quad \gamma\hbar H_0 & \\ +1/2 \;\underline{\hspace{3cm}} & N_+ \end{array}$$

FIG. 1.2. Energy levels for $I = \frac{1}{2}$.

The total number of spins, N, is a constant, but application of an alternating field will cause N_+ or N_- to change as a result of the transitions induced. Let us denote the probability per second of inducing the transition of a spin with $m = +1/2$ to a state $m = -1/2$ by $W_{(+)\to(-)}$. We shall denote the reverse transition by $W_{(-)\to(+)}$. We can then write a differential equation for the change of the population N_+.

$$\frac{dN_+}{dt} = N_- W_{(-)\to(+)} - N_+ W_{(+)\to(-)} \tag{1}$$

Without as yet attempting to compute $W_{(+)\to(-)}$ or $W_{(-)\to(+)}$, we note a famous formula from time-dependent perturbation theory for the probability per second, $P_{a\to b}$, that an interaction $V(t)$ induces a transition from a state (a) with energy E_a to a state (b) whose energy is E_b:

$$P_{a\to b} = \frac{2\pi}{\hbar}\,|(b|V|a)|^2\,\delta(E_a - E_b - \hbar\omega) \tag{2}$$

Since $|(a|V|b)|^2 = |(b|V|a)|^2$, we note that $P_{a\to b}$ is the same as the rate $P_{b\to a}$. Such an argument describes many situations and leads to the condition $W_{(+)\to(-)} = W_{(-)\to(+)} \equiv W$.

$$\frac{dN_+}{dt} = W(N_- - N_+) \tag{3}$$

It is convenient to introduce the variable $n = N_+ - N_-$, the difference in population of the two levels. The two variables N_+ and N_- may be replaced by n and N, using the equations

$$\begin{aligned} N &= N_+ + N_- \\ n &= N_+ - N_- \end{aligned} \tag{4}$$

$$\begin{aligned} N_+ &= \tfrac{1}{2}(N + n) \\ N_- &= \tfrac{1}{2}(N - n) \end{aligned} \tag{4a}$$

Substitution of Eq. (4a) into Eq. (3) gives us

$$\frac{dn}{dt} = -2Wn \tag{5}$$

the solution of which is

$$n = n(0)e^{-2Wt} \tag{6}$$

where $n(0)$ is the value of n at $t = 0$. We note that if initially we have a population difference, it will eventually disappear under the action of the induced transitions.

The rate of absorption of energy, dE/dt, is given by computing the number of spins per second that go from the lower energy to the upper, and by subtracting the number that drops down, emitting energy in the process:

$$\frac{dE}{dt} = N_+W\hbar\omega - N_-W\hbar\omega = \hbar\omega Wn \tag{7}$$

Therefore, for a net absorption of energy, n must be non-zero; that is, there must be a population difference. We see that when the upper state is more highly populated than the lower, the net absorption of energy is negative—the system supplies more energy than it receives. This state of affairs is the basis of the oscillators or amplifiers known as *masers* (*m*icrowave *a*mplification by *s*timulated *e*mission of *r*adiation).

We see that if the equations we have put down were complete, the resonant absorption of energy would eventually stop and the resonance would disappear. A more serious difficulty is seen if we assume $W = 0$ (that is, we do not apply the alternating magnetic field). Under these circumstances our equations say that $dN_+/dt = 0$. The populations cannot change. On the other hand, if we applied a static field to a piece of unmagnetized material, we should expect it to become magnetized. The preferential alignment of the nuclear moments parallel to the field corresponds to N_+ being greater than N_-. ($N_- = 0$ would represent perfect polarization, a state we should not expect to find at temperatures above absolute zero.) The process of magnetization of an unmagnetized sample, therefore requires a net number of transitions from the upper to the lower energy state. In the process, the spins give up energy—there is, so to speak, a heat transfer. Therefore there must be some other system to accept the energy. If we ask how big a population difference will eventually be found, the answer must depend upon the willingness of the other system to continue accepting energy. Speaking in thermodynamic terms, the heat flow will continue until the relative populations N_-/N_+ correspond to the temperature T of the reservoir to which the energy is given.

The final equilibrium populations, N_+^0 and N_-^0, are then given by

$$\frac{N_-^0}{N_+^0} = e^{-\Delta E/kT} = e^{-\gamma\hbar H_0/kT} \tag{8}$$

We must postulate, therefore, that there exists a mechanism for inducing transitions between N_+ and N_-, which arises because of the coupling of the spins to some other system. Let us denote the probability per second that such a coupling will induce a spin transition upward in energy (from $+ \to -$) by $W_\uparrow$, and the reverse process by $W_\downarrow$. Then we have a rate equation

$$\frac{dN_+}{dt} = +N_-W_\downarrow - N_+W_\uparrow \tag{9}$$

Let us again introduce the variables N and n; but now we no longer can assume equality of the two transition probabilities, since we know such an assumption would not give the preference for downward transitions, which is necessary for the establishment of the magnetization. In fact, since in the steady-state dN_+/dt is zero, Eq. (9) tells us that

$$\frac{N_-^0}{N_+^0} = \frac{W_\uparrow}{W_\downarrow} \tag{10}$$

By using Eq. (8), we find that the ratio of $W_\downarrow$ to $W_\uparrow$ is not unity but rather is

$$\frac{W_\downarrow}{W_\uparrow} = e^{\gamma\hbar H_0/kT} \tag{10a}$$

It is natural to wonder why the argument given to show the equality of $W_{(+)\to(-)}$ and $W_{(-)\to(+)}$ does not also apply here. The resolution of this paradox is that the thermal transition requires not only a coupling but also another system in an energy state that permits a transition. We can illustrate by assuming that the reservoir has only two levels whose spacing is equal to that of the nuclear system. If the nucleus and reservoir are initially in the states of Fig. 1.3a given by the

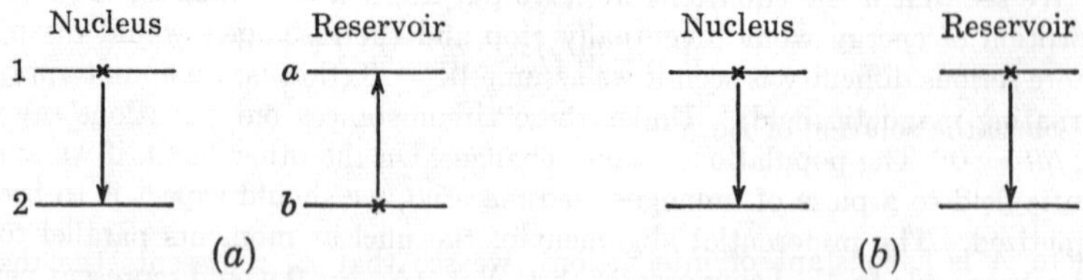

FIG. 1.3. (a) A possible transition. (b) A forbidden transition.

crosses, conservation of energy is satisfied by simultaneous transitions indicated by the arrows. The nucleus may therefore give up energy to the lattice. On the other hand, if both systems are in the upper state (Fig. 1.3b), the simultaneous transition cannot occur because it does not conserve energy. The rate of transition of the nucleus will therefore depend not only on the matrix elements but *also* on the probability that the reservoir will be in a state that permits the transition.

Thus, if we label the nuclear states 1 and 2 with populations N_1 and N_2, and label the lattice states (a) and (b) with populations N_a and N_b, the number of transitions per second, such as shown in Fig. 1.3a, will be

$$\text{number/sec} = N_1 N_b W_{1b\to 2a} \tag{11}$$

where $W_{1b\to 2a}$ is the probability per second of such a transition under the condition that the nucleus is actually in state 1 and the lattice is actually in state (b). The steady-state condition is found by equating the rate of such transitions to the rate of the inverse transition:

$$N_1 N_b W_{1b\to 2a} = N_2 N_a W_{2a\to 1b} \tag{12}$$

Since the quantum theory requires that $W_{1b\to 2a} = W_{2a\to 1b}$, we see that in thermal equilibrium,

$$\frac{N_1}{N_2} = \frac{N_a}{N_b} \tag{13}$$

That is, the nuclear levels will have the same relative populations as do the lattice's. The nuclear population will therefore be in thermal equilibrium with the lattice's. Note, moreover, that for this simple model, we can compute $W_\uparrow$ and $W_\downarrow$:

$$W_\uparrow = N_a W_{2a\to 1b} \qquad W_\downarrow = N_b W_{1b\to 2a} = N_b W_{2a\to 1b} \tag{14}$$

so that $W_\uparrow$ and $W_\downarrow$ are seen to be unequal.

We now leave our special model and return to Eq. (9). By making the substitutions of Eq. (4a) for N_+ and N_-, we find

$$\frac{dn}{dt} = N(W_\downarrow - W_\uparrow) - n(W_\downarrow + W_\uparrow) \tag{15}$$

which can be rewritten as

$$\frac{dn}{dt} = \frac{n_0 - n}{T_1} \tag{16}$$

where

$$n_0 = N\left(\frac{W_\downarrow - W_\uparrow}{W_\downarrow + W_\uparrow}\right) \qquad \frac{1}{T_1} = (W_\downarrow + W_\uparrow) \tag{17}$$

Since the solution of Eq. (16) is

$$n = n_0 + Ae^{-t/T_1} \tag{18}$$

(where A is a constant of integration), we see that n_0 represents the thermal equilibrium population difference, and T_1 is a characteristic time associated with the approach to thermal equilibrium. T_1 is called the "spin-lattice relaxation time." For example, if we deal with a sample that is initially unmagnetized, the magnetization process is described by an exponential rise to the equilibrium:

$$n = n_0(1 - e^{-t/T_1}) \tag{19}$$

That is, T_1 characterizes the time needed to magnetize an unmagnetized sample.

We may now combine the two rate equations for dn/dt, to find the combined transition rate due to both thermal processes and transitions induced by the applied alternating field:

$$\frac{dn}{dt} = -2Wn + \frac{n_0 - n}{T_1} \tag{20}$$

In the steady state, Eq. (20) tells us that

$$n = \frac{n_0}{1 + 2WT_1} \tag{21}$$

Therefore, as long as $2WT_1 \ll 1$, $n = n_0$, and the absorption of energy from the alternating field does not disturb the populations much from their thermal equilibrium values. The rate of absorption of energy dE/dt is given by

$$\frac{dE}{dt} = n\hbar\omega W = n_0\hbar\omega \frac{W}{1 + 2WT_1} \tag{22}$$

We shall see later that W is proportional to the square of the alternating magnetic field. Therefore Eq. (22) tells us that we can increase the power absorbed by the nuclei by increasing the amplitude of the alternating field, as long as $2WT_1 \ll 1$. However, once W is large enough so that $W \sim 1/2T_1$, this statement is no longer true. The power absorbed levels off despite an increase in W. This effect is called "saturation." Provided one has enough information to compute W (a situation often realized), one can measure T_1 by observing the saturation effect.

We have now seen several quantities that will be important in describing a magnetic resonance. The quantity T_1 will clearly be related to the microscopic details of both the nuclear system and the reservoir. We shall wish to consider what mechanisms may give rise to spin-lattice relaxation, and how to compute T_1 for any assumed mechanism. In the early work on nuclear resonance, it was feared that the spin-lattice relaxation might be so slow that a population excess might not be achieved within reasonable times. The famous Dutch physicist C. J. Gorter, who has made so many of the important discoveries and proposals in connection with magnetic relaxation, was the first person to look for a magnetic resonance in bulk matter.† That he failed was probably due to his bad luck in having a sample which was easily saturated because of its long T_1.

When Purcell, Pound, and Torrey†† first looked for a resonance of protons in paraffin, they allowed the nuclei to sit in the magnetic field H_0 for a long time before even attempting a resonance. They used a value of alternating field sufficiently low to allow them time to observe a resonance even though T_1 were many seconds. Their efforts, as with those of Bloch, Hansen, and Packard,§ were made independently of Gorter's.

We have also seen that the rate of absorption is related to the transition rate W. An estimate of the size of the resonance absorption is basic to a decision about whether or not a resonance might be observed. We shall wish to consider how to calculate W. Moreover, since no resonance line is perfectly sharp, we expect that

---

† C. J. Gorter and L. J. F. Broer, *Physica*, **9**: 591 (1942).
†† E. M. Purcell, H. C. Torrey, and R. V. Pound, *Phys. Rev.*, **69**: 37 (1946).
§ F. Bloch, W. W. Hansen, and M. Packard, *Phys. Rev.*, **69**: 127 (1946).

the factors governing the width of the spectral line will be of interest. Closely related is the question of what magnetic field to use in the relation $\omega = \gamma H_0$, for the nuclei are never bare. There will be magnetic fields due to electrons as well as due to other nuclei, which must be added to the external field. These fields produce effects of greatest interest, such as the splitting of the proton resonance of ethyl alcohol (CH_3CH_2OH) into three lines of relative intensities 3:2:1. They are also responsible for the fact that there is a nuclear resonance in ferromagnets even in the absence of an applied static magnetic field.

CHAPTER 2

BASIC THEORY

2·1 MOTION OF ISOLATED SPINS—CLASSICAL TREATMENT

We begin our study of the basic theory with a classical description of the motion of a spin in an external magnetic field **H**, assuming that **H** may possibly vary with time. **H** will produce a torque on the magnetic moment $\boldsymbol{\mu}$ of amount $\boldsymbol{\mu} \times \mathbf{H}$. If we applied a magnetic field to an ordinary bar magnet, mounted with bearings so that it could turn at will, the magnet would attempt to line up along the direction of **H**. If **H** were constant in time and if the bearings were frictionless, the magnet would actually oscillate about the equilibrium direction. If the bearings were not frictionless, the oscillations would die out as the magnet gave up energy to the bearings, until eventually it would be lined up along **H**.

When the magnet also possesses angular momentum, the situation is modified, since it now acts like a gyroscope. As we shall see, in the event of frictionless bearings, the moment would remain at fixed angle with respect to **H** (providing **H** is constant in time), but would precess about it. The conversion of energy back and forth between potential energy and kinetic energy would not occur. It would still be true, however, that if the bearings possessed friction, the magnet would eventually become parallel to a static field **H**. As we shall see, the friction corresponds to relaxation processes such as T_1.

The equation of motion of the magnet is found by equating the torque with the rate of change of angular momentum, **J**.

$$\frac{d\mathbf{J}}{dt} = \boldsymbol{\mu} \times \mathbf{H} \tag{1}$$

Since $\boldsymbol{\mu} = \gamma \mathbf{J}$, we may eliminate **J**, getting

$$\frac{d\boldsymbol{\mu}}{dt} = \boldsymbol{\mu} \times (\gamma \mathbf{H}) \tag{2}$$

This equation, which holds regardless of whether or not **H** is time dependent, tells us that at any instant the changes in $\boldsymbol{\mu}$ are perpendicular to both $\boldsymbol{\mu}$ and **H**. Refer to Fig. 2.1 and consider the tail of the vector $\boldsymbol{\mu}$ as fixed; the tip of the vector is therefore moving out of the paper. The angle θ between $\boldsymbol{\mu}$ and **H** does not change. If **H** is independent of time, the vector $\boldsymbol{\mu}$ therefore generates a cone.

One can proceed with the solution of Eq. (2) by standard methods of differential equations for various assumed time dependences of **H**. We shall find it most useful for our future work, however, to introduce a special technique: the use of a rotating coordinate system.

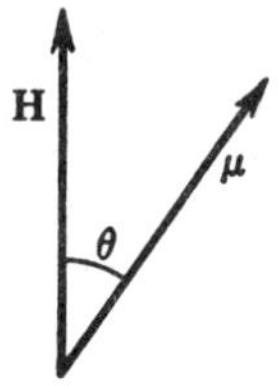

FIG. 2.1. Relation of $\boldsymbol{\mu}$ to **H**.

Consider a vector function of time $\mathbf{F}(t)$, which we may write in terms of its components $F_x(t)$, $F_y(t)$, $F_z(t)$, along a set of rectangular coordinates. In terms of the corresponding unit vectors **i**, **j**, and **k**, we have

$$\mathbf{F} = \mathbf{i}F_x + \mathbf{j}F_y + \mathbf{k}F_z \tag{3}$$

Ordinarily we think of **i**, **j**, and **k** as being constant in time, but we shall wish to be more general. Since their lengths are fixed, they can at most rotate. We shall assume they rotate with an instantaneous angular velocity $\boldsymbol{\Omega}$. Then

$$\frac{d\mathbf{i}}{dt} = \boldsymbol{\Omega} \times \mathbf{i} \tag{4}$$

The time derivative of **F** is therefore

$$\begin{aligned}\frac{d\mathbf{F}}{dt} &= \mathbf{i}\frac{dF_x}{dt} + F_x\frac{d\mathbf{i}}{dt} + \mathbf{j}\frac{dF_y}{dt} + F_y\frac{d\mathbf{j}}{dt} + \mathbf{k}\frac{dF_z}{dt} + F_z\frac{d\mathbf{k}}{dt} \\ &= \mathbf{i}\frac{dF_x}{dt} + \mathbf{j}\frac{dF_y}{dt} + \mathbf{k}\frac{dF_z}{dt} + \boldsymbol{\Omega} \times (\mathbf{i}F_x + \mathbf{j}F_y + \mathbf{k}F_z) \\ &= \frac{\delta\mathbf{F}}{\delta t} + \boldsymbol{\Omega} \times \mathbf{F}\end{aligned} \tag{5}$$

where we have introduced the symbol $\delta\mathbf{F}/\delta t$, representing the time rate of change of **F** with respect to the coordinate system **i**, **j**, **k**. For example, when $\delta\mathbf{F}/\delta t = 0$, the components of **F** along **i**, **j**, and **k** do not change in time.

By making use of Eq. (5), we can rewrite the equation of motion of $\boldsymbol{\mu}$ in terms of a coordinate system rotating with an as yet arbitrary angular velocity $\boldsymbol{\Omega}$:

$$\frac{\delta\boldsymbol{\mu}}{\delta t} + \boldsymbol{\Omega} \times \boldsymbol{\mu} = \boldsymbol{\mu} \times \gamma\mathbf{H} \tag{6}$$

or

$$\frac{\delta\boldsymbol{\mu}}{\delta t} = \boldsymbol{\mu} \times (\gamma\mathbf{H} + \boldsymbol{\Omega}) \tag{7}$$

Equation (7) tells us that the motion of $\boldsymbol{\mu}$ in the rotating coordinate system obeys the same equation as in the laboratory system, *provided* we replace the actual magnetic field **H** by an effective field $\mathbf{H}_e$:

$$\mathbf{H}_e = \mathbf{H} + \frac{\boldsymbol{\Omega}}{\gamma} \tag{8}$$

We can now readily solve for the motion of $\boldsymbol{\mu}$ in a static field $\mathbf{H} = \mathbf{k}H_0$ by choosing $\boldsymbol{\Omega}$ such that $\mathbf{H}_e = 0$. That is, we take $\boldsymbol{\Omega} = -\gamma H_0\mathbf{k}$. Since in this reference frame $\delta\boldsymbol{\mu}/\delta t = 0$, $\boldsymbol{\mu}$ remains fixed with respect to **i**, **j**, and **k**. The motion with respect to the laboratory is therefore that of a vector fixed in a set of axes which themselves rotate at $\boldsymbol{\Omega} = -\gamma H_0\mathbf{k}$. In other words, $\boldsymbol{\mu}$ rotates at an angular velocity $\boldsymbol{\Omega} = -\gamma H_0\mathbf{k}$ with respect to the laboratory. The angular frequency γH_0 is called the "Larmor frequency."

We are struck by the fact that the classical precession frequency $\boldsymbol{\Omega}$ is identical in magnitude with the angular frequency needed for magnetic resonance absorption, as found by elementary quantum theory. Let us therefore look more closely at the quantum mechanical description.

2.2 QUANTUM MECHANICAL DESCRIPTION OF SPIN IN A STATIC FIELD

We have seen that the quantum mechanical description of a spin in a static field gave energies in terms at the quantum number m, which was an eigenvalue of the component of spin, I_z, parallel to the static field H_0. The energies E_m were

$$E_m = -\gamma\hbar H_0 m \tag{1}$$

The corresponding eigenfunctions of the time-independent Schrödinger equation may then be denoted by $u_{I,m}$. The time-dependent solution corresponding to a particular value of m is therefore

$$\Psi_{I,m}(t) = u_{I,m}e^{-(i/\hbar)E_m t} \tag{2}$$

The most general time-dependent solution $\Psi(t)$ is therefore

$$\Psi(t) = \sum_{m=-I}^{+I} c_m u_{I,m}e^{-(i/\hbar)E_m t} \tag{3}$$

where the c_m's are complex constants. We may compute the expectation value of any observable by means of $\Psi(t)$, as we can illustrate with the x-component of magnetic moment:

$$\langle\mu_x(t)\rangle = \int \Psi^*(t)\mu_x\Psi(t)\,d\tau^\dagger \tag{4}$$

We have emphasized that the expectation value of μ_x, $\langle\mu_x\rangle$ will vary in time by explicitly writing it as a function of time.

By using the fact that $\mu_x = \gamma\hbar I_x$, and that $\Psi(t)$ is given by Eq. (3), we find

$$\langle\mu_x(t)\rangle = \sum_{m,m'} \gamma\hbar c_{m'}^* c_m (m'|I_x|m)e^{(i/\hbar)(E_{m'}-E_m)t} \tag{5}$$

where

$$(m'|I_x|m) \equiv \int u_{Im'}^* I_x u_{Im}\,d\tau \tag{6}$$

† We write a variable of integration $d\tau$ in the expression for the expectation value, in analogy to that which we would do for a spatial coordinate x, y, z or angular coordinates θ, ϕ. For spin, the notation is to be thought of as a symbolic representation of the scalar product of the two functions $\Psi(t)$ and $\mu_x\Psi(t)$.

is a time-independent matrix element. Expressions similar to Eq. (5) would hold for any operator. We note that the expectation value will in general be time dependent, will consist of a number of terms oscillating harmonically, and that the possible frequencies

$$\frac{E_{m'} - E_m}{\hbar} \tag{7}$$

are just those which correspond to the frequency of absorption or emission between states m and m'. Of course it was the assumption that observable properties of any quantum system had to be given by expressions such as Eq. (5), which was the basis of Heisenberg and Born's formulation of the quantum theory in matrix form.

Since matrix elements $(m'|I_x|m)$ vanish unless $m' = m \pm 1$, we see that all the terms of Eq. (5) have an angular frequency of either $+\gamma H_0$ or $-\gamma H_0$. Their sum must also contain just γH_0. The expectation value $\langle \mu_x(t) \rangle$ therefore oscillates in time at the classical precession frequency.

It is convenient at this point to introduce the famous raising and lowering operators I^+ and I^-, defined by the equations

$$\begin{aligned} I^+ &= I_x + iI_y \\ I^- &= I_x - iI_y \end{aligned} \tag{8}$$

We may express I_x or I_y in terms of I^+ and I^- by solving Eq. (8), getting

$$\begin{aligned} I_x &= \frac{1}{2}\,[I^+ + I^-] \\ I_y &= \frac{1}{2i}\,[I^+ - I^-] \end{aligned} \tag{9}$$

The operators are called "raising" or "lowering" because of the effect they produce when they operate on a function u_{Im}:

$$\begin{aligned} I^+ u_{I,m} &= \sqrt{I(I+1) - m(m+1)}\; u_{I,m+1} \\ I^- u_{I,m} &= \sqrt{I(I+1) - m(m-1)}\; u_{I,m-1} \end{aligned} \tag{10}$$

I^+ turns $u_{I,m}$ into a function whose m value has been raised by one unit. We see, therefore, that $(m'|I^+|m)$ vanishes unless $m' = m + 1$, while $(m'|I^-|m)$ vanishes unless $m' = m - 1$. Van Vleck has characterized these as "sharper" selection rules than those of the operators I_x or I_y, which may join a state $u_{I,m}$ with either $u_{I,m+1}$ or $u_{I,m-1}$.

In order to gain further insight into the physical significance of the general expression for $\langle \mu_x(t) \rangle$, Eq. (5), we now consider the form it takes for a spin of $\frac{1}{2}$. By using the fact that the diagonal matrix elements of I_x vanish, we get

$$\begin{aligned} \langle \mu_x(t) \rangle = \gamma\hbar[&c^*_{1/2}c_{-1/2}(\tfrac{1}{2}|I_x|-\tfrac{1}{2})e^{-(i\gamma H_0 t)} \\ &+ c^*_{-1/2}c_{1/2}(-\tfrac{1}{2}|I_x|\tfrac{1}{2})e^{(i\gamma H_0 t)}] \end{aligned} \tag{11}$$

It is convenient to define a quantity $\omega_0 = \gamma H_0$. As we have seen, ω_0 is the angular frequency we must apply to produce resonance and is also the classical precession frequency. By utilizing the fact that $(\frac{1}{2}|I_x|-\frac{1}{2})$ is the complex conjugate of

$(-\frac{1}{2}|I_x|\frac{1}{2})$, and using the symbol "Re" for "take the real part of," we get

$$\langle\mu_x(t)\rangle = 2\gamma\hbar \mathrm{Re}[c_{1/2}^{*}c_{-1/2}(\tfrac{1}{2}|I_x|-\tfrac{1}{2})e^{-i\omega_0 t}] \tag{12}$$

We evaluate the matrix element by means of Eqs. (9) and (10), getting $(\frac{1}{2}|I_x|-\frac{1}{2}) = \frac{1}{2}$.

It is convenient at this point to express the c's in terms of two real, positive quantities a and b, and two other real quantities (which may be positive or negative) α and β:

$$\begin{aligned} c_{1/2} &= ae^{i\alpha} \\ c_{-1/2} &= be^{i\beta} \end{aligned} \tag{13}$$

The normalization of the wave function gives us $a^2 + b^2 = 1$. These give us

$$\langle\mu_x(t)\rangle = \gamma\hbar ab\cos(\alpha - \beta + \omega_0 t) \tag{14a}$$

Similarly we find

$$\begin{aligned} \langle\mu_y(t)\rangle &= -\gamma\hbar ab\sin(\alpha - \beta + \omega_0 t) \\ \langle\mu_z(t)\rangle &= \gamma\hbar\left(\frac{a^2 - b^2}{2}\right) \end{aligned} \tag{14b}$$

We note that both $\langle\mu_x\rangle$ and $\langle\mu_y\rangle$ oscillate in time at the Larmor frequency γH_0, but that $\langle\mu_z\rangle$ is independent of time. Moreover the maximum amplitudes of $\langle\mu_x\rangle$ and $\langle\mu_y\rangle$ are the same. If we define

$$\langle\boldsymbol{\mu}\rangle \equiv \mathbf{i}\langle\mu_x\rangle + \mathbf{j}\langle\mu_y\rangle + \mathbf{k}\langle\mu_z\rangle \tag{15}$$

and utilize the fact that $\langle\mu_x\rangle^2 + \langle\mu_y\rangle^2 =$ constant, a fact readily verified from Eq. (14), we see that $\langle\boldsymbol{\mu}\rangle$ behaves as does a vector making a fixed angle with the z-direction, precessing in the x-y plane.

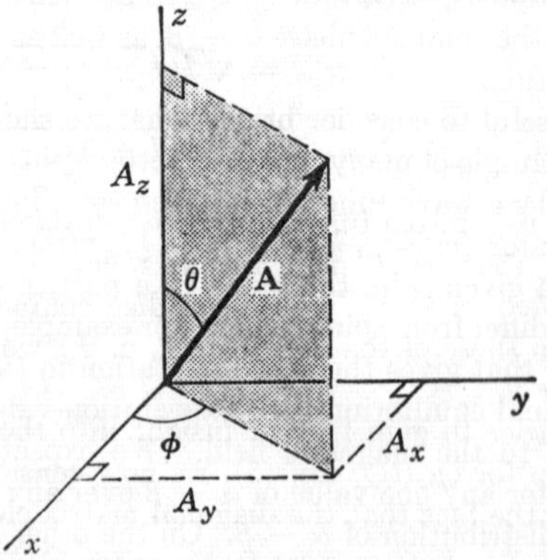

FIG. 2.2. Relationship of the components A_x, A_y, and A_z of a vector **A** to the polar angles θ, ϕ, and the magnitude A.

In terms of polar coordinates θ, ϕ, (see Fig. 2.2), any vector **A** may be written as

$$\begin{aligned} A_x &= \mathrm{A}\sin\theta\cos\phi \\ A_y &= \mathrm{A}\sin\theta\sin\phi \\ A_z &= \mathrm{A}\cos\theta \end{aligned} \tag{16}$$

By means of algebraic manipulation one can show that

$$\langle \mu_x \rangle = \frac{\gamma\hbar}{2} \sin\theta \cos\phi$$
$$\langle \mu_y \rangle = \frac{\gamma\hbar}{2} \sin\theta \sin\phi \tag{17}$$
$$\langle \mu_z \rangle = \frac{\gamma\hbar}{2} \cos\theta$$

provided

$$\phi = \beta - \alpha - \omega_0 t$$
$$a^2 = \frac{1 + \cos\theta}{2} \tag{18}$$

One may look on Eq. (18) as a formal change of variables, of course, but the results of Eq. (17) tell us that there is a simple physical significance; the expectation value of the operator $\boldsymbol{\mu}$ acts as does a vector of length $\gamma\hbar/2$, whose direction is given by the spherical coordinates θ, ϕ. If the orientation is specified at any time, it can be found at future times by recognizing that it precesses at angular velocity ω_0 in the negative ϕ direction. The orientation may be specified quite arbitrarily (by specifying a or b and $\beta - \alpha$). We emphasize that an *arbitrary* orientation can be specified, since sometimes the belief is erroneously held that spins may only be found pointing either parallel or antiparallel to the quantizing field. One of the beauties of the quantum theory is that it contains features of both discreteness and continuity. In terms of the two quantum states with $m = \pm\frac{1}{2}$ we can describe an *expectation* value of magnetization which may go all the way from parallel to antiparallel, including all values in between. Thus a wave function with $a = b$ has an expectation value corresponding to a magnetization lying somewhere in the x-y plane (that is, with vanishing z-component). Just where in the plane it points is given by the complex phase $\alpha - \beta$, as well as the time at which we wish to know the orientation.

It is useful to consider briefly what we should expect for the wave function if we took a sample of many non-interacting spins which were in thermal equilibrium. There will be a wave function for each spin, but in general it will not be in one of the eigenstates ($m = +\frac{1}{2}$ or $m = -\frac{1}{2}$); rather it will be in some linear combination. For a given spin, there will be a particular set of values for a, b, α, β. The values will differ from spin to spin. For example, we have a distribution of the quantity $\alpha - \beta$ that gives the spin orientation in the x-y plane at $t = 0$. If the spins are in thermal equilibrium, the expectation value of the total magnetization must be parallel to the magnetic field. We expect, therefore, that there will be no preference for any one value of $\alpha - \beta$ over any other. That is, the spins will have a random distribution of $\alpha - \beta$. On the other hand, since the spins will be polarized to some extent, we expect to find a larger than b more often than b is larger than a. That is, the average value of a must be larger than the average value of b. Since an observable quantity can be expressed in the form of Eq. (5), we see that we can specify either the individual c_m's or the complex products $c_{m'}^* c_m$, which we shall label $P_{mm'}$ for convenience.

$$P_{mm'} = c_{m'}^* c_m$$

For our example:

$$P_{1/2\ 1/2} = a^2$$
$$P_{-1/2\ -1/2} = b^2$$
$$P_{1/2\ -1/2} = abe^{i(\alpha-\beta)}$$
$$P_{-1/2\ 1/2} = abe^{i(\beta-\alpha)}$$

We may consider the $P_{mm'}$'s to be the elements of a complex matrix P. Notice that the diagonal elements ($m = m'$) give the probabilities of occupation of the various states, while the off-diagonal elements are closely related to the components of magnetic moment perpendicular to the static field. We shall make use in a subsequent section of the average of the matrix P over a statistical ensemble. The statement that in thermal equilibrium the magnetization will be parallel to the field amounts to saying that the average over the ensemble of $P_{mm'}$ for $m' \neq m$ is zero, whereas the average for $m = m'$ is the Boltzmann factor describing the probability of finding the state occupied.

(Of course, in the quantum theory, even for a number of spins with *identical* wave functions, any experiment that counts the number of spins in the various m states will find a statistical distribution not related, however, to temperature.)

2·3 EQUATIONS OF MOTION OF THE EXPECTATION VALUE

The close correspondence of the classical and quantum mechanical treatments is made particularly clear by examination of a differential equation relating the time variations of the expectation values $\langle\mu_x\rangle$, $\langle\mu_y\rangle$, and $\langle\mu_z\rangle$. The equation is based on a well-known formula whose derivation we sketch.

Suppose we have a pair of wave functions $\Psi(t)$ and $\Phi(t)$, both of which are solutions of the same Schrödinger equation:

$$-\frac{\hbar}{i}\frac{\partial\Psi}{\partial t} = \mathcal{H}\Psi \qquad -\frac{\hbar}{i}\frac{\partial\Phi}{\partial t} = \mathcal{H}\Phi \tag{1}$$

Let us have some operator F that has no explicit time dependence. Then

$$\frac{d}{dt}\int \Phi^* F\Psi\, d\tau = \frac{i}{\hbar}\int \Phi^*(\mathcal{H}F - F\mathcal{H})\Psi\, d\tau \tag{2}$$

This equation is readily derived from the fact that

$$\frac{d}{dt}\int \Phi^* F\Psi\, d\tau = \int \frac{\partial\Phi^*}{\partial t} F\Psi\, dt + \int \Phi^* F \frac{\partial\Psi}{\partial t}\, d\tau \tag{3}$$

into which we substitute expressions for the time derivative taken from Eq. (1).†

It is convenient to write Eq. (2) in operator form. There is no problem with the right-hand side: It is simply $(i/\hbar)(\mathcal{H}F - F\mathcal{H})$. For the left-hand side we must define some new notation. We define the operator dF/dt by the equation

$$\int \Phi^* \frac{dF}{dt}\Psi\, d\tau = \frac{d}{dt}\int \Phi^* F\Psi\, d\tau \tag{4}$$

† To prove Eq. (2), one must use the fact that $\mathcal{H}$ is an Hermitian operator. (See discussion in Section 2.5.)

That is to say, dF/dt does *not* mean to take the derivative of F with respect to t. Such a derivative vanishes, since F does not contain the variable t. Rather dF/dt is a symbol that has the meaning of Eq. (4). By using dF/dt in this symbolic sense, we have

$$\frac{dF}{dt} = \frac{i}{\hbar}[\mathcal{H}, F] \tag{5}$$

where $[\mathcal{H}, F]$ is the usual commutator $\mathcal{H}F - F\mathcal{H}$. We may use this formalism to compute the time derivative of the expectation values of μ_x, μ_y, and μ_z. We define the x-, y-, z-axes as being fixed in space but with the z-axis coinciding at an instant with the direction of the magnetic field. (In this way we include both static and time-varying fields.) Then

$$\mathcal{H} = -\gamma\hbar H I_z \tag{6}$$

We shall wish to use the commutation relations for the components of angular momentum, all of which may be obtained by cyclic permutation from

$$[I_x, I_y] = iI_z \tag{7}$$

Then

$$\begin{aligned} \frac{dI_x}{dt} &= \frac{i}{\hbar}[\mathcal{H}, I_x] \\ &= -\gamma H_0 i[I_z, I_x] \\ &= \gamma H_0 I_y \end{aligned} \tag{8a}$$

Similarly,

$$\begin{aligned} \frac{dI_y}{dt} &= -\gamma H_0 I_x \\ \frac{dI_z}{dt} &= 0 \end{aligned} \tag{8b}$$

These equations are the component equations of the vector operator equation

$$\frac{d\mathbf{I}}{dt} = \mathbf{I} \times \gamma\mathbf{H} \tag{9}$$

where

$$\frac{d\mathbf{I}}{dt} = \mathbf{i}\frac{dI_x}{dt} + \mathbf{j}\frac{dI_y}{dt} + \mathbf{k}\frac{dI_z}{dt} \tag{10}$$

Therefore, since $\boldsymbol{\mu} = \gamma\hbar\mathbf{I}$, we have the equation for the expectation value of magnetization,

$$\frac{d\langle\boldsymbol{\mu}\rangle}{dt} = \langle\boldsymbol{\mu}\rangle \times \gamma\mathbf{H} \tag{11}$$

which is just the classical equation. In words, Eq. (11) tells us that the expectation value of the magnetic moment obeys the classical equation of motion. Equation (11) was derived for the expectation value of a magnetic moment of a single spin. If we have a group of spins with moments $\boldsymbol{\mu}_k$, for the kth spin, their total magnetic moment $\boldsymbol{\mu}$ is defined as

$$\boldsymbol{\mu} = \sum_k \boldsymbol{\mu}_k \tag{12}$$

If the spins do not interact with one another, it is easy to prove that Eq. (11) also holds true for the expectation value of the total magnetization. Since, in practice we measure the results of a number of spins simultaneously, the experimental measurements of magnetization measure the expectation value of the various components of magnetization. That is, the experimentally determined bulk magnetization is simply the expectation value of the total magnetic moment. Therefore the classical equation correctly describes the dynamics of the magnetization, provided the spins may be thought of as not interacting with one another.

It is important to bear in mind that *Eq. (11) holds true for a time dependent* **H**, *not simply a static one*. Therefore it enables us to use a classical picture for studying the effects produced by alternating magnetic fields. We turn to that in the next section.

2·4 EFFECT OF ALTERNATING MAGNETIC FIELDS

The effect of an alternating magnetic field $H_x(t) = H_{x0} \cos \omega t$ is most readily analyzed by breaking it into two rotating components, each of amplitude H_1, one rotating clockwise and the other counterclockwise.

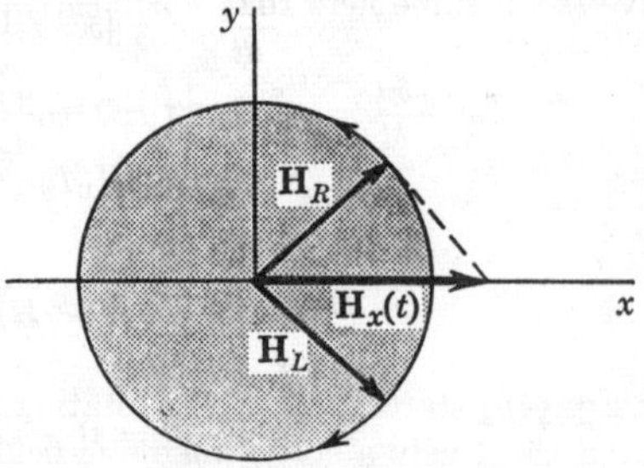

FIG. 2.3. Decomposition of a linear oscillating field into two rotating elements.

We denote the rotating fields by $\mathbf{H}_R$ and $\mathbf{H}_L$:

$$\begin{aligned} \mathbf{H}_R &= H_1[\mathbf{i} \cos \omega t + \mathbf{j} \sin \omega t] \\ \mathbf{H}_L &= H_1[\mathbf{i} \cos \omega t - \mathbf{j} \sin \omega t] \end{aligned} \tag{1}$$

Note that $\mathbf{H}_L$ and $\mathbf{H}_R$ differ simply by a replacement of ω by $-\omega$. Since one component will rotate in the same sense as the precession of the moment, and the other in the opposite sense, one can show that near resonance the counter-rotating component may be neglected. We shall make that approximation in what follows. Alternatively we can assume that we are finding the exact solution of a problem in which the experimental arrangement has produced a rotating field; for example, by use of two identical coils at right angles to each other and with alternating currents 90 degrees out of phase.

We shall assume we have only the field $\mathbf{H}_R$, but this is no loss in generality because the use of a negative ω will convert it to $\mathbf{H}_L$. In order to reserve the symbol ω for a positive quantity, we shall introduce the symbol ω_z, the component of ω along the z-axis. ω_z may therefore be positive or negative. We may, therefore write

$$\mathbf{H}_1 = H_1[\mathbf{i} \cos \omega_z t + \mathbf{j} \sin \omega_z t] \tag{2}$$

which will give us either sense of rotation, depending on the sign of ω_z.

We now ask for the equation of motion of a spin including the effects both of $\mathbf{H}_1(t)$ and of the static field $\mathbf{H}_0 = \mathbf{k}H_0$.

$$\frac{d\boldsymbol{\mu}}{dt} = \boldsymbol{\mu} \times \gamma[\mathbf{H}_0 + \mathbf{H}_1(t)] \tag{3}$$

The time dependence of $\mathbf{H}_1$ can be eliminated by using a coordinate system that rotates about the z-direction at frequency ω_z. In such a coordinate system, $\mathbf{H}_1$ will be static. Since the axis of rotation coincides with the direction of $\mathbf{H}_0$, $\mathbf{H}_0$ will also be static. Let us take the x-axis in the rotating frame along $\mathbf{H}_1$. Then Eq. (3) becomes

$$\frac{\delta\boldsymbol{\mu}}{\delta t} = \boldsymbol{\mu} \times [\mathbf{k}(\omega_z + \gamma H_0) + \mathbf{i}\gamma H_1] \tag{4a}$$

Notice that we have encountered two effects in making the transformation of Eq. (3) to Eq. (4). The first is associated with the derivative of the rotating unit vectors and gives the term ω_z. The second is associated with expressing the vectors $\mathbf{H}_0$ and $\mathbf{H}_1$ in terms of their components in the rotating system and gives rise to the conversion of $\mathbf{H}_1$ from a rotating to a static field. Eq. (4) may be rewritten to emphasize that near resonance $\omega_z + \gamma H_0 \cong 0$, by setting $\omega_z = -\omega$, where ω is now positive (we assume here that γ is positive). Then

$$\begin{aligned}\frac{\delta\boldsymbol{\mu}}{\delta t} &= \boldsymbol{\mu} \times \gamma\left[\left(H_0 - \frac{\omega}{\gamma}\right)\mathbf{k} + H_1\mathbf{i}\right] \\ &= \boldsymbol{\mu} \times \mathbf{H}_{\text{eff}}\end{aligned} \tag{4b}$$

where

$$\mathbf{H}_{\text{eff}} = \mathbf{k}\left(H_0 - \frac{\omega}{\gamma}\right) + H_1\mathbf{i}$$

Physically Eq. (4b) states that in the rotating frame, the moment acts as though it experienced effectively a static magnetic field $\mathbf{H}_{\text{eff}}$. The moment therefore precesses in a cone of fixed angle about the direction of $\mathbf{H}_{\text{eff}}$ at angular frequency γH_{eff}. The situation is illustrated in Fig. 2.4 for a magnetic moment which, at $t = 0$, was oriented along the z-direction.

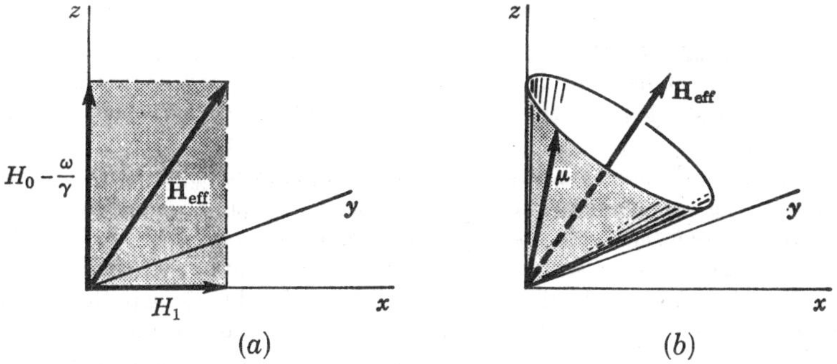

FIG. 2.4. (a) Effective field. (b) Motion of the moment μ in the rotating coordinate system.

We notice that the motion of the moment is periodic. If it is initially oriented along the z-direction, it periodically returns to that direction. As it increases its angle with the z-direction, its magnetic potential energy in the laboratory reference system changes (in the laboratory system the magnetic energy with respect to H_0 is much larger than that with respect to H_1, so we customarily neglect the latter). However, all the energy it takes to tilt $\boldsymbol{\mu}$ away from $\mathbf{H}_0$ is returned in a complete cycle of $\boldsymbol{\mu}$ around the cone. There is no net absorption of energy from the alternating field but rather alternately receiving and returning of energy.

Note that if H_0 is above resonance (that is, $H_0 > \omega/\gamma$), the effective field has a positive z-component, but when H_0 lies below the resonance ($H_0 < \omega/\gamma$), the effective field has a negative z-component.

If the resonance condition is fulfilled exactly ($\omega = \gamma H_0$), the effective field is then simply $\mathbf{i}H_1$. A magnetic moment that is parallel to the static field initially will then precess in the y-z plane. That is, it will precess but remaining always perpendicular to $\mathbf{H}_1$. Periodically it will be lined up *opposed* to $\mathbf{H}_0$. If we were to turn on H_1 for a short time (that is, apply a wave train of duration t_w), the moment would precess through an angle $\theta = \gamma H_1 t_w$. If t_w were chosen such that $\theta = \pi$, the pulse would simply invert the moment. Such a pulse is referred to in the literature as a "180 degree pulse." If $\theta = \pi/2$ (90 degree pulse), the magnetic moment is turned from the z-direction to the y-direction. Following the turn-off of H_1, the moment would then remain at rest in the rotating frame, and hence precess in the laboratory, pointing normal to the static field.

These remarks suggest a very simple method of observing magnetic resonance, illustrated in Fig. 2.5. We put a sample of material we wish to study in a coil, the axis of which is oriented perpendicular to $\mathbf{H}_0$. In thermal equilibrium there

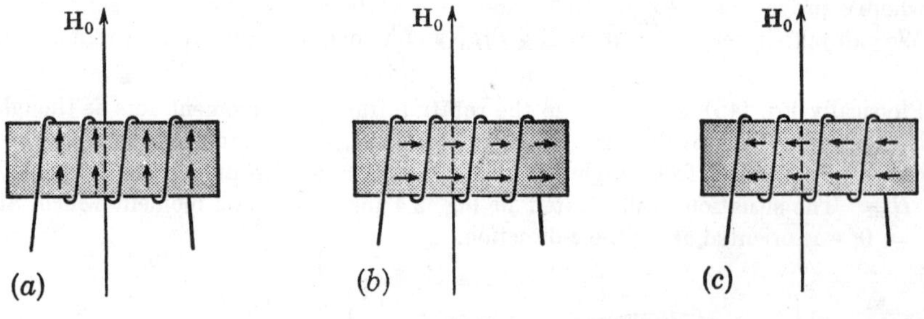

FIG. 2.5. (a) Coil containing sample. In thermal equilibrium an excess of moments is parallel to H_0. (b) and (c) Following a 90-degree pulse, the excess moments precess perpendicular to H_0.

will be an excess of moments pointing along $\mathbf{H}_0$. Application of an alternating voltage to the coil produces an alternating magnetic field perpendicular to H_0. By properly adjusting H_1 and t_w, we may apply a 90 degree pulse. Following the pulse, the excess magnetization will be perpendicular to $\mathbf{H}_0$ and will precess at angular frequency γH_0. As a result, the moments will produce a flux through the coil which will alternate as the spins precess. The resultant induced emf may be observed.

What we have suggested so far would indicate that the induced emf would persist indefinitely, but in practice, the interactions of the spins with their surroundings cause a decay. The decay may last in liquids for many milliseconds, but in solids it is more typically 100 μsec. Even during that short time, however, there are many precession periods. The technique we have described of observing the "free induction decay" (that is, decay "free" of H_1) is a commonly used technique for observing resonances. It has the great virtue of enabling one to study the resonance signal in the absence of the voltages needed to produce H_1. Since oscillators always generate noise, such a scheme may be advantageous.

One interesting application of the rotating reference frame is to prove the following theorem, which is the basis of another technique for producing resonance signals. Suppose we have a magnetic field $\mathbf{H}_0$ of fixed magnitude whose direction we may vary (no other magnetic field is present). Let the magnetization $\mathbf{M}$ be parallel to $\mathbf{H}_0$ at $t = 0$. We may describe the changing direction of $\mathbf{H}_0$ by an angular velocity $\boldsymbol{\omega}$. Then the theorem states that if

$$\gamma H_0 \gg \omega$$

the magnetization $\mathbf{M}$ will turn with $\mathbf{H}_0$, always remaining aligned along $\mathbf{H}_0$ as $\mathbf{H}_0$ turns.

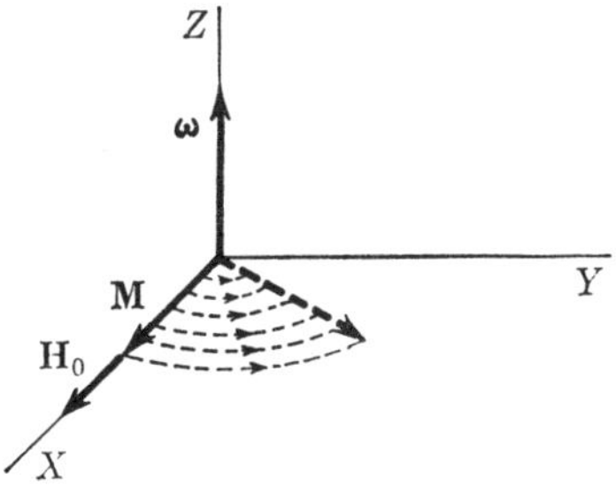

FIG. 2.6. Magnetic field $\mathbf{H}_0$, magnetization $\mathbf{M}$, and angular velocity $\boldsymbol{\omega}$ at $t = 0$.

To prove this theorem, let us assume $\boldsymbol{\omega}$ to be a constant in the z-direction. We can take it perpendicular to $\mathbf{H}_0$, since a component parallel to $\mathbf{H}_0$ produces no

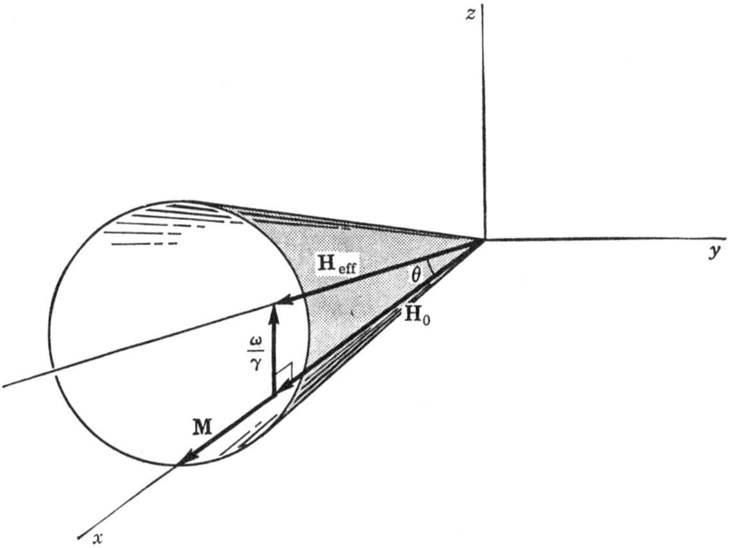

FIG. 2.7. Magnetization $\mathbf{M}$ and effective field $\mathbf{H}_{\text{eff}}$ in the rotating coordinate system x, y, z. The magnetization will precess about the effective field in the cone of angle θ shown.

effect. The relationships are shown in Fig. 2.6 at $t = 0$, with $\mathbf{M}$ and $\mathbf{H}_0$ taken parallel to each other and pointing in the X-direction in the laboratory. If we choose a reference frame x, y, z rotating at angular velcoity $\mathbf{\Omega}_R = \boldsymbol{\omega}$, $\mathbf{H}_0$ appears static, but we must add an effective field $\mathbf{\Omega}_R/\gamma$. Choosing the z- and Z-axes as parallel, and x to coincide with X at $t = 0$, the effective fields and magnetization at $t = 0$ are shown in Fig. 2.7.

The effective field in the rotating frame is static and given by

$$\mathbf{H}_{\text{eff}} = \mathbf{H}_0 + \frac{\mathbf{\Omega}_R}{\gamma}$$
$$= \mathbf{H}_0 + \frac{\boldsymbol{\omega}}{\gamma}$$

$\mathbf{M}$ will precess about $\mathbf{H}_{\text{eff}}$, making an angle θ such that

$$\tan\theta = \frac{\omega}{\gamma H_0} \tag{6}$$

$\mathbf{M}$ will therefore remain within an angle 2θ of $\mathbf{H}_0$. We see that if $\omega/\gamma H_0 \ll 1$, $\mathbf{M}$ and $\mathbf{H}_0$ remain parallel.

The fact that the magnetization follows the direction of the magnetic field when the field changes direction sufficiently slowly is described by the term *adiabatic.*

By utilizing this principle, one can turn to the case of a rotating magnetic field H_1 of frequency ω, perpendicular to a static field H_0. If one starts far below resonance, the magnetization is nearly parallel to the effective field in the rotating frame, $\sqrt{H_1^2 + [(\omega/\gamma) - H_0]^2}$. As one approaches resonance, both magnitude and direction of the effective field change, but if resonance is approached sufficiently slowly, $\mathbf{M}$ will remain parallel to $\mathbf{H}_{\text{eff}}$ in the rotating frame according to the theorem we have just proved. Thus, exactly at resonance, the magnetization will lie along H_1, making a 90 degree angle with H_0 (Fig. 2.8).

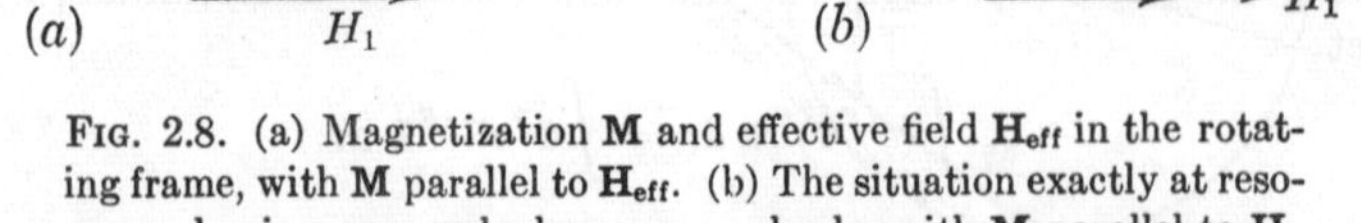

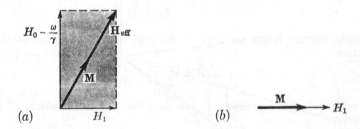

FIG. 2.8. (a) Magnetization $\mathbf{M}$ and effective field $\mathbf{H}_{\text{eff}}$ in the rotating frame, with $\mathbf{M}$ parallel to $\mathbf{H}_{\text{eff}}$. (b) The situation exactly at resonance, having approached resonance slowly, with $\mathbf{M}$ parallel to $\mathbf{H}_0$ when H_0 was far above resonance.

If one were to continue on through the resonance, the magnetization would end up by pointing in the negative z-direction. This technique of inverting $\mathbf{M}$ is very useful experimentally and is called "adiabatic inversion."

2.5 EXPONENTIAL OPERATORS

It will be useful to consider the quantum mechanical equivalent of the rotating coordinate transformation, but to do so, we shall need to employ several useful relations. We review them here for the convenience of the reader.

Suppose we have two wave functions, Φ and Ψ, that satisfy appropriate boundary conditions and have other satisfactory properties for some region of space, and suppose we have an operator F. F may be, for example, a component of spin. The operator is said to be Hermitian when

$$\int \Phi^* F \Psi \, d\tau = \int (F\Phi)^* \Psi \, d\tau \tag{1}$$

where the integrals are over the region of space designated. To prove that an operator is Hermitian requires some statement about the conditions Ψ and Φ are to satisfy, as well as a definition of the region. For example, if F is an operator involving derivatives, the proof that it is Hermitian may involve transforming the volume integral to a surface integral and requiring the integrand of the surface integral to vanish on the surface of the region.

Hermitian operators are important because their expectation values and eigenvalues are real. Therefore any operator that corresponds to a physically observable quantity must be Hermitian. Thus the operators I_x, I_y, and I_z are Hermitian. If they are Hermitian, it is easy to show from Eq. (1) that the operators $I^+ = I_x + iI_y$ and $I^- = I_x - iI_y$ are not.

In the theory of functions, it is useful to define the exponential function of the complex variable z:

$$e^z = 1 + z + \frac{z^2}{2!} + \frac{z^3}{3!} + \cdots$$

the power series converging for all z.

We define the function

$$e^F = 1 + F + \frac{F^2}{2!} + \frac{F^3}{3!} + \cdots$$

similarly, where F is now an operator. We shall be particularly interested in the function

$$e^{iF} = 1 + iF + \frac{(iF)^2}{2!} + \frac{(iF)^3}{3!} + \cdots \tag{2}$$

By using the series expansion, one can show that if F is Hermitian, e^{iF} is not. In fact

$$\int (e^{iF}\Phi)^* \Psi \, d\tau = \int \Phi^* e^{-iF} \Psi \, d\tau \tag{3}$$

The exponential function of operators obeys some of the same algebra as does the function of ordinary number, but as usual with operators, care must be taken whenever two non-commuting operators are encountered. Thus, if A and B are two operators, one can verify by means of the series expansion that

$$Ae^{iB} = e^{iB}A \tag{4a}$$

only if A and B commute. Likewise,

$$e^{i(A+B)} = e^{iA}e^{iB} \tag{4b}$$

only if A and B commute.

If A and B do not commute, another useful equation may still hold. Let us define C as the commutator of A and B:

$$[A, B] = AB - BA \equiv C$$

Suppose that C commutes with both A and B:

$$[A, C] = 0$$
$$[B, C] = 0$$

Then

$$e^{(A+B)} = e^{A}e^{B}e^{-C/2} = e^{C/2}e^{B}e^{A}$$

This theorem is proved in Appendix A.

Use of the exponential function provides a particularly simple method for obtaining a formal solution of Schrödinger's equation if the Hamiltonian does not depend explicitly on time. That is, if $\Psi(t)$ is the solution of

$$-\frac{\hbar}{i}\frac{\partial\Psi(t)}{\partial t} = \mathcal{H}\Psi(t) \tag{5}$$

then we can express $\Psi(t)$ in terms of its value at $t = 0$, $\Psi(0)$, by the equation

$$\Psi(t) = e^{-(i/\hbar)\mathcal{H}t}\Psi(0) \tag{6}$$

Equation (6) may be verified by direct substitution into Equation (5). If, for example, we consider the motion of a spin in a magnetic field so that $\mathcal{H} = -\gamma\hbar H_0 I_z$

$$\begin{aligned} \Psi(t) &= e^{-(i/\hbar)(-\gamma\hbar H_0 I_z)t}\Psi(0) \\ &= e^{i\omega_0 t I_z}\Psi(0) \end{aligned} \tag{7}$$

where $\omega_0 = \gamma H_0$.

We know that H_0 produces a rotation of the magnetic moment at angular velocity $\mathbf{\Omega}$ given by $\mathbf{\Omega} = -\gamma H_0\mathbf{k}$. We shall call such a rotation "negative," since the component of angular velocity along the z-axis is negative. It is logical to suppose, then, that $\Psi(t)$ must correspond to the function $\Psi(0)$, referred, however, to axes rotated in the negative direction through an angle $\omega_0 t$. Thus $e^{-iI_z\phi}\Psi(0)$ should correspond to a function identical to $\Psi(0)$ referred to axes rotated through the positive angle ϕ. If we compute the expectation value or matrix elements of, for example, I_x, we find

$$\begin{aligned} \int \Psi^*(t) I_x \Psi(t)\, d\tau &= \int (e^{i\omega_0 t I_z}\Psi(0))^* I_x e^{i\omega_0 t I_z}\Psi(0)\, d\tau \\ &= \int \Psi^*(0) e^{-i\omega_0 t I_z} I_x e^{i\omega_0 t I_z}\Psi(0)\, d\tau \\ &= \int \Psi^*(0) I_{x'}(t)\Psi(0)\, d\tau \end{aligned} \tag{8a}$$

where

$$I_{x'}(t) \equiv e^{-i\omega_0 t I_z} I_x e^{i\omega_0 t I_z} \tag{8b}$$

The last line defines the operator $I_{x'}$. We can give a simple interpretation of Eq. (8) as follows:

The first integral, which gives $\langle I_x(t)\rangle$, corresponds to a precessing angular momentum arising from the effect on a time-independent operator I_x of a time-dependent function $\Psi(t)$. The last integral describes the effect on a time-dependent operator $I_{x'}(t)$ of a wave function $\Psi(0)$, which is independent of time. Since the precession is in the negative sense, the first integral involves a fixed operator and a wave function fixed with respect to axes that rotate in the negative sense. Therefore the last integral must describe an operator rotating in the *positive* sense with respect to the "fixed" wave function $\Psi(0)$.

It is a simple matter to show that $I_{x'}$ is related to I_x through a rotation of axes. Let us consider

$$e^{-iI_z\phi} I_x e^{iI_z\phi} = f(\phi) \tag{9}$$

We wish to find $f(\phi)$, to see what meaning we can ascribe to it. Of course we could simply expand the exponentials, and using the commutation laws, try to reduce the function to something tractable. A simpler method is to show first that $f(\phi)$ satisfies a simple differential equation and then solve the equation. We have

$$\frac{df}{d\phi} = e^{-iI_z\phi}(-iI_zI_x + iI_xI_z)e^{iI_z\phi} \tag{10}$$

But, since $[I_z, I_x] = iI_y$,

$$\frac{df}{d\phi} = e^{-iI_z\phi} I_y e^{iI_z\phi} \tag{11}$$

Likewise

$$\begin{aligned} \frac{d^2f}{d\phi^2} &= e^{-iI_z\phi}(-iI_zI_y + iI_yI_z)e^{iI_z\phi} \\ &= -e^{-iI_z\phi}(I_x)e^{iI_z\phi} = -f \qquad \text{or} \qquad \frac{d^2f}{d\phi^2} + f = 0 \end{aligned} \tag{12}$$

Therefore

$$f(\phi) = A\cos\phi + B\sin\phi$$

where we must evaluate the constants of integrations. (As we shall see, the "constants" are actually operators.) Clearly, $A = f(0)$, but from Eq. (9), $f(0) = I_x$.

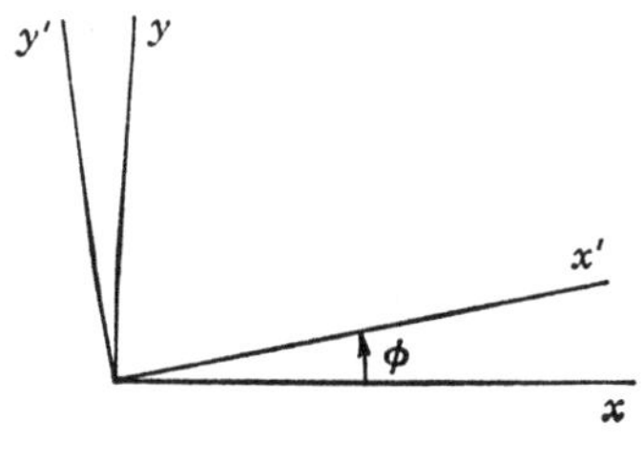

FIG. 2.9. Relation of axes x, y to x', y' and the angle ϕ.

Likewise, $B = f'(0) = I_y$, using Eq. (11). In this way we get

$$I_{x'} \equiv e^{-iI_z\phi} I_x e^{iI_z\phi} = I_x \cos\phi + I_y \sin\phi$$
$$I_{y'} \equiv e^{-iI_z\phi} I_y e^{iI_z\phi} = -I_x \sin\phi + I_y \cos\phi \tag{13}$$
$$I_{z'} \equiv e^{-iI_z\phi} I_z e^{iI_z\phi} = I_z$$

The quantities $I_{x'}$, $I_{y'}$, and $I_{z'}$ are clearly the components of angular momentum along a set of axes x', y', z' rotated with respect to x, y, z, as shown in Fig. 2.9. Therefore we see that we can use the exponential operator $e^{iI_z\phi}$ to generate rotations.

2·6 QUANTUM MECHANICAL TREATMENT OF A ROTATING MAGNETIC FIELD

We shall now use the exponential operators to perform the quantum mechanical equivalent of the classical "rotating coordinate" transformation. We shall consider a magnetic field H_1, which rotates at angular velocity ω_z, in addition to the static field $\mathbf{k}H_0$. The total field $\mathbf{H}(t)$ is then

$$\mathbf{H}(t) = \mathbf{i}H_1 \cos\omega_z t + \mathbf{j}H_1 \sin\omega_z t + \mathbf{k}H_0 \tag{1}$$

and the Schrödinger equation

$$-\frac{\hbar}{i}\frac{\partial\Psi}{\partial t} = -\boldsymbol{\mu}\cdot\mathbf{H}\Psi = -\gamma\hbar[H_0 I_z + H_1(I_x \cos\omega_z t + I_y \sin\omega_z t)]\Psi \tag{2}$$

By using Eq. (13) of the preceding section, we can write the Hamiltonian of Eq. (2) as

$$\mathcal{H} = -\gamma\hbar[H_0 I_z + H_1 e^{-i\omega_z t I_z} I_x e^{i\omega_z t I_z}] \tag{3}$$

We are tempted to try to "remove" the operator $e^{i\omega_z t I_z}$ from I_x and transfer it onto Ψ, much as the reverse of the steps of Eq. (8) of the preceding section. Accordingly we let

$$\Psi' = e^{i\omega_z t I_z}\Psi \tag{4}$$

or

$$\Psi = e^{-i\omega_z t I_z}\Psi'$$

The physical interpretation of Eq. (4) is that Ψ and Ψ' differ by a rotation of axes through an angle $\omega_z t$ (a rotating coordinate transformation).

Then

$$\frac{\partial\Psi}{\partial t} = -i\omega_z I_z e^{-i\omega_z t I_z}\Psi' + e^{-i\omega_z t I_z}\frac{\partial\Psi'}{\partial t} \tag{5}$$

We may substitute Eqs. (4) and (5) into Eq. (3), multiply both sides from the left by $e^{i\omega_z t I_z}$, and obtain

$$-\frac{\hbar}{i}\frac{\partial\Psi'}{\partial t} = -[\hbar(\omega_z + \gamma H_0)I_z + \gamma\hbar H_1 I_x]\Psi' \tag{6}$$

In Eq. (6) the time dependence of $\mathbf{H}_1(t)$ has been eliminated. In fact we recognize it as representing the coupling of the spins with an effective *static* field

$$\mathbf{k}\left(H_0 + \frac{\omega_z}{\gamma}\right) + \mathbf{i}H_1$$

the effective field of our classical equations. The spins are therefore quantized along the effective field in the rotating coordinate system, the energy spacing being $\gamma\hbar H_{\text{eff}}$.

The wave function Ψ' given by Eq. (4) is related to the function Ψ by a coordinate rotation, the "forward" motion of I_x relative to a stationary Ψ having been replaced by a stationary I_x and "backward" rotating Ψ'. As usual, resonance occurs when $\omega_z \approx -\gamma H_0$. If we define the transformed Hamiltonian $\mathcal{H}'$ by

$$\mathcal{H}' = -[(\hbar\omega_z + \gamma\hbar H_0)I_z + \gamma\hbar H_1 I_x] \tag{7}$$

we can formally solve Eq. (6):

$$\Psi'(t) = e^{-(i/\hbar)\mathcal{H}'t}\Psi'(0) \tag{8a}$$

whence, using Eq. (4),

$$\Psi(t) = e^{-i\omega_z tI_z}e^{-(i/\hbar)\mathcal{H}'t}\Psi'(0) \tag{8b}$$

[Note that at $t = 0$, $\Psi(0) = \Psi'(0)$.]

Equation (8b) gives us a particularly compact way to express the solution of Schrödinger's equation when a rotating field is present.

We can illustrate the use of the wave function of Eq. (8b) by computing the time dependence of the expectation value of μ_z. Of course we know already what the result must be, since we have proved that the classical picture applies. Let us for simplicity assume that H_1 is applied exactly at resonance. Then, from Eq. (7),

$$\mathcal{H}' = -\gamma\hbar H_1 I_x \tag{9}$$

Then we have, using Eqs. (8b) and (9),

$$\begin{aligned}\langle\mu_z(t)\rangle &= \int \Psi^*(t)\mu_z\Psi(t)\,d\tau \\ &= \gamma\hbar\int (e^{-i\omega_z tI_z}e^{+i\gamma H_1 I_x t}\Psi(0))^* I_z(e^{-i\omega_z tI_z}e^{+i\gamma H_1 I_x t}\Psi(0))\,d\tau\end{aligned} \tag{10}$$

If we define ω_1,

$$\omega_1 \equiv \gamma H_1 \tag{11}$$

and use the fact that I_x and I_z are Hermitian, we get

$$\begin{aligned}\langle\mu_z(t)\rangle &= \gamma\hbar\int \Psi^*(0)e^{-i\omega_1 tI_x}e^{i\omega_z tI_z}I_z e^{-i\omega_z tI_z}e^{i\omega_1 tI_x}\Psi(0)\,d\tau \\ &= \gamma\hbar\int \Psi^*(0)e^{-i\omega_1 tI_x}I_z e^{i\omega_1 tI_x}\Psi(0)\,d\tau\end{aligned} \tag{12}$$

By using Eq. (13) of Section 2.6, we can write

$$e^{-i\omega_1 tI_x}I_z e^{i\omega_1 tI_x} = -I_y\sin\omega_1 t + I_z\cos\omega_1 t \tag{13}$$

Substituting in Eq. (12) we get

$$\langle\mu_z(t)\rangle = -\langle\mu_y(0)\rangle \sin \omega_1 t + \langle\mu_z(0)\rangle \cos \omega_1 t \tag{14}$$

If the magnetization lies along the z-axis at $t = 0$ so that $\langle\mu_y(0)\rangle = 0$, we get

$$\langle\mu_z(t)\rangle = \langle\mu_z(0)\rangle \cos \gamma H_1 t \tag{15}$$

Thus the z-magnetization oscillates in time at γH_1, corresponding to the precession of $\langle\boldsymbol{\mu}\rangle$ about H_1 in the rotating reference frame. It is important to note that in this picture, which neglects all interactions of spins with one another or the lattice, the magnetization continues oscillating between $+\langle\mu_z(0)\rangle$ and $-\langle\mu_z(0)\rangle$ indefinitely. This behavior is very different from that which we should expect from a time-independent transition probability such as we assumed in Chapter 1. The time-independent transitions occur only if some physical process spoils the coherent precession about H_1 in the rotating reference frame.

2·7 BLOCH EQUATIONS

Both quantum mechanical and classical descriptions of the motion of non-interacting spins have in common a periodic motion of the magnetization in the rotating frame. For example, if $\gamma H_0 = \omega$ and if the magnetization is parallel to the static field at $t = 0$, the magnetization precesses around H_1 in the rotating frame, becoming alternately parallel and antiparallel to the direction of the static field. Viewed from the laboratory frame, the magnetization is continuously changing its orientation with respect to the large static field. However, the energy that must be supplied to turn the spins from parallel to antiparallel to the static field is recovered as the spins return to being parallel to the static field. Thus there is no cumulative absorption over long times but rather an alternate absorption and recovery. The situation is reminiscent of that we described in the first chapter prior to introduction of the coupling to a thermal reservoir. (We note that there the system, however, simply equalized populations, whereas our present model predicts an alternating reversal of populations. The two models must therefore be based on differing assumptions.)

Without contact to a reservoir, we have no mechanism for the establishment of the magnetization. By analogy to the equation

$$\frac{dn}{dt} = \frac{n_0 - n}{T_1} \tag{1}$$

and recognizing that $M_z = \gamma\hbar n/2$, we expect that it would be reasonable for M_z to be established according to the equation

$$\frac{dM_z}{dt} = \frac{M_0 - M_z}{T_1} \tag{2}$$

where M_0 is the thermal equilibrium magnetization. In terms of the static magnetic susceptibility χ_0 and the static magnetic field H_0, we have

$$M_0 = \chi_0 H_0 \tag{3}$$

We combine Eq. (2) with the equation for the driving of $\mathbf{M}$ by the torque to get

$$\frac{dM_z}{dt} = \frac{M_0 - M_z}{T_1} + \gamma(\mathbf{M} \times \mathbf{H})_z \tag{4}$$

Furthermore we wish to express the fact that in thermal equilibrium under a static field, the magnetization will wish to be parallel to H_0. That is, the x- and y-components must have a tendency to vanish. Thus

$$\begin{aligned} \frac{dM_x}{dt} &= \gamma(\mathbf{M} \times \mathbf{H})_x - \frac{M_x}{T_2} \\ \frac{dM_y}{dt} &= \gamma(\mathbf{M} \times \mathbf{H})_y - \frac{M_y}{T_2} \end{aligned} \tag{5}$$

We have here introduced the same relaxation time T_2 for the x- and y-directions, but have implied that it is different from T_1. That the transverse rate of decay may differ from the longitudinal is reasonable if we recall that, in contrast to the longitudinal decay, the transverse decay conserves energy in the static field. Therefore there is no necessity for transfer of energy to a reservoir for the transverse decay. (This statement is not strictly true and gives rise to important effects when saturating resonances in solids, as has been described by Redfield.)

On the other hand, the postulate of the particular (exponential) form of relaxation we have assumed must be viewed as being rather arbitrary. It provides a most useful postulate to describe certain important effects, but must not be taken too literally. According to Eq. (5), under the influence of a static field the transverse components would decay with a simple exponential. (This result is readily seen by transforming to a frame rotating at γH_0, where the effective field vanishes.)

A possible simple mechanism for T_2 for a solid in which each nucleus has nearby neighbors arises from the spread in precession rates produced by the magnetic field that one nucleus produces at another. If the nearest neighbor distance is r, we expect a typical nucleus to experience a local field $H_{\text{loc}} \sim \mu/r^3$ (due to the neighbors) either aiding or opposing the static field. As a result, if all nuclei were precessing in phase at $t = 0$, they would get out of step. In a time τ such that $\gamma H_{\text{loc}}\tau \cong 1$, there would be significant dephasing, and the vector sum of the moments would have thus diminished significantly. Since τ must therefore be comparable to T_2, a rough estimate for T_2 on this model is

$$T_2 = \frac{1}{\gamma H_{\text{loc}}} = \frac{r^3}{\gamma^2 \hbar} \tag{6}$$

often about 100 μsec for nuclei. Equations (4) and (5) were first proposed by Felix Bloch and are commonly referred to as the "Bloch equations." Although they have some limitations, they have nevertheless played a most important role in understanding resonance phenomena, since they provide a very simple way of introducing relaxation effects.

2.8 SOLUTION OF THE BLOCH EQUATIONS FOR LOW H_1

At this stage we shall be interested in the solution of the Bloch equations for low values of the alternating field, values low enough to avoid saturation. We immediately transform to the coordinate frame rotating at ω_z, taking H_1 along the x-axis and denoting $H_0 + (\omega_z/\gamma)$ by h_0. Then

$$\frac{dM_z}{dt} = -\gamma M_y H_1 + \frac{M_0 - M_z}{T_1} \tag{1a}$$

$$\frac{dM_x}{dt} = +\gamma M_y h_0 - \frac{M_x}{T_2} \tag{1b}$$

$$\frac{dM_y}{dt} = \gamma[M_z H_1 - M_x h_0] - \frac{M_y}{T_2} \tag{1c}$$

Since M_x and M_y must vanish as $H_1 \to 0$, we realize from Eq. (1a) that in a steady state, M_z differs from M_0 to order H_1^2. We therefore replace M_z by M_0 in Eq. (1c). The solution is further facilitated by introducing $M_+ = M_x + iM_y$. By adding Eq. (1b) to i times Eq. (1c), we get

$$\frac{dM_+}{dt} = -M_+\alpha + i\gamma M_0 H_1 \tag{2}$$

where

$$\alpha = \frac{1}{T_2} + \gamma h_0 i \tag{3}$$

Therefore

$$M_+ = Ae^{-\alpha t} + \frac{i\gamma M_0 H_1}{(1/T_2) + i\gamma h_0} \tag{4}$$

If we neglect the transient term and substitute $M_0 = \chi_0 H_0$, and define $\omega_0 = \gamma H_0$, $\omega_z = -\omega$, we get

$$\begin{aligned} M_x &= \chi_0(\omega_0 T_2) \frac{(\omega_0 - \omega)T_2}{1 + (\omega - \omega_0)^2 T_2^2} H_1 \\ M_y &= \chi_0(\omega_0 T_2) \frac{1}{1 + (\omega - \omega_0)^2 T_2^2} H_1 \end{aligned} \tag{5}$$

Equations (5) show that the magnetization is a constant in the rotating reference frame, and therefore is rotating at frequency ω in the laboratory. In a

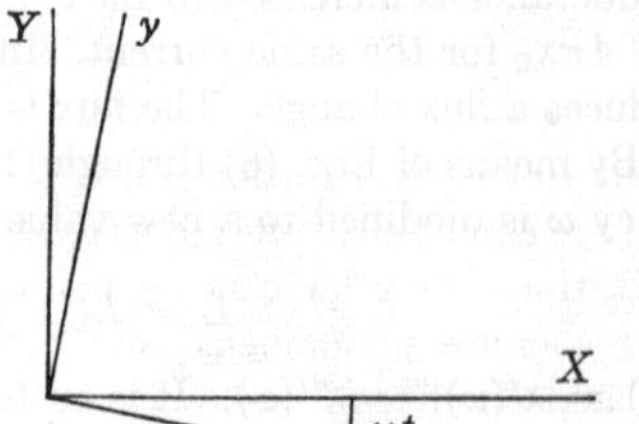

FIG. 2.10. Rotating axes x, y relative to laboratory axes X, Y.

typical experimental arrangement we observe the magnetization by studying the emf it induces in a fixed coil in the laboratory. If the coil is oriented with its axis along the X-direction in the laboratory, we can calculate the emf from knowledge of the time-dependent component of magnetization M_X along the X-direction.

By referring to Fig. 2.10, we can relate the laboratory component M_X to the components M_x and M_y in the rotating frame. Thus

$$M_X = M_x \cos \omega t + M_y \sin \omega t \tag{6}$$

If we write the magnetic field as being a linear field,

$$H_X(t) = H_{X0} \cos \omega t \qquad 2H_1 = H_{X0} \tag{7}$$

then we see that both M_x and M_y are proportional to H_{X0}, and we can write

$$M_X(t) = [\chi' \cos \omega t + \chi'' \sin \omega t]H_{X0} \tag{8}$$

defining the quantities χ' and χ''. By using Eqs. (5) and (8), we get

$$\begin{aligned} \chi' &= \frac{\chi_0}{2}\,\omega_0 T_2 \frac{(\omega_0 - \omega)T_2}{1 + (\omega - \omega_0)^2 T_2^2} \\ \chi'' &= \frac{\chi_0}{2}\,\omega_0 T_2 \frac{1}{1 + (\omega - \omega_0)^2 T_2^2} \end{aligned} \tag{8a}$$

It is convenient to regard both $M_X(t)$ and $H_X(t)$ as being the real parts of complex functions $M_X^C(t)$ and $H_X^C(t)$. Then, defining the complex susceptibility χ by

$$\chi = \chi' - i\chi'' \tag{9}$$

and writing

$$H_X^C(t) = H_{X0}e^{i\omega t} \tag{10}$$

we find

$$M_X^C(t) = \chi H_X^C(t) \tag{11}$$

or

$$M_X(t) = \mathrm{Re}[\chi H_{X0}e^{i\omega t}] \tag{11a}$$

Although Eqs. (7) and (11a) were arrived at by considering the Bloch equations, they are in fact quite general. Any resonance is characterized by a complex susceptibility expressing the linear relationship between magnetization and applied field.

Ordinarily, if a coil of inductance L_0 is filled with a material of susceptibility χ_0, the inductance is increased to $L_0(1 + 4\pi\chi_0)$, since the flux is increased by the factor $1 + 4\pi\chi_0$ for the same current. In a similar manner the complex susceptibility produces a flux change. The flux is not only changed in magnitude but *also* in phase. By means of Eqs. (8) through (11), it is easy to show that the inductance at frequency ω is modified to a new value L, given by

$$L = L_0[1 + 4\pi\chi(\omega)] \tag{12}$$

where $\chi(\omega) = \chi'(\omega) - i\chi''(\omega)$. It is customary in electric circuits to use the symbol j for $\sqrt{-1}$. However, in order to avoid the confusion of using two symbols for the same quantity, we use only i.†

† In practice, the sample never completely fills all space, and we must introduce the "filling factor" q. Its calculation depends on a knowledge of the spatial variation of the alternating field. Then Eq. (12) becomes

$$L = L_0[1 + 4\pi q\chi(\omega)]$$

Denoting the coil resistance in the absence of a sample as R_0, the coil impedance Z becomes

$$\begin{aligned} Z &= iL_0\omega(1 + 4\pi\chi' - i4\pi\chi'') + R_0 \\ &= iL_0\omega(1 + 4\pi\chi') + L_0\omega 4\pi\chi'' + R_0 \end{aligned} \tag{13}$$

The real part of the susceptibility χ' therefore changes the inductance, whereas the imaginary part, χ'', modifies the resistance. The fractional change in resistance $\Delta R/R_0$ is

$$\frac{\Delta R}{R_0} = \frac{L_0\omega}{R_0} 4\pi\chi'' = 4\pi\chi''Q \tag{14}$$

where we have introduced the so-called quality factor Q, typically in a range of 50 to 100 for radio frequency coils or 1,000 to 10,000 for microwave cavities.

Assuming uniform magnetic fields occupying a volume V, the peak stored magnetic energy produced by an alternating current, whose peak value is i_0, is

$$\frac{1}{2} L_0 i_0^2 = \frac{1}{8\pi} H_{x0}^2 V \tag{15}$$

The average power dissipated in the nuclei $\overline{P}$ is

$$\overline{P} = \tfrac{1}{2} i_0^2 \, \Delta R = \tfrac{1}{2} i_0^2 L_0 \omega 4\pi\chi'' \tag{16}$$

By substituting from Eq. (15), we find

$$\overline{P} = \tfrac{1}{2}\omega H_{x0}^2 \chi'' V \tag{17}$$

This equation provides a simple connection between the power absorbed, χ'', and the strength of the alternating field. We shall use it as the basis of a calculation of χ'' from atomic considerations, since the power absorbed can be computed in terms of such quantities as transition probabilities. Since χ' and χ'' are always related, as we shall see shortly, a calculation of χ'' will enable us to compute χ'. Moreover, we recognize that the validity of Eq. (17) does not depend on the assumption of the Bloch equations.

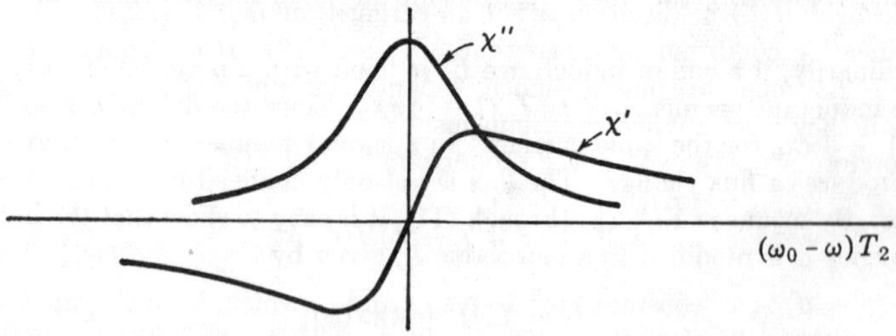

FIG. 2.11. χ' and χ'' from the Bloch equations plotted versus $x \equiv (\omega_0 - \omega)T_2$.

The particular functions χ' and χ'', which are solutions of the Bloch equations, are frequently encountered. They are shown in the graph of Fig. 2.11. The term *Lorentzian line* is often applied to them.

At this time we should point out that we have computed the magnetization produced in the X-direction by an alternating field applied in the X-direction. Since the magnetization vector rotates about the Z-direction, we see that there will also be magnetization in the Y-direction. To describe such a situation, we may consider χ to be a tensor, such that

$$M^C_{\alpha'}(t) = \chi_{\alpha'\alpha} H_{\alpha 0} e^{i\omega t} \qquad \begin{array}{l} \alpha = X, Y, Z \\ \alpha' = X, Y, Z \end{array}$$

In general we shall be interested in χ_{XX}.

2·9 RELATIONSHIP BETWEEN TRANSIENT AND STEADY-STATE RESPONSE OF A SYSTEM AND OF THE REAL AND IMAGINARY PARTS OF THE SUSCEPTIBILITY

Suppose, to avoid saturation, we deal with sufficiently small magnetic fields. The magnetic system may then be considered linear. That is, the magnetization produced by the sum of two weak fields when applied together is equal to the sum of the magnetization produced by each one alone. (We shall not include the static field H_0 as one of the fields, but may find it convenient to consider small *changes* in the static field.) In a similar manner, an ordinary electric circuit is linear, since the current produced by two voltage sources simultaneously present is the sum of the currents each source would produce if the other voltage were zero.

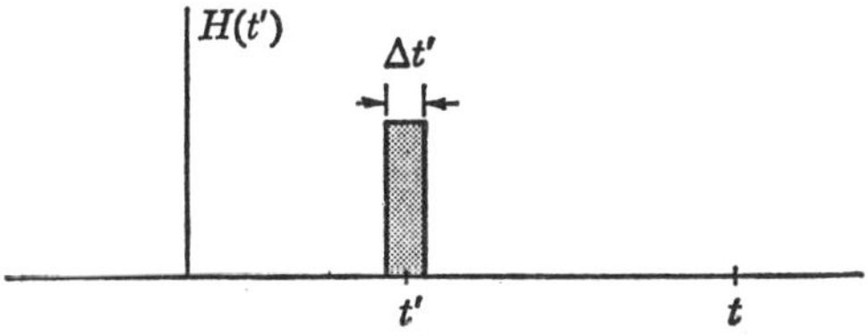

FIG. 2.12. Pulse of magnetic field.

Let us think of the magnetization $\Delta M(t)$ produced at a time t and due to a magnetic field $H(t')$ of duration $\Delta t'$ at an earlier time (see Fig. 2.12). As a result of the linearity condition we know that $\Delta M(t) \propto H(t')$. It is also $\propto \Delta t'$ as long as $\Delta t' \ll t - t'$, since two pulses slightly separate in time must produce the same effect as if they were applied simultaneously.

Therefore we may express the proportionality by writing

$$\Delta M(t) = m(t - t')H(t')\,\Delta t' \tag{1}$$

where $m(t - t')$ is a "constant" for a given t and t', which, however, must depend on how long $(t - t')$ after the pulse of field we wish to know the magnetization. The total magnetization at time t is obtained by integrating Eq. (1) over the history of the magnetic field $H(t')$:

$$M(t) = \int_{-\infty}^{t} m(t - t')H(t')\,dt' \tag{2}$$

Note that $m(t - t') = 0$ if $t' > t$, since the effect cannot precede the cause.

To understand just what $m(t - t')$ is, let us assume $H(t')$ is a δ-function at $t = 0$. Then the magnetization at $t > 0$ (which we shall denote by M_δ) is

$$M_\delta(t) = \int_{-\infty}^{t} m(t - t')\, \delta(t')\, dt' = m(t) \tag{3}$$

That is, $m(t)$ is the response to a δ-function at $t = 0$. Knowledge of $m(t)$ enables us to determine from Eq. (2) the magnetization resulting from a magnetic field of arbitrary time variation.

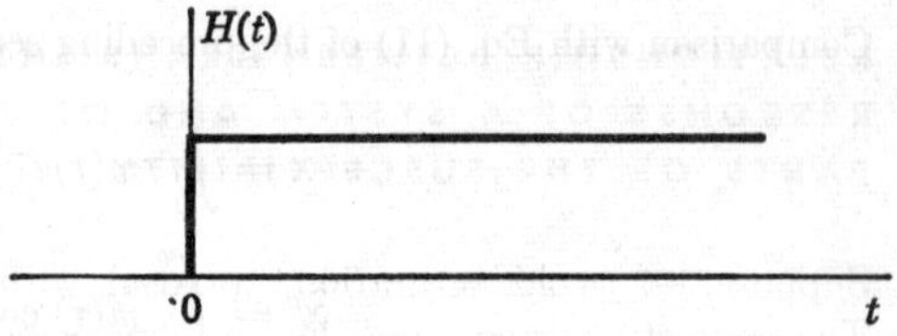

FIG. 2.13. Step function.

If a unit step were applied at $t = 0$ (Fig. 2.13), we should have magnetization, which we shall denote as M_{step}:

$$M_{\text{step}}(t) = \int_0^t m(t - t')\, dt' = \int_0^t m(\tau)\, d\tau \tag{4}$$

By taking the derivative of Eq. (4), we find

$$m(t) = \frac{d}{dt}\,(M_{\text{step}}) \tag{5}$$

Equation (5) therefore shows us that knowledge of $M_{\text{step}}(t)$ enables us to compute $m(t)$.

For example, suppose we discuss the magnetization of a sample following application of a unit magnetic field in the z-direction for a system obeying the Bloch equations. We know from the Bloch equations that

$$M_z(t) = \chi_0[1 - e^{-t/T_1}] = M_{\text{step}} \tag{6}$$

Therefore, using Eq. (5),

$$m(t) = \frac{\chi_0}{T_1}\, e^{-t/T_1} \tag{7}$$

Note that in any real system, the magnetization produced by a step is bounded, so that

$$\int_0^\infty m(\tau)\, d\tau \tag{8}$$

converges.

Suppose we apply an alternating magnetic field. We shall write it as complex for simplicity:

$$H_X^C(t) = H_{X0}e^{i\omega t} \tag{9}$$

Then

$$
\begin{aligned}
M_X^C(t) &= \int_{-\infty}^{t} m(t-t')H_{X0}e^{i\omega t'}\,dt' \\
&= H_{X0}e^{i\omega t}\int_{-\infty}^{t} m(t-t')e^{i\omega(t'-t)}\,dt' \\
&= H_{X0}e^{i\omega t}\int_{0}^{\infty} m(\tau)e^{-i\omega\tau}\,d\tau
\end{aligned}
\tag{10}
$$

Comparison with Eq. (11) of the preceding section shows that

$$
\begin{aligned}
\chi &= \int_0^\infty m(\tau)e^{-i\omega\tau}\,d\tau \\
\chi' &= \int_0^\infty m(\tau)\cos\omega\tau\,d\tau \\
\chi'' &= \int_0^\infty m(\tau)\sin\omega\tau\,d\tau\dagger
\end{aligned}
\tag{11}
$$

It is simple to show, using the integral representation of the δ function,

$$
\delta(x) = \frac{1}{2\pi}\int_{-\infty}^{+\infty} e^{ixt}\,dt \tag{12}
$$

that

$$
m(\tau) = \frac{1}{2\pi}\int_{-\infty}^{+\infty} \chi(\omega)e^{i\omega\tau}\,d\omega \tag{13}
$$

That is, $m(\tau)$ and $\chi(\omega)$ are Fourier transforms of each other. Knowledge of one completely determines the other. One may attempt to predict the properties of

† Strictly speaking, we should turn on the alternating field adiabatically and consider the limit of slower and slower turn-on. Thus we can take

$$
H_X^C(t) = H_{X0}e^{i\omega t}e^{st}
$$

As $t \to -\infty$, this function goes to zero. We compute the limit as $s \to 0$. Thus

$$
\begin{aligned}
M_X^C(t) &= \int_{-\infty}^{t} m(t-t')H_{X0}e^{i\omega t'}e^{st'}dt' \\
&= H_{X0}e^{i\omega t}e^{st}\int_{-\infty}^{t} m(t-t')e^{i\omega(t'-t)}e^{s(t'-t)}\,dt' \\
&= H_{X0}e^{(i\omega+s)t}\int_0^\infty m(\tau)e^{-(s+i\omega)\tau}\,d\tau
\end{aligned}
$$

and

$$
\chi(\omega) = \lim_{s\to 0}\int_0^\infty m(\tau)e^{-(s+i\omega)\tau}\,d\tau
$$

The advantage of this definition is that it has meaning for the case of a "lossless resonator" (magnetic analogue of an undamped harmonic oscillator), in which a sudden application of a field would excite a transient that would never die out.

resonance lines either by analyzing the response to an alternating signal or by analyzing the transient response. Kubo and Tomita,† for example, base their general theory of magnetic resonance on the transient response, calculating the response of the system to a step.

Examination of Eq. (11) enables us to say something about χ' and χ'' at both zero and infinite frequencies. Clearly, χ'' vanishes at $\omega = 0$, since sin 0 vanishes, but χ' does not vanish at $\omega = 0$. Moreover, if $m(\tau)$ is a finite, reasonably continuous function whose total integral $\int_0^\infty m(\tau)\,d\tau$ is bounded, both χ' and χ'' will go to zero as $\omega \to \infty$, since the oscillations of the $\sin \omega\tau$ or $\cos \omega\tau$ will "average" the integrand to zero. Actually we may permit $m(\tau)$ to be infinite at $\tau = 0$. We can see this by thinking of $\int_0^t m(\tau)\,d\tau$, the response to a step. We certainly do not expect the response to a step to be discontinuous at any time other than that when the step is discontinuous ($t = 0$). Therefore $m(\tau)$ can have at most an integrable infinity at $t = 0$, since the response must be bounded. We shall represent this by a δ-function. Thus, if

$$m(\tau) = m_1(\tau) + c_1\,\delta(\tau) \tag{14}$$

where $m_1(\tau)$ has no δ-function, we get

$$\chi'(\omega) = \int_0^\infty m_1(\tau)\cos\omega\tau\,d\tau + c_1 \tag{15}$$

The integral vanishes as $\omega \to \infty$, leaving us $c_1 = \chi'(\infty)$. It is therefore convenient to subtract the δ-function part from $m(\tau)$, which amounts to saying that

$$\chi(\omega) - \chi'(\infty) = \int_0^\infty m(\tau)e^{-i\omega\tau}\,d\tau \tag{16}$$

where *now* $m(\tau)$ has no δ-function part.

[Of course no physical system could have a magnetization that follows the excitation at infinite frequency. However, if one were rather making a theorem about permeability μ, $\mu(\infty)$ is *not* zero. We keep $\chi'(\infty)$ to emphasize the manner in which such a case would be treated.]

We wish now to prove a theorem relating χ' and χ'', the so-called Kramers-Kronig theorem. To do so, we wish to consider χ to be a function of a complex variable $z = x + iy$. The real part of z will be the frequency ω, but we use the symbol x for ω to make the formulas more familiar. Therefore

$$\begin{aligned}\chi(z) - \chi'(\infty) &= \int_0^\infty m(\tau)e^{-iz\tau}\,d\tau \\ &= \int_0^\infty m(\tau)e^{y\tau}e^{-ix\tau}\,d\tau\end{aligned} \tag{17}$$

Since an integral is closely related to a sum, we see that $\chi(z)$ is essentially a sum of exponentials of z. Since each exponential is an analytic function of z, so is the integral, providing nothing too bizarre results from integration.

† R. Kubo and K. Tomita, *J. Phys. Soc. Japan*, **9**: 888 (1954).

To prove that $\chi(z) - \chi'(\infty)$ is an analytic function of z, one may apply the Cauchy derivative test, which says that if

$$\chi(z) - \chi'(\infty) \equiv u + iv \tag{18}$$

where u and v are real, u and v must satisfy the equations

$$\frac{\partial u}{\partial x} = \frac{\partial v}{\partial y} \qquad \text{and} \qquad \frac{\partial v}{\partial x} = -\frac{\partial u}{\partial y} \tag{19}$$

From Eq. (17) we have

$$\begin{aligned} u &= \int_0^\infty m(\tau) \cos x\tau \, e^{y\tau} \, d\tau \\ v &= -\int_0^\infty m(\tau) \sin x\tau \, e^{y\tau} \, d\tau \end{aligned} \tag{20}$$

giving

$$\begin{aligned} \frac{\partial u}{\partial x} &= -\int_0^\infty m(\tau)\tau \sin x\tau \, e^{y\tau} \, d\tau = \frac{\partial v}{\partial y} \\ \frac{\partial u}{\partial y} &= \int_0^\infty m(\tau)\tau \cos x\tau \, e^{y\tau} \, d\tau = -\frac{\partial v}{\partial x} \end{aligned} \tag{21}$$

which satisfy the Cauchy relations, *provided* it is permissible to take derivatives under the integral sign. There are a variety of circumstances under which one can do this, and we refer the reader to the discussion in E. W. Hobson's book†. For our purposes, the key requirement is that the integrals in both Eqs. (20) and (21) must not diverge. This prevents us in general from considering values of y that are too positive. For any reasonable $m(\tau)$ such as that of Eq. (7), the integrals will be convergent for $y \leq 0$, so that $\chi(z) - \chi'(\infty)$ will be analytic on the real axis and in the lower half of the complex z-plane.

Whenever we use functions $m(\tau)$ that are *not* well behaved, we shall also imply that they are to be taken as the limit of a well-behaved function. (Thus an absorption line that has zero width is physically impossible, but may be thought of as the limit of a very narrow line.)

The presence of the term $e^{y\tau}$ tells us that

$$|\chi(z) - \chi'(\infty)| \to 0 \qquad \text{as} \qquad y \to -\infty$$

We already know that

$$|\chi(z) - \chi'(\infty)| \to 0 \qquad \text{as} \qquad x \to \pm\infty$$

Therefore $\chi(z) - \chi'(\infty)$ is a function that is analytic for $y \leq 0$ and goes to zero as $|z| \to \infty$ in the lower half of the complex plane.

---

† E. W. Hobson, *The Theory of Functions of a Real Variable and the Theory of Fourier's Series.* Cambridge University Press, 1926, p. 353 ff.

Let us consider a contour integral along the path of Fig. 2.14 of the function

$$\frac{\chi(z') - \chi'(\infty)}{z' - \omega}$$

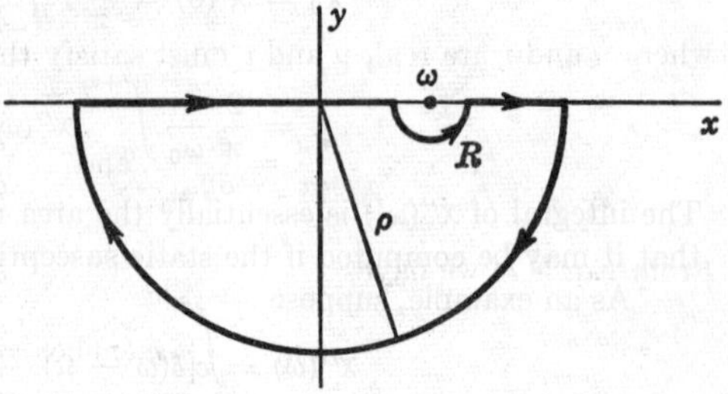

FIG. 2.14. Contour integral.

By Cauchy's integral theorem this integral vanishes, since $\chi(z)$ has no poles inside the contour.

$$\int_C \frac{\chi(z') - \chi'(\infty)}{z' - \omega}\, dz' = 0 \tag{22}$$

Since $|\chi(z') - \chi'(\infty)|$ goes to zero on the large circle of radius ρ, that part of the integral gives zero contribution. There remains the contribution on the real axis plus that on the circle $z' - \omega = Re^{i\phi}$. Thus

$$\begin{aligned}\int_{-\infty}^{\omega-R} \frac{\chi(\omega') - \chi'(\infty)}{\omega' - \omega}\, d\omega' + \int_{\pi}^{2\pi} \frac{[\chi(\omega') - \chi'(\infty)]}{Re^{i\phi}}\, Rie^{i\phi} d\phi \\ + \int_{\omega+R}^{+\infty} \frac{\chi(\omega') - \chi'(\infty)}{\omega' - \omega} \\ = 0 = P\int_{-\infty}^{+\infty} \frac{\chi(\omega') - \chi'(\infty)}{\omega' - \omega}\, d\omega' \\ + \pi i[\chi(\omega) - \chi'(\infty)]\end{aligned} \tag{23}$$

where the symbol P stands for taking the principal part of the integral (that is, takes the limit of the sum of the integrals $\int_{-\infty}^{\omega-R}$ and $\int_{\omega+R}^{+\infty}$ as $R \to 0$ simultaneously in the two integrals).

Solving for the real and imaginary parts, we find

$$\begin{aligned}\chi'(\omega) - \chi'(\infty) &= \frac{1}{\pi} P\int_{-\infty}^{+\infty} \frac{\chi''(\omega')}{\omega' - \omega}\, d\omega' \\ \chi''(\omega) &= -\frac{1}{\pi} P\int_{-\infty}^{+\infty} \frac{\chi'(\omega') - \chi'(\infty)}{\omega' - \omega}\, d\omega'\end{aligned} \tag{24}$$

These are the famous Kramers-Kronig equations. Similar equations can be worked out for analogous quantities such as the dielectric constant or the electrical susceptibility.

The significance of these equations is that there are restrictions placed, for example, on the dispersion by the absorption. One cannot dream up arbitrary $\chi'(\omega)$

and $\chi''(\omega)$. To phrase alternately, we may say that knowledge of χ'' for all frequencies enables one to compute the χ' at any frequency. Note in particular that for a narrow resonance line, assuming $\chi'(\infty) = 0$, the static suscep ibility χ_0 is given by

$$\chi_0 = \chi'(0) = \frac{1}{\pi} P \int_{-\infty}^{+\infty} \frac{\chi''(\omega')}{\omega'} d\omega' \tag{25}$$
$$= \frac{2}{\pi} \frac{1}{\omega_0} \int_0^{+\infty} \chi''(\omega')\, d\omega'$$

The integral of $\chi''(\omega')$ is essentially the area under the absorption curve. We see that it may be computed if the static susceptibility is known.†

As an example, suppose

$$\chi''(\omega) = c[\delta(\omega - \Omega) - \delta(-\omega - \Omega)] \tag{26}$$

The first term corresponds to absorption at frequency Ω. The second term simply makes χ'' an odd function of ω. For this function, what is $\chi'(\omega)$?

$$\chi'(\omega) - \chi'(\infty) = \frac{1}{\pi} P \int_{-\infty}^{+\infty} \frac{c[\delta(\omega' - \Omega) - \delta(-\omega' - \Omega)]\, d\omega'}{\omega' - \omega} \tag{27}$$
$$= \frac{c}{\pi}\left[\frac{1}{\Omega - \omega} - \frac{1}{-\Omega - \omega}\right] = \frac{c}{\pi}\left[\frac{1}{\Omega - \omega} + \frac{1}{\Omega + \omega}\right]$$

where we have used the fact that $\delta(x) = \delta(-x)$.††

Of course, near resonance ($\omega \cong \Omega$), only the first term is large. The function is shown in Fig. 2.15.

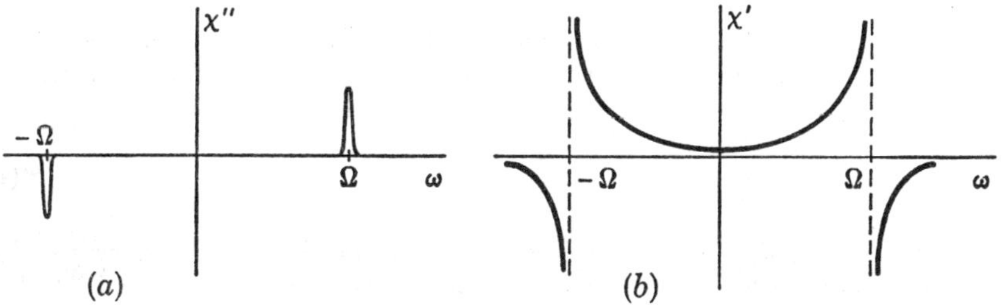

FIG. 2.15. (a) Absorption spectrum. (b) Corresponding dispersion spectrum.

---

† Of course, if we are talking about a magnetic resonance experiment with the static field in the z-direction and the alternating field in the x-direction, we are discussing χ_{xx}. Then $\chi'(0)$ of Eq. (25) is $\chi'_{xx}(0)$, whereas χ_0 is usually thought of as relating the total magnetization M_0 to the field H_0, which produces it, and is thus $\chi'_{zz}(0)$. However, a small static field H_x in the x-direction simply rotates M_0, giving

$$M_x = M_0 \frac{H_x}{H_0} = \chi'_{zz}(0) H_x$$

Thus $\chi'_{xx}(0) = \chi'_{zz}(0) = \chi_0$.

†† That the Dirac δ-function is an even function of x follows from evaluating $\int_{-\infty}^{+\infty} f(x)\, \delta(-x)\, dx$ and changing variables to $x' = -x$, which shows this equals $\int_{-\infty}^{+\infty} f(-x')\, \delta(x')\, dx' = f(0) = \int_{-\infty}^{+\infty} f(x)\, \delta(x)\, dx$. Thus $\delta(x) = \delta(-x)$

2·10 ATOMIC THEORY OF ABSORPTION AND DISPERSION

We shall now turn to obtaining expressions for the absorption and dispersion in terms of atomic properties such as the wave functions, matrix elements, and energy levels of the system under study. We shall compute χ'' directly and obtain χ' from the Kramers-Kronig equations.

We make the connection between the macroscopic and the microscopic properties by computing the average power absorbed, $\overline{P}$, from an alternating magnetic field $H_{x0} \cos \omega t$. From Eq. (17) of Section 2.8 we have

$$\overline{P} = \frac{\omega}{2} \chi'' H_{x0}^2 V \tag{1}$$

in a volume V. It will be convenient henceforth to refer everything to a unit volume. (We shall have to remember this fact when we compute the atomic expressions in particular cases.)

On the other hand, the alternating field couples to the magnetic moment μ_{xk} of the kth spin. Therefore, in our Hamiltonian we shall have a time-dependent perturbation $\mathcal{H}_{\text{pert}}$ of

$$\begin{aligned} \mathcal{H}_{\text{pert}} &= -\sum_k \mu_{xk} H_{x0} \cos \omega t \\ &= -\mu_x H_{x0} \cos \omega t \end{aligned} \tag{2}$$

where μ_x is the x-component of the total magnetic moment

$$\mu_x \equiv \sum_k \mu_{xk} \tag{3}$$

In the absence of the perturbation, the Hamiltonian will typically consist of the interactions of the spins with the external static field and of the coupling $\mathcal{H}_{jk}$ between spins j and k. Thus

$$\mathcal{H} = -\sum_k \mu_{zk} H_0 + \sum_{j,k} \mathcal{H}_{jk} \tag{4}$$

We shall denote the eigenvalues of energy of this many-spin Hamiltonian as E_a, E_b, and so on, with corresponding many-spin wave functions as $|a)$ and $|b)$. See Fig. 2.16. Because of the large number of degrees of freedom there will be a quasi-continuum of energy levels.

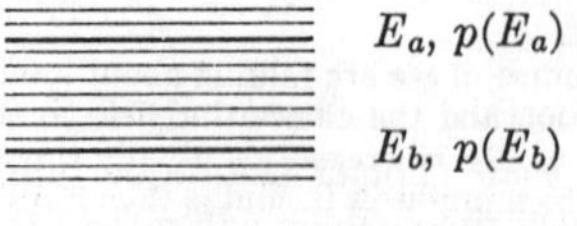

FIG. 2.16. Eigenvalues of energy.

The states $|a)$ and $|b)$ are eigenstates of the Hamiltonian. The most general wave function would be a linear combination of such eigenstates:

$$\Psi = \sum_a c_a |a) e^{-(i/\hbar)E_a t} \tag{5}$$

where the c_a's are complex constants. The square of the absolute value of c_a gives the probability, $p(a)$, of finding the system in the eigenstate a:

$$p(a) = |c_a|^2$$

If the system is in thermal equilibrium, all states will be occupied to some extent, the probability of occupation, $p(a)$, being given by the Boltzmann factor

$$p(E_a) = \frac{e^{-E_a/kT}}{\sum_{E_c} e^{-E_c/kT}} \tag{6}$$

where the sum E_c goes over the entire eigenvalue spectrum. The denominator is just the classical partition function, Z, inserted to guarantee that the total probability of finding the system in any of the eigenstates is equal to unity; that is,

$$\sum_{E_a} p(E_a) = 1$$

We can compute the absorption rate $\overline{P}_{ab}$, due to transitions between states a and b in terms of W_{ab}, the probability per second that a transition would be induced from a to b if the system were entirely in state a initially:

$$\overline{P}_{ab} = \hbar\omega W_{ab}[p(E_b) - p(E_a)] \tag{7}$$

The terms $p(E_b)$ and $p(E_a)$ come in because the states $|a)$ and $|b)$ are only fractionally occupied.

The calculation of the transition probability W_{ab} is well known from elementary quantum mechanics. Suppose we have a time-dependent perturbation $\mathcal{H}_{\text{pert}}$ given by

$$\mathcal{H}_{\text{pert}} = Fe^{-i\omega t} + Ge^{i\omega t} \tag{8}$$

where F and G are two operators. In order that $\mathcal{H}_{\text{pert}}$ will be Hermitian, F and G must be related so that for all states $|a)$ or $|b)$,

$$(a|F|b) = (b|G|a)^* \tag{9}$$

Under the action of such a perturbation we can write that W_{ab} is time independent and is given by the formula

$$W_{ab} = \frac{2\pi}{\hbar} |(a|F|b)|^2 \, \delta(E_a - E_b - \hbar\omega) \tag{10}$$

provided certain conditions are satisfied: We do not ask for details that appear on a time scale shorter than a certain characteristic time τ. It must be possible to find such a time, which will satisfy the conditions that (1) the populations change only a small amount in τ and (2) the possible states between which absorption can occur must be spread in energy continuously over a range ΔE such that $\Delta E \gg \hbar/\tau$.

These conditions are violated if the perturbation matrix element $|(a|F|b)|$ exceeds the line width, as it does when a very strong alternating field is applied. We can see this point as follows: The quantity ΔE may be taken as the line width. We have, then, that $\Delta E < |(a|F|b)|$. But under these circumstances one can show that the populations change significantly in a time of order $\hbar/|(a|F|b)|$. Thus to satisfy the condition 1 that the populations change only a small amount during τ, τ must be chosen less than $\hbar/|(a|F|b)|$. This gives us

$$|(a|F|b)| < \frac{\hbar}{\tau}$$

But, by hypothesis,

$$\Delta E < |(a|F|b)|$$

Therefore

$$\Delta E < \frac{\hbar}{\tau}$$

which violates condition 2 above. Thus it is not possible to satisfy both conditions, and the transition probability is not independent of time.

This example shows why we did not get a simple time-independent rate process in Section 2.6, since for that problem, the energy levels in the absence of H_1 are perfectly sharp ($\Delta E = 0$), $|(a|F|b)| > \Delta E$.

In our formula for W_{ab} we use the δ-function. This implies that we shall eventually sum over a quasi-continuum of energy states. In writing the transition probability, it is preferable to use the δ-function form to the integrated form involving density of states in order to keep track of quantum numbers of individual states.

By summing over all states with $E_a > E_b$, we find

$$\begin{aligned}\overline{P} &= \frac{2\pi}{\hbar}\frac{H_{x0}^2}{4}\hbar\omega \sum_{E_a>E_b} [p(E_b) - p(E_a)]\,|(a|\mu_x|b)|^2\,\delta(E_a - E_b - \hbar\omega) \\ &= \frac{\omega}{2}\chi'' H_{x0}^2\end{aligned} \tag{11}$$

Therefore

$$\chi''(\omega) = \pi \sum_{E_a>E_b} [p(E_b) - p(E_a)]\,|(a|\mu_x|b)|^2\,\delta(E_a - E_b - \hbar\omega) \tag{12}$$

As long as $E_a > E_b$, only positive ω will give absorption because of the δ-function in Eq. (12). Removal of the restriction $E_a > E_b$ extends the meaning of $\chi''(\omega)$ formally to negative ω. Note that since $p(E_b) - p(E_a)$ changes sign when a and b are interchanged, $\chi''(\omega)$ is an odd function of ω, as described in the preceding section.

$$\chi''(\omega) = \pi \sum_{E_a, E_b} [p(E_b) - p(E_a)]\,|(a|\mu_x|b)|^2\,\delta(E_a - E_b - \hbar\omega) \tag{13}$$

Assuming $\chi'(\infty) = 0$ for our system, we can easily compute $\chi'(\omega)$, since

$$\begin{aligned}\chi'(\omega) &= \frac{1}{\pi} P\int_{-\infty}^{+\infty} \frac{\chi''(\omega')}{\omega' - \omega}\,d\omega' \\ &= \pi \sum_{E_a, E_b} [p(E_b) - p(E_a)]\,|(a|\mu_x|b)|^2\,\frac{1}{\pi} P\int_{-\infty}^{+\infty} \frac{\delta(E_a - E_b - \hbar\omega')}{\omega' - \omega}\,d\omega'\end{aligned} \tag{14}$$

or, evaluating the integral,

$$\chi'(\omega) = \sum_{E_a, E_b} [p(E_b) - p(E_a)] |(a|\mu_x|b)|^2 \frac{1}{E_a - E_b - \hbar\omega} \tag{15}$$

By using the fact that a and b are dummy indices, one may also rewrite Eq. (15) to give

$$\chi'(\omega) = \sum_{E_a, E_b} p(E_b)|(a|\mu_x|b)|^2 \left[\frac{1}{E_a - E_b - \hbar\omega} + \frac{1}{E_a - E_b + \hbar\omega}\right] \tag{15a}$$

The quanta $\hbar\omega$ correspond crudely to the energy required to invert a spin in the static field. This energy is usually much smaller than kT. For nuclear moments in strong laboratory fields ($\sim 10^4$ gauss), T must be as low as 10^{-3} °K so that $\hbar\omega$ will be as large as kT. This fact accounts for the difficulty in producing polarized nuclei. For electrons, $kT \sim \hbar\omega$ at about 1°K in a field of 10^4 gauss. Therefore we may often approximate

$$E_a - E_b \ll kT \tag{16}$$

We may call this the "high-temperature approximation." By using Eq. (6) and Eq. (16), we have

$$\begin{aligned} p(E_b) - p(E_a) &= \frac{e^{-E_a/kT}[e^{(E_a - E_b)/kT} - 1]}{Z} \\ &= \frac{e^{-E_a/kT}}{Z}\left(\frac{E_a - E_b}{kT}\right) \end{aligned} \tag{17}$$

Substitution of Eq. (17) into Eq. (13) together with recognition that $E_a - E_b = \hbar\omega$, owing to the δ-functions, gives

$$\chi''(\omega) = \frac{\hbar\omega\pi}{kTZ} \sum_{E_a, E_b} e^{-E_a/kT}|(a|\mu_x|b)|^2 \, \delta(E_a - E_b - \hbar\omega) \tag{18}$$

Another expression for $\chi''(\omega)$ is frequently encountered. It is the basis, for example, of P. W. Anderson's theory of motional narrowing [*J. Phys. Soc. Japan*, **9**: 316 (1954)]. We discuss it in Appendix B because a proper discussion requires reference to some of the materials in Chapters 3 and 5.

It is important to comment on the role of the factors $e^{-E_a/kT}$. If one is dealing with water, for example, the proton absorption lines are found to be quite different at different temperatures. Ice, if cold enough, possesses a resonance several kilocycles broad, whereas the width of the proton resonance in liquid water is only about 1 cycle. Clearly the only difference is associated with the relative mobility of the H_2O molecule in the liquid as opposed to the solid. The position coordinates of the protons therefore play an important role in determining the resonance. Formally we should express this fact by including the kinetic and potential energies of the atoms as well as the spin energies in the Hamiltonian. Then the energies E_a and E_b contain contributions from both spin and positional coordinates. Some states $|a)$ correspond to a solid, some to a liquid. The factor $e^{-E_a/kT}$ picks out the type of "lattice" wave functions or states that are representative of the temperature, that is, whether the water molecules are in liquid, solid, or gaseous phase.

Commonly the exponential factor is omitted from the expression for χ'', but the states $|a)$ and $|b)$ are chosen to be representative of the known state. The classic papers of Gutowsky and Pake, on the effect of hindered molecular motion on the width of resonance, use such a procedure.

Evaluation of χ'' by using Eq. (18) would require knowledge of the wave functions and energy levels of the system. As we shall see, we rarely have that information, but we shall be able to use Eq. (18) to compute the so-called moments of the absorption line. We see that the only frequencies at which strong absorption will occur must correspond to transitions among states between which the magnetic moment has large matrix elements.

CHAPTER 3

MAGNETIC DIPOLAR BROADENING OF RIGID LATTICES

3·1 INTRODUCTION

A number of physical phenomena may contribute to the width of a resonance line. The most prosaic is the lack of homogeneity of the applied static magnetic field. By dint of hard work and clever techniques, this source can be reduced to a few milligauss out of 10^4 gauss, although more typically magnet homogeneities are a few tenths of a gauss. The homogeneity depends on sample size. Typical samples have a volume between 0.1 cc to several cubic centimeters. Of course fields of ultrahigh homogeneity place severe requirements on the frequency stability of the oscillator used to generate the alternating fields. Although these matters are of great technical importance, we shall not discuss them here. If a nucleus possesses a non-vanishing electric quadrupole moment, the degeneracy of the resonance frequencies between different m-values may be lifted, giving rise to either resolved or unresolved splittings. The latter effectively broaden the resonance. The fact that T_1 processes produce an equilibrium population by balancing rates of transitions puts a limit on the lifetime of the Zeeman states, which effectively broadens the resonance lines by an energy of the order of $\hbar/T_1$.

In this chapter, however, we shall ignore all these effects and concentrate on the contribution of the magnetic dipole coupling between the various nuclei to the width of the Zeeman transition. This approximation is often excellent, particularly when the nuclei have spin $\frac{1}{2}$ (thus a vanishing quadrupole moment) and a rather long spin-lattice relaxation time.

A rough estimate of the effect of the dipolar coupling is easily made. If typical neighboring nuclei are a distance r apart and have magnetic moment μ, they produce a magnetic field H_{loc} of the order

$$H_{\text{loc}} = \frac{\mu}{r^3} \tag{1}$$

By using $r = 2\text{Å}$ and $\mu = 10^{-23}$ erg/gauss (10^{-3} of a Bohr magneton), we find $H_{\text{loc}} \cong 1$ gauss. Since this field may either aid or oppose the static field H_0, a spread in the resonance condition results, with significant absorption occurring over a range of $H_0 \sim 1$ gauss. The resonance width on this argument is independent of H_0, but for typical laboratory fields of 10^4 gauss, we see there is indeed a sharp resonant line. Since the width is substantially greater than the magnet inhomogeneity, it is possible to study the shape in detail without instrumental limitations.

3·2 BASIC INTERACTION

The classical interaction energy E between two magnetic moments $\boldsymbol{\mu}_1$ and $\boldsymbol{\mu}_2$ is

$$E = \frac{\boldsymbol{\mu}_1 \cdot \boldsymbol{\mu}_2}{r^3} - \frac{3(\boldsymbol{\mu}_1 \cdot \mathbf{r})(\boldsymbol{\mu}_2 \cdot \mathbf{r})}{r^5} \tag{1}$$

where $\mathbf{r}$ is the radius vector from $\boldsymbol{\mu}_1$ to $\boldsymbol{\mu}_2$. (The expression is unchanged if $\mathbf{r}$ is taken as the vector from $\boldsymbol{\mu}_2$ to $\boldsymbol{\mu}_1$.) For the quantum mechanical Hamiltonian we simply take Eq. (1), treating $\boldsymbol{\mu}_1$ and $\boldsymbol{\mu}_2$ as operators as usual:

$$\begin{aligned} \boldsymbol{\mu}_1 &= \gamma_1 \hbar \mathbf{I}_1 \\ \boldsymbol{\mu}_2 &= \gamma_2 \hbar \mathbf{I}_2 \end{aligned} \tag{2}$$

where we have assumed that both the gyromagnetic ratios and spins may be different. The general dipolar contribution to the Hamiltonian for N spins then becomes

$$\mathcal{H}_d = \frac{1}{2} \sum_{j=1}^{N} \sum_{k=1}^{N} \left[\frac{\boldsymbol{\mu}_j \cdot \boldsymbol{\mu}_k}{r_{jk}^3} - \frac{3(\boldsymbol{\mu}_j \cdot \mathbf{r}_{jk})(\boldsymbol{\mu}_k \cdot \mathbf{r}_{jk})}{r_{jk}^5} \right] \tag{3}$$

where the $\frac{1}{2}$ is needed, since the sums over j and k would count each pair twice, and where, of course, we exclude terms with $j = k$.

By writing $\boldsymbol{\mu}_1$ and $\boldsymbol{\mu}_2$ in component form and omitting the subscripts from $\mathbf{r}$, we see from Eq. (1) that the dipolar Hamiltonian will contain terms such as

$$\begin{aligned} &\gamma_1 \gamma_2 \hbar^2 I_{1x} I_{2x} \frac{1}{r^3} \\ &\gamma_1 \gamma_2 \hbar^2 I_{1x} I_{2x} \frac{xy}{r^5} \end{aligned} \tag{4}$$

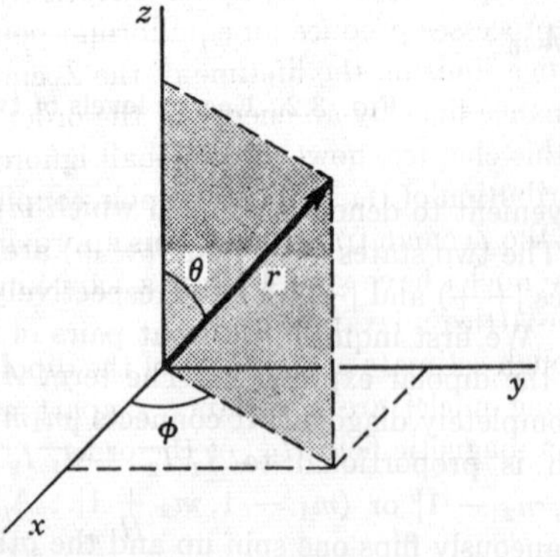

Fig. 3.1. Relationship between rectangular coordinates x, y, z (describing the position of nucleus 2 relative to nucleus 1) and the polar coordinates r, θ, ϕ.

If we express I_{1x} and I_{1y} in terms of the raising and lowering operators I_1^+ and I_1^-, respectively, and express the rectangular coordinates x, y, z in terms of spherical coordinates r, θ, ϕ (Fig. 3.1), we may write the Hamiltonian in a form that is particularly convenient for computing matrix elements:

$$\mathcal{H}_d = \frac{\gamma_1\gamma_2\hbar^2}{r^3}[A + B + C + D + E + F] \tag{5}$$

where

$$\begin{aligned} A &= I_{1z}I_{2z}(1 - 3\cos^2\theta) \\ B &= -\tfrac{1}{4}[I_1^+I_2^- + I_1^-I_2^+](1 - 3\cos^2\theta) \\ C &= -\tfrac{3}{2}[I_1^+I_{2z} + I_{1z}I_2^+]\sin\theta\cos\theta e^{-i\phi} \\ D &= -\tfrac{3}{2}[I_1^-I_{2z} + I_{1z}I_2^-]\sin\theta\cos\theta e^{i\phi} \\ E &= -\tfrac{3}{4}I_1^+I_2^+\sin^2\theta e^{-2i\phi} \\ F &= -\tfrac{3}{4}I_1^-I_2^-\sin^2\theta e^{2i\phi} \end{aligned} \tag{6}$$

As we have remarked, $(\gamma_1\gamma_2\hbar^2)/r^3$ corresponds to the interaction of a nuclear moment with a field of about 1 gauss, whereas the Zeeman Hamiltonian ($\mathcal{H}_Z = -\gamma_1\hbar H_0 I_{1z} - \gamma_2\hbar H_0 I_{2z}$) corresponds to an interaction with a field of 10^4 gauss. It is therefore appropriate to solve the Zeeman problem first and then treat the dipolar term as a small perturbation. (Actually, for two spins of $\frac{1}{2}$, an exact solution is possible.)

To see the significance of the various terms A, B, C, and so on, we shall consider a simple example of two identical moments, both of spin $\frac{1}{2}$.

The Zeeman energy and wave functions can be given in terms of the individual quantum numbers m_1 and m_2, which are the eigenvalues of I_{1z} and I_{2z}. Then the Zeeman energy is

$$E_Z = -\gamma\hbar H_0 m_1 - \gamma\hbar H_0 m_2 \tag{7}$$

We shall diagram the appropriate matrix elements and energy levels in Fig. 3.2.

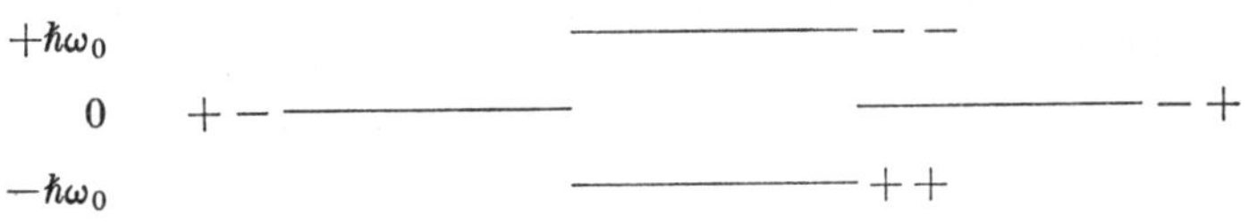

FIG. 3.2. Energy levels of two identical spins.

It is convenient to denote a state in which $m_1 = +\frac{1}{2}$, $m_2 = -\frac{1}{2}$ by the notation $(+-)$. The two states $|+-)$ and $|-+)$ are degenerate, and both have $E_Z = 0$. The states $|++)$ and $|--)$ have respectively $-\hbar\omega_0$ and $+\hbar\omega_0$, where $\omega_0 = \gamma H_0$ as usual. We first inquire into what pairs of states are connected by the various terms in the dipolar expression. The term A, which is proportional to $I_{1z}I_{2z}$, is clearly completely diagonal: It connects $|m_1m_2)$ with $(m_1m_2|$. On the other hand, B, which is proportional to $I_1^+I_2^- + I_1^-I_2^+$, only connects $|m_1m_1)$ to states $(m_1 + 1, m_2 - 1|$ or $(m_1 - 1, m_2 + 1|$. A customary parlance is to say that B simultaneously flips one spin up and the other down. B therefore can join only the states $|+-)$ and $|-+)$. The states joined by A and B are shown diagrammatically in Fig. 3.3.

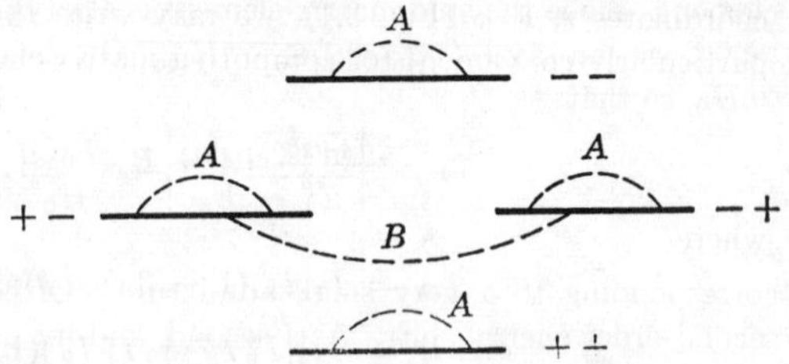

FIG. 3.3. States joined by matrix elements A and B. The dashed lines go between states that are joined.

Note that B has no diagonal matrix elements for the m_1m_2 representation, but it has off-diagonal elements between two states which are degenerate. The fact that off-diagonal elements join the degenerate states $|+\,-)$ and $|-\,+)$ tells us, of course, that they are not the proper zero-order states. B therefore plays an important role in determining the proper zero-order functions. When the proper zero-order functions are determined, B turns out to have diagonal matrix elements. We shall return to this point later.

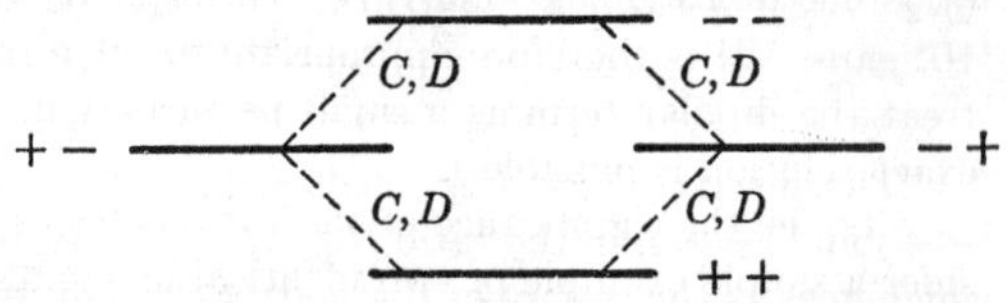

FIG. 3.4. States joined by the terms C and D.

Since terms C and D each flip one spin only, they join states shown in Fig. 3.4, all of which differ by $\hbar\omega_0$ in energy. Finally E and F flip both spins up or both spins down, connecting states that differ by $2\hbar\omega_0$ (Fig. 3.5).

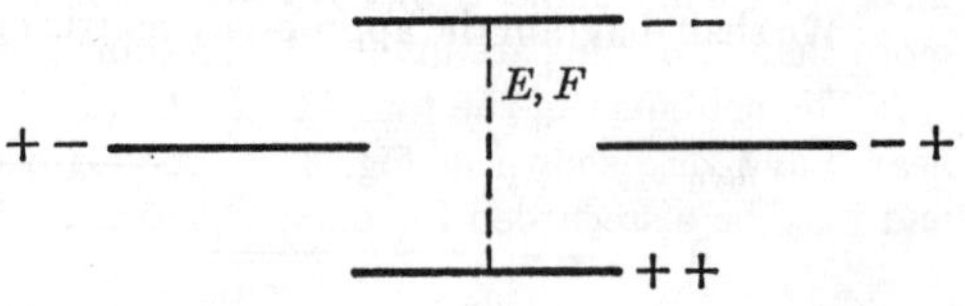

FIG. 3.5. States joined by the dipolar terms E and F.

The terms C, D, E, and F therefore are off-diagonal. They produce slight admixtures of our zero-order states into the exact states. The amount of the admixture can be computed by second-order perturbation theory, using the well-known expression for the correction to the zero-order functions u_n^0 of zero-order energy E_n:

$$u_n = u_n^0 + \sum_{n'} \frac{(n'|\mathcal{H}_{\text{pert}}|n)}{E_n - E_{n'}} u_{n'}^0 \tag{8}$$

where u_n is the wave function corrected for the effect of the perturbation $\mathcal{H}_{\text{pert}}$ and where, of course, the matrix elements $(n'|\mathcal{H}_{\text{pert}}|n)$ are computed between the unperturbed states of $u_{n'}^0$ and u_n^0.

By means of Eq. (8) we can see that the state $|+\,+)$ will have a small admixture of $|+\,-)$, $|-\,+)$, and $|-\,-)$. The amount of admixture will depend on $(n'|\mathcal{H}_{\text{pert}}|n)$ and $E_n - E_{n'}$. The former will be $\gamma^2\hbar^2/r^3$ multiplied by a spin matrix element. Since the spin matrix element is always of order unity, and since $H_{\text{loc}} = \gamma\hbar/r^3$, we can say $(n'|\mathcal{H}_{\text{pert}}|n) \cong \gamma\hbar H_{\text{loc}}$. On the other hand, $E_n - E_{n'} = \hbar\omega_0 = \gamma\hbar H_0$, so that

$$\left|\frac{(n'|\mathcal{H}_{\text{pert}}|n)}{E_n - E_{n'}}\right| \approx \frac{H_{\text{loc}}}{H_0} \sim 10^{-4} \tag{9}$$

corresponding to a very small admixture. Of course the admixture produces a second-order energy shift. As a second, and for us more important, effect, the admixture enables the alternating field to induce transitions that would otherwise be forbidden. Thus the transition from $|++)$ to $|--)$, which would be forbidden if these were exactly the states, can now take place by means of the small admixture of the states $|+-)$ and $|-+)$. (See Fig. 3.6.)

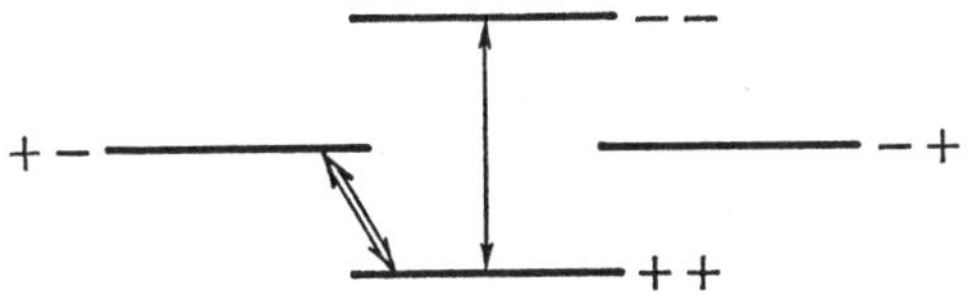

FIG. 3.6. The strong transition is indicated by the double arrow. The transition by the light arrow has non-vanishing matrix elements due to the dipole admixtures.

The matrix element is smaller than the normal one, for example, between $|++)$ and $|+-)$, in the ratio H_{loc}/H_0. Therefore the intensity of the absorption, which goes as the square of the matrix element, is weaker in the ratio $(H_{\text{loc}}/H_0)^2$. This transition occurs, of course, at $\omega = 2\omega_0$. A further consequence of the admixture of states is that a transition near $\omega = 0$ can be induced. [Actually this transition is forbidden for a pair of spins, each of spin $\frac{1}{2}$, because the eigenstates of $M = m_1 + m_2 = 0$ are of different symmetry under exchange of the particle labels (the singlet and triplet states), whereas the perturbation is symmetric. If more than two spins are involved, the transition is permitted.]

The net effect of the terms C, D, E, and F is therefore to give the absorption near 0 and $2\omega_0$, shown in Fig. 3.7. The extra peaks at 0 and $2\omega_0$ are very weak and may be disregarded for our purposes. Since they are the principal effects of

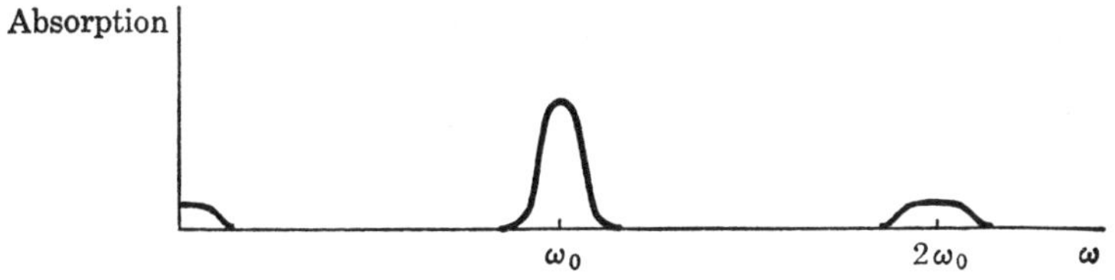

FIG. 3.7. Absorption versus frequency, including dipolar couplings. The three absorption regions have width $\sim\gamma H_{\text{loc}}$, but the intensity of the peaks at 0 and $2\omega_0$ are $\sim(H_{\text{loc}}/H_0)^2$ smaller than that at ω_0.

the terms C, D, E, and F, it will be an excellent approximation to drop C, D, E, and F from the Hamiltonian. For some of our later calculations we shall see that failure to drop these terms can lead us into erroneous results. The remaining dipolar term $A + B$ may be combined to give what we shall call $\mathcal{H}_d^0$:

$$\mathcal{H}_d^0 = \frac{1}{2}\frac{\gamma^2\hbar^2}{r^3}(1 - 3\cos^2\theta)(3I_{1z}I_{2z} - \mathbf{I}_1 \cdot \mathbf{I}_2) \tag{10}$$

and the total simplified Hamiltonian becomes

$$\mathcal{H} = \sum_k (-\gamma\hbar H_0 I_{zk}) + \frac{1}{4}\gamma^2\hbar^2 \sum_{j,k} \frac{(1 - 3\cos^2\theta_{jk})}{r_{jk}^3}(3I_{jz}I_{kz} - \mathbf{I}_j \cdot \mathbf{I}_k) \tag{11}$$

Now the terms $\mathcal{H}_Z$ and $\mathcal{H}_d^0$ commute. {This can be seen by considering a pair of spins 1 and 2. Clearly $I_z = I_{1z} + I_{2z}$ commutes with $3I_{1z}I_{2z}$. How about the terms $\mathbf{I}_1 \cdot \mathbf{I}_2$? I_z commutes with $(\mathbf{I}_1 + \mathbf{I}_2)^2$, since $\mathbf{I}_1 + \mathbf{I}_2 = \mathbf{I}$ is the operator of the total angular momentum (any component of angular momentum commutes with the square of the total angular momentum). By writing $\mathbf{I}^2 = (\mathbf{I}_1 + \mathbf{I}_2)^2$, we have

$$\mathbf{I}^2 = \mathbf{I}_1^2 + \mathbf{I}_2^2 + 2\mathbf{I}_1 \cdot \mathbf{I}_2 \tag{12}$$

We see that $I_{1z} + I_{2z}$ commutes with the left side and the first two terms on the right. Therefore it must commute with $\mathbf{I}_1 \cdot \mathbf{I}_2$.} If two operators commute, we may choose an eigenfunction to be simultaneously an eigenfunction of both. Let us use α to denote the eigenvalues of $\mathcal{H}_d^0$. Then we have

$$\begin{aligned} \mathcal{H}_d^0 u_\alpha &= E_\alpha u_\alpha \\ \mathcal{H}_Z u_M &= (-\gamma\hbar H_0 M) u_M \end{aligned} \tag{13}$$

so that

$$(\mathcal{H}_Z + \mathcal{H}_d^0)|M\alpha) = (-\gamma\hbar H_0 M + E_\alpha)|M\alpha) \tag{14}$$

These quantum numbers will prove useful later. Unfortunately all we can say about the quantum numbers α is that they exist, although we do not know them or the corresponding eigenfunctions. If $\mathcal{H}_d^0$ consisted of only the term $I_{1z}I_{2z}$, we could solve the resonance shape exactly. We could do the same if all we had was $\mathbf{I}_1 \cdot \mathbf{I}_2$. But the presence of both together, since they do not commute, spoils the two solutions. In fact, to proceed further, we are forced to go to the so-called method of moments, a clever technique due to Van Vleck, which enables one to compute properties of the resonance line without solving explicitly for the eigenstates and eigenvalues of energy.

3·3 METHOD OF MOMENTS†

Before outlining the method of moments, we must return to our original expression for $\chi''(\omega)$:

$$\chi''(\omega) = \frac{\pi\hbar\omega}{kTZ}\sum_{a,b} e^{-E_a/kT}|(a|\mu_x|b)|^2\,\delta(E_a - E_b - \hbar\omega) \tag{1}$$

† See references under "Second Moment" in the Bibliography.

Since we shall treat the lattice variables as parameters, the only variables coming into the problem are due to spin; that is, the quantum numbers a and b refer to spins. We shall therefore assume $E_a \ll kT$ and replace the exponentials by 1. The validity of this approximation requires some justification since the E_a's are energies of the total Hamiltonian of all N spins. If the nuclei had spin $\frac{1}{2}$, and if the only energy were the Zeeman energy, an individual spin could have energy $\pm\gamma_n\hbar H_0/2$, but the energy E_a could range between $\pm N\gamma_n\hbar H_0/2$. Since N may be very large, there are values of E_a that clearly violate the restriction $|E_a| \ll kT$. But the largest energy, $N\gamma_n\hbar H_0/2$, is realized only when all spins are parallel. The next smallest energy may be obtained by turning over one spin, it is $E_a = (N - 2)\gamma\hbar H_0/2$. However, we could turn over any of the N spins, so that this energy is N-fold degenerate. We expect, in fact, that a Gaussian distribution will describe the number of states of any given energy. Typical energies E_a will therefore be of order $\sqrt{N}\,\gamma\hbar H_0/2$ which is still much larger than the Zeeman energy of a single spin. However, we know that the energy levels of a single spin give a very good prediction of the frequency of absorption, so that we suspect the $\sqrt{N}$ effect must in some sense be a red herring. That such is the case is shown in Appendix E where we demonstrate that the high temperature approximation is valid if $\gamma\hbar H_0 I \ll kT$.

With this approximation the shape of the line is then given by the factor ω and by the function $f(\omega)$ defined as

$$f(\omega) = \sum_{a,b} |(a|\mu_x|b)|^2\,\delta(E_a - E_b - \hbar\omega) \tag{2}$$

In fact, experimental determinations of $\chi''(\omega)$ enable us to compute $f(\omega)$ from Eq. (1), and conversely a theoretical determination of $f(\omega)$ gives us $\chi''(\omega)$. We focus therefore on $f(\omega)$. First we note that since $\chi''(\omega)$ was an odd function of ω, $f(\omega)$ is an even function. [This fact is also evident by explicit examination of $f(\omega)$.] We now define the nth moments of $f(\omega)$ by the equation

$$\langle\omega^n\rangle = \frac{\int_0^\infty \omega^n f(\omega)\,d\omega}{\int_0^\infty f(\omega)\,d\omega} \tag{3}$$

and

$$\langle\Delta\omega^n\rangle = \frac{\int_0^\infty (\omega - \langle\omega\rangle)^n f(\omega)\,d\omega}{\int_0^\infty f(\omega)\,d\omega} \tag{4}$$

The expression (4) for $n = 2$ is called the "second moment." Clearly $\langle\Delta\omega^2\rangle$ is of the order of the square of the line width, so that

$$\langle\Delta\omega^2\rangle \cong (\gamma H_{\text{loc}})^2 \tag{5}$$

The two moments of Eqs. (3) and (4) are closely related, as may readily be seen for $n = 2$ as follows: Expanding $(\omega - \langle\omega\rangle)^2 = \omega^2 - 2\omega\langle\omega\rangle + \langle\omega\rangle^2$, one easily shows from Eqs. (3) and (4) that

$$\langle \Delta\omega^2 \rangle = \langle \omega^2 \rangle - \langle \omega \rangle^2 \tag{6}$$

Therefore we can compute either $\langle \Delta\omega^2 \rangle$ directly or compute it from the calculations of $\langle \omega^2 \rangle$ and $\langle \omega \rangle$. (We shall do the latter.)

To illustrate the general methods, we shall first compute $\int_0^\infty f(\omega)\, d\omega$, which is, of course, closely related to the area under the absorption curve. Then we shall compute $\langle \omega \rangle$ and $\langle \Delta\omega^2 \rangle$. Since $f(\omega)$ is an even function,

$$\int_0^\infty f(\omega)\, d\omega = \frac{1}{2}\int_{-\infty}^{+\infty} f(\omega)\, d\omega = \frac{1}{2}\int_{-\infty}^{+\infty} \sum_{a,b} (a|\mu_x|b)(b|\mu_x|a)\, \delta(E_a - E_b - \hbar\omega)\, d\omega \tag{7}$$

The integrand picks up a contribution from the δ-function integral every time $\hbar\omega = E_a - E_b$. But for any pair of states $|a)$ and $|b)$, there is *some* value of ω between $-\infty$ and $+\infty$ which satisfies the condition $\hbar\omega = E_a - E_b$. (Note, if we had the integral from 0 to ∞, we should have zero from states for which $E_a - E_b$ was negative. It is for this reason that we let the integral range from $-\infty$ to $+\infty$.) Thus, changing the variable of integration from ω to $\hbar\omega$, we get

$$\int_0^\infty f(\omega)\, d\omega = \frac{1}{2\hbar} \sum_{a,b} (a|\mu_x|b)(b|\mu_x|a) \tag{8}$$

But it is a basic theorem of quantum mechanics that for any complete set $|\beta')$ and for any operators A and B,

$$\sum_{\beta'} (\beta|A|\beta')(\beta'|B|\beta'') = (\beta|AB|\beta'') \tag{8a}$$

So, we can rewrite Eq. (8) as

$$\int_0^\infty f(\omega)\, d\omega = \frac{1}{2\hbar} \sum_a (a|\mu_x^2|a) = \frac{1}{2\hbar}\, \mathrm{Tr}\mu_x^2 \tag{9}$$

where the symbol "Tr" stands for "trace" or sum of the diagonal matrix elements. Another important theorem tells us that when we go from one complete set of orthogonal functions $|\beta)$ to an alternate one $|\xi)$, [$|\beta)$ can thus be expressed as a linear combination of the $|\xi)$'s], the trace is unchanged. We may therefore choose any complete set of functions to compute the trace. In fact we shall choose a set of functions that is simply the product of the individual spin functions of quantum numbers $m_1, m_2, m_3 \cdots m_N$ for the N-spins. Therefore

$$\int_0^\infty f(\omega)\, d\omega = \frac{1}{2\hbar} \sum_{m_1, m_2, m_3 \cdots} (m_1 m_2 m_3 \cdots |\mu_x^2| m_1 m_2 m_3 \cdots) \tag{10}$$

Now, since $\mu_x = \sum_j \mu_{xj}$,

$$\mu_x^2 = \sum_{j,k} \mu_{xj}\mu_{xk} \tag{11}$$

There are two types of terms: $j \neq k$ and $j = k$. We examine the first kind first.

Let us consider $j = 1$, $k = 2$. Then, holding $m_2, m_3, m_4 \cdots$ fixed, we can first sum over m_1. Now,

$$(m_1 m_2 m_3 \cdots |\mu_{1x}\mu_{2x}| m_1 m_2 \cdots) = (m_1|\mu_{1x}|m_1)(m_2|\mu_{2x}|m_2) \tag{12}$$

so that summing over m_1 gives us

$$\left[\sum_{m_1} (m_1|\mu_{1x}|m_1)\right](m_2|\mu_{2x}|m_2) \tag{13}$$

Now, $\sum_{m_1}(m_1|\mu_{1x}|m_1) = 0$. This may be seen by noting that when we take m_1 as eigenvalues of I_{1z}, all the diagonal elements of I_{1x} and μ_{1x} are zero. Or, alternatively, one may let m_1 be the eigenvalues of I_{1x}. But for every $+m$ value there is a corresponding negative one, so that

$$\sum_{m_1} (m_1|\mu_{1x}|m_1) = \gamma\hbar \sum_{m_1} (m_1|I_{1x}|m_1) = 0 \tag{14}$$

Therefore the contribution from terms $j \neq k$ vanishes. For $j = k$, we get, taking $j = 1$,

$$\frac{1}{2\hbar} \sum_{m_1, m_2 \cdots} (m_1 m_2 \cdots |\mu_{1x}^2| m_1 m_2 \cdots) = \frac{\gamma^2\hbar^2}{2\hbar} \sum_{m_1, m_2 \cdots} (m_1 m_2 \cdots |I_{1x}^2| m_1 m_2 \cdots) \tag{15}$$

The matrix element is independent of m_2, m_3, and so on, but it is *repeated* for each combination of the other quantum numbers. Since there are $(2I + 1)$ values of m_2, $(2I + 1)$ values of m_3, and so on, we get the matrix for each value of m_1 repeated $(2I + 1)^{N-1}$ times. On the other hand, using Tr_1 to mean a trace only over quantum numbers of spin 1, we have that $\mathrm{Tr}_1\mu_{1x}^2 = \mathrm{Tr}_1\mu_{1y}^2$. This equation is most simply proved by first evaluating $\mathrm{Tr}_1\mu_{1x}^2$, using eigenfunctions of I_{1x}. Then

$$\mathrm{Tr}_1\mu_{1x}^2 = \gamma^2\hbar^2 \sum_{m=-I}^{+I} m^2 \tag{16}$$

In a similar way, $\mathrm{Tr}_1\mu_{1y}^2$ may be evaluated by using eigenfunctions of I_{1y}:

$$\mathrm{Tr}_1\mu_{1y}^2 = \gamma^2\hbar^2 \sum_{m=-I}^{+I} m^2 \tag{16a}$$

Therefore

$$\mathrm{Tr}_1\mu_{1x}^2 = \mathrm{Tr}_1\mu_{1y}^2 = \mathrm{Tr}_1\mu_{1z}^2 = \tfrac{1}{3}\mathrm{Tr}\mu_1^2 \tag{16b}$$

There are $2I + 1$ diagonal matrix elements of μ_1^2, each of magnitude $\gamma^2\hbar^2 I(I + 1)$. Therefore

$$\mathrm{Tr}_1\mu_{1x}^2 = \frac{\gamma^2\hbar^2 I(I + 1)}{3}(2I + 1)$$

Since there are N identical terms of $j = k$, finally we get as our answer:

$$\int_0^\infty f(\omega)\, d\omega = \frac{1}{2\hbar}\gamma^2\hbar^2 \frac{I(I + 1)}{3} N(2I + 1)^N \tag{17}$$

We turn now to a calculation of the effect of the dipolar coupling on the average frequency of absorption, $\langle\omega\rangle$. The existence of such a shift implies that the local field produced by the neighbors has a preferential orientation with respect to the applied field. Since such an effect must correspond to a Lorentz local field, ΔH, it must be of general order $\chi_n H_0$, where χ_n is the static nuclear susceptibility. χ_n is given by the Langevin-Debye formula: $\chi_n = N\gamma^2\hbar^2 I(I+1)/3kT$, where N is the number of nuclei per unit volume. If the distance between nearest neighbors is a, $N \cong 1/a^3$, we have, therefore, that $\Delta H \cong (\gamma\hbar/a^3)(\gamma\hbar H_0/kT) \cong H_{\text{loc}}(\gamma\hbar H_0/kT)$. Since the nuclear Zeeman energy $\gamma\hbar H_0$ is very small compared with kT, we see ΔH is very small compared with the line breadth H_{loc} and is presumably negligible. Notice that the physical significance of our expression for ΔH is that the neighbors have a slight preferential orientation parallel to the static field given by the exponent of the Boltzmann factor $(\gamma\hbar H_0/kT)$. H_{loc} has a non-zero average to this extent. Since $f(\omega)$ of Eq. (2) corresponds to infinite temperature, it must lead to a $\Delta H = 0$, and $\langle\omega\rangle = \omega_0$.

To compute the average frequency or first moment rigorously

$$\langle\omega\rangle = \frac{\int_0^\infty \omega f(\omega)\,d\omega}{\int_0^\infty f(\omega)\,d\omega}$$

is a bit more difficult than the calculation of $\int_0^\infty f(\omega)\,d\omega$. In Eq. (7) it was convenient to extend the limits of integration to go from $-\infty$ to $+\infty$. As a result, for every pair of energies E_a and E_b, there was some frequency ω such that $E_a - E_b = \hbar\omega$, regardless of whether E_a was higher or lower than E_b. We cannot do the same thing for $\langle\omega\rangle$, since

$$\int_{-\infty}^{+\infty} \omega f(\omega)\,d\omega = 0 \tag{18}$$

because the integrand is an odd function of ω. We therefore are forced to compute $\int_0^\infty \omega f(\omega)\,d\omega$:

$$\begin{aligned}\int_0^\infty \omega f(\omega)\,d\omega &= \frac{1}{\hbar^2}\sum_{a,b}\int_0^{+\infty} (a|\mu_x|b)(b|\mu_x|a)(\hbar\omega)\,\delta(E_a - E_b - \hbar\omega)\,d(\hbar\omega)\\ &= \frac{1}{\hbar^2}\sum_{E_a>E_b}(a|\mu_x|b)(b|\mu_x|a)(E_a - E_b)\end{aligned} \tag{19}$$

The energies E_a and E_b are the sum of dipolar and Zeeman contributions $(-\gamma\hbar H_0 M + E_\alpha)$, as we have remarked previously. We shall assume that the dipolar energy changes are always small compared with the changes in Zeeman energy and that the latter correspond to absorption near ω_0 (our earlier discussion of the role of the terms $A, B, \cdots F$ shows us this fact). Therefore, since $E_a > E_b$, we write

$$\begin{aligned}E_a &= -\gamma\hbar H_0 M + E_\alpha\\ E_b &= -\gamma\hbar H_0(M+1) + E_{\alpha'}\\ E_a - E_b &= \hbar\omega_0 + E_\alpha - E_{\alpha'}\end{aligned} \tag{20}$$

By using these relations, we can write Eq. (19) as

$$\int_0^\infty \omega f(\omega)\,d\omega = \frac{1}{\hbar^2}\sum_{M,\alpha,\alpha'} (M\alpha|\mu_x|M+1\alpha')(M+1\alpha'|\mu_x|M\alpha)(\hbar\omega_0 + E_\alpha - E_{\alpha'}) \tag{21}$$

We shall first discuss the contribution of the $\hbar\omega_0$ term in the parentheses. It is

$$\frac{\hbar\omega_0}{\hbar^2}\sum_{M,\alpha,\alpha'} (M\alpha|\mu_x|M+1\alpha')(M+1\alpha'|\mu_x|M\alpha) \tag{22}$$

Were it not for the restriction to $M+1$, Eq. (22) could be converted to a trace by means of Eq. (8a). This restriction can be removed by using the properties of the raising and lowering operators and by noting that

$$\mu_x = \tfrac{1}{2}(\mu^+ + \mu^-)$$

Thus (23)

$$(M+1\alpha'|\mu_x|M\alpha) = \tfrac{1}{2}(M+1\alpha'|\mu^+|M\alpha)$$

Since μ^+ connects only states M' and M in a matrix element, $(M'\alpha'|\mu^+|M\alpha)$ where $M' = M+1$, we can rewrite Eq. (22), summing over *all* values of M' as

$$\begin{aligned}\frac{\hbar\omega_0}{4\hbar^2}\sum_{\substack{M,M'\\ \alpha,\alpha'}} (M\alpha|\mu^-|M'\alpha')(M'\alpha'|\mu^+|M\alpha) &= \frac{\omega_0}{4\hbar}\,\mathrm{Tr}\mu^-\mu^+ \\ &= \frac{\omega_0}{4\hbar}\,\mathrm{Tr}[\mu_x - i\mu_y)(\mu_x + i\mu_y) \\ &= \frac{\omega_0}{4\hbar}\,\mathrm{Tr}[\mu_x^2 + \mu_y^2 + i(\mu_x\mu_y - \mu_y\mu_x)] \\ &= \frac{\omega_0}{2\hbar}\,\mathrm{Tr}\mu_x^2\end{aligned} \tag{24}$$

where we have used the facts that $\mathrm{Tr}\mu_x^2 = \mathrm{Tr}\mu_y^2$, and

$$\begin{aligned}\mathrm{Tr}(\mu_x\mu_y - \mu_y\mu_x) &= \gamma^2\hbar^2\,\mathrm{Tr}(I_xI_y - I_yI_x) \\ &= \gamma^2\hbar^2 i\,\mathrm{Tr}I_z = 0\end{aligned} \tag{25}$$

We have so far handled the $\hbar\omega_0$ term of Eq. (21). The technique for handling the term $E_\alpha - E_{\alpha'}$ is very simple. We know that $\mathcal{H}_d^0|M\alpha') = E_{\alpha'}|M\alpha')$. Therefore, for an operator P, we have

$$\begin{aligned}(M'\alpha'|P\mathcal{H}_d^0|M\alpha) &= \int u_{M'\alpha'}^* P\mathcal{H}_d^0 u_{M\alpha}\,d\tau \\ &= \int u_{M'\alpha'}^* PE_\alpha u_{M\alpha}\,d\tau \\ &= E_\alpha(M'\alpha'|P|M\alpha)\end{aligned} \tag{26}$$

Likewise, using the fact that $\mathcal{H}_d^0$ is Hermitian,

$$
\begin{aligned}
(M'\alpha'|\mathcal{H}_d^0 P|M\alpha) &= \int u^*_{M'\alpha'}\mathcal{H}_d^0 P u_{M\alpha}\, d\tau \\
&= \int (\mathcal{H}_d^0 u_{M'\alpha'})^* P u_{M\alpha}\, d\tau \\
&= E_{\alpha'}\int u^*_{M'\alpha'} P u_{M\alpha}\, d\tau \\
&= E_{\alpha'}(M'\alpha'|P|M\alpha)
\end{aligned}
\tag{27}
$$

Therefore

$$
\begin{aligned}
\sum_{\substack{\alpha,\alpha'\\ M,M'}} (M\alpha|\mu^-|M'\alpha')(M'\alpha'|\mu^+|M\alpha)(E_\alpha - E_{\alpha'}) \\
= \sum_{\substack{\alpha,\alpha'\\ M,M'}} (M\alpha|[\mathcal{H}_d^0, \mu^-]|M'\alpha')(M'\alpha'|\mu^+|M\alpha) \\
= \mathrm{Tr}([\mathcal{H}_d^0, \mu^-]\mu^+)
\end{aligned}
\tag{28}
$$

A detailed evaluation of this trace shows that it vanishes. Therefore, combining the results of Eqs. (21), (24), and (28), we get

$$
\int_0^\infty \omega f(\omega)\, d\omega = \frac{\omega_0}{2\hbar}\,\mathrm{Tr}\mu_x^2 \tag{29}
$$

But from Eq. (9),

$$
\int_0^\infty f(\omega)\, d\omega = \frac{1}{2\hbar}\,\mathrm{Tr}\mu_x^2
$$

Therefore

$$
\langle\omega\rangle = \frac{\displaystyle\int_0^\infty \omega f(\omega)\, d\omega}{\displaystyle\int_0^\infty f(\omega)\, d\omega} = \omega_0 \tag{30}
$$

The "average" value of the frequency is therefore unshifted by the broadening as we had expected. To get the local field correction that we mentioned in our qualitative discussion, we should, in fact, have to go back to Eq. (2) and include the exponential factors that we deleted in going from Eq. (1). (That this is true follows from the fact that the expression $\Delta H \approx H_{\text{loc}}(\gamma\hbar H_0/kT)$ depends on temperature. The only place the temperature enters is in the exponentials.)

We can compute the second moment, $\langle\omega^2\rangle$, by similar techniques:

$$
\langle\omega^2\rangle = \frac{\displaystyle\int_0^\infty \omega^2 f(\omega)\, d\omega}{\displaystyle\int_0^\infty f(\omega)\, d\omega} \tag{31}
$$

Since we have already evaluated the denominator, all that remains is to compute the numerator:

$$\int_0^\infty \omega^2 f(\omega)\,d\omega = \frac{1}{2}\int_{-\infty}^{+\infty} \omega^2 f(\omega)\,d\omega$$
$$= \frac{1}{2}\int_{-\infty}^{+\infty} \sum_{a,b} \omega^2 (a|\mu_x|b)(b|\mu_x|a)\,\delta(E_a - E_b - \hbar\omega)\,d\omega \tag{32}$$
$$= \frac{1}{2\hbar^3}\sum_{a,b}(E_a - E_b)^2(a|\mu_x|b)(b|\mu_x|a)$$

By using the fact that $\mathcal{H}|a) = E_a|a)$, we see, as in Eqs. (27) and (28),

$$\int_0^\infty \omega^2 f(\omega)\,d\omega = -\frac{1}{2\hbar^3}\sum_{a,b}(a|\mathcal{H}\mu_x - \mu_x\mathcal{H}|b)(b|\mathcal{H}\mu_x - \mu_x\mathcal{H}|a)$$
$$= -\frac{1}{2\hbar^3}\,\mathrm{Tr}[\mathcal{H}, \mu_x]^2 \tag{33}$$

We can expand, using $\mathcal{H} = \mathcal{H}_Z + \mathcal{H}_d^0$ to get

$$\int_0^\infty \omega^2 f(\omega)\,d\omega = -\frac{1}{2\hbar^3}\,\mathrm{Tr}[\mathcal{H}_Z, \mu_x]^2 - \frac{2}{2\hbar^3}\,\mathrm{Tr}[\mathcal{H}_Z, \mu_x][\mathcal{H}_d^0, \mu_x] - \frac{1}{2\hbar^3}\,\mathrm{Tr}[\mathcal{H}_d^0, \mu_x]^2 \tag{34}$$

where in the "cross-term" involving $[\mathcal{H}_Z, \mu_x]$ and $[\mathcal{H}_d^0, \mu_x]$, we have used the basic relation true for any pair of operators A and B:

$$\mathrm{Tr}AB = \mathrm{Tr}BA \tag{35}$$

which is readily proved by applying Eq. (8a). If the dipolar coupling were zero, only the first term on the right would survive, and of course the resonance would be a δ-function at $\omega = \omega_0$. In this case $\langle\omega^2\rangle = \omega_0^2$. Therefore we see that the first term must contribute ω_0^2 to $\langle\omega^2\rangle$. Explicit evaluation in fact verifies this result. The second, or "cross," term vanishes, since every term involves factors such as $\mathrm{Tr}_1\mu_{1x}$. The last term, when divided by $\int_0^\infty f(\omega)\,d\omega$ gives

$$\frac{3}{4}\gamma^4\hbar^2 I(I+1)\left(\frac{1}{N}\right)\sum_{j,k}\frac{(1 - 3\cos^2\theta_{jk})^2}{r_{jk}^6} \tag{36}$$

Now, by Eq. (6),

$$\langle\Delta\omega^2\rangle = \langle\omega^2\rangle - \langle\omega\rangle^2$$

Therefore, since $\langle\omega\rangle = \omega_0$, we have

$$\langle\Delta\omega^2\rangle = \frac{3}{4}\gamma^4\hbar^2 I(I+1)\,\frac{1}{N}\sum_{j,k}\frac{(1 - 3\cos^2\theta_{jk})^2}{r_{jk}^6} \tag{37}$$

We can get a clearer understanding of Eq. (37) by considering an example in which all spins are located in equivalent positions, so that

$$\sum_k \frac{(1 - 3\cos^2\theta_{jk})^2}{r_{jk}^6}$$

is independent of j. There are then N equivalent sums, one for each value of j, giving us

$$\langle\Delta\omega^2\rangle = \frac{3}{4}\gamma^4\hbar^2 I(I+1)\sum_k \frac{(1 - 3\cos^2\theta_{jk})^2}{r_{jk}^6} \tag{38}$$

Each term is clearly of order $(\gamma H_{\text{loc}}^k)^2$ where H_{loc}^k is the contribution of the kth spin to the local field at spin j. The important point about Eq. (38) is that it gives a precise meaning to the concept of a local field, which enables one to compare a precisely defined theoretical quantity with experimental values.

So far we have considered only the second moment for a case where all nuclei are identical. If more than one species is involved, we get a somewhat different answer. The basic difference is in the terms of type B in the dipolar coupling that connect states such as $|+\,-)$ to $|-\,+)$. If the two states are degenerate, as in the case when the spins are identical, B makes a first-order shift in the energy. On the other hand, when the states are non-degenerate, B merely produces second-order energy shifts and gives rise to weak, otherwise forbidden transitions. It is therefore appropriate to omit B when the spins are unlike.†

The interactions between like and unlike nuclei spins may be compared and the second moment readily obtained. If we use the symbol I for the species under observation, and S for the other species, the effective dipolar coupling between like nuclei is

$$(\mathcal{H}_d^0)_{II} = \frac{1}{4}\gamma_I^2\hbar^2\sum_{k,l}\frac{(1 - 3\cos^2\theta_{kl})}{r_{kl}^3}(3I_{zk}I_{zl} - \mathbf{I}_k\cdot\mathbf{I}_l) \tag{39}$$

In computing the second moment for like spins, the terms $\mathbf{I}_k\cdot\mathbf{I}_l$ do not contribute, since they commute with μ_x (see Eq. 34). The coupling between unlike spins is

$$(\mathcal{H}_d^0)_{IS} = \gamma_I\gamma_S\hbar^2\sum_{k,l}\frac{(1 - 3\cos^2\theta_{kl})}{r_{kl}^3}I_{zk}S_{zl} \tag{40}$$

Equations (39) and (40) differ primarily in the numerical factor of the zz-term, Eq. (40) being small by a factor of $\frac{2}{3}$. This numerical factor becomes $\frac{4}{9}$ in the second moment, giving for the final answer:

$$\langle\Delta\omega^2\rangle_{IS} = \frac{1}{3}\gamma_I^2\gamma_S^2\hbar^2 S(S+1)\frac{1}{N}\sum_{j,k}\frac{(1 - 3\cos^2\theta_{jk})^2}{r_{jk}^6} \tag{41}$$

Notice that it is $S(S+1)$, not $I(I+1)$, that comes into Eq. (41), expressing the fact that the local magnetic field seen by nuclei I is proportional to the magnetic

† Van Vleck points out that omitting these terms for unlike spins as well as the terms C, D, E, and F for like spins is crucial in computing $\langle\Delta\omega^2\rangle$. The reason is that in computing $\langle\Delta\omega^2\rangle$, the rather weak satellite lines at $\omega = 0$ and $\omega = 2\omega_0$ correspond to a typical frequency from the center of the resonance, which is H_0/H_{loc} larger than those of the main transition. The second moment measures the square of the frequency deviation. Therefore, although the satellites are down in intensity by $(H_{\text{loc}}/H_0)^2$, they contribute an amount quite comparable to the second moment. Since we are concerned with the width of the main transition, we do not wish to include the satellites. We must exclude the terms that produce them from the Hamiltonian.

moment $(\gamma_S \hbar \sqrt{S(S+1)})$ of the other species. The total second moment of the resonance line of spin I is given by adding the second-moment contributions of like nuclei to that of unlike nuclei.

3·4 EXAMPLE OF THE USE OF SECOND MOMENTS

Since the pioneering work of Pake and Gutowsky, numerous studies of second moments have been reported. A particularly interesting example is provided by the work of Andrew and Eades† on solid benzene. By studying the various isotopic compositions in which protons were replaced by deuterons, they were able to measure the proton-proton distance between adjacent protons in the ring and to show that at temperatures above about 90° K, the benzene molecules are relatively free to reorient about the axis perpendicular to the plane of the molecule. We shall describe their work.

The three isotopic species studied by Andrew and Eades are shown in Fig. 3.8.

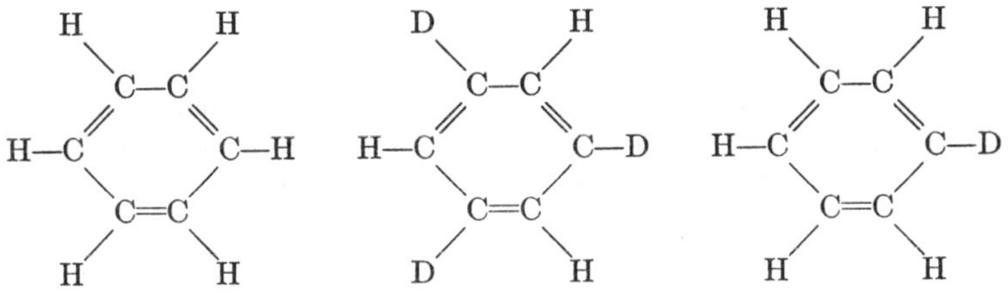

FIG. 3.8. Three species of benzene studied by Andrew and Eades.

The structure of the benzene crystal is very similar to that of a face-centered cubic crystal with the benzene molecules on the corners and face centers of the cube. However, although the sides of the unit cell are perpendicular, they are not equal in length, the a-, b-, and c-axes being respectively 7.44 Å, 9.65 Å, and 6.81 Å. All benzenes have their planes parallel to the crystalline b-axis. A rough sketch of the

FIG. 3.9. Unit cell of the benzene crystal. Solid lines represent molecules in the $y = 0$ plane; dashed lines represent molecules $b/2$ above.

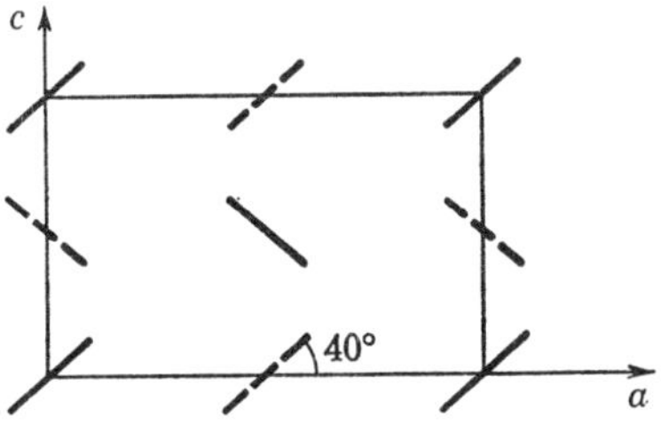

crystal structure is shown in Fig. 3.9, looking down to the b-axis edge onto the plane of the molecules. The plane of the molecules is represented by straight lines, solid for those atoms in the $y = 0$ plane, dashed for those $b/2$ above the $y = 0$ plane. (Since the samples studied by Andrew and Eades were polycrystalline, studies of the effect of the orientation of the magnetic field relative to the crystalline axes were not possible.)

† E. R. Andrew and R. G. Eades, *Proc. Soc., Roy.* **A218**: 537 (1953).

As we can see, there will be contributions to the second moment from nuclei within the same molecule and from nuclei outside the molecule. In principle, if one knew the location and orientation of all molecules, the only unknown parameter would be the distance R between adjacent protons in the ring. By using isotopic substitution, however, Andrew and Eades were able to obtain an *experimental* division of the total second moment into contributions within and outside. We can see this readily by noting that replacement of a proton by a deuteron on any given site reduces the contribution of that site to the second moment by the factor α:

$$\alpha = \frac{4}{9}\frac{\gamma_D^2 I_D(I_D+1)}{\gamma_P^2 I_P(I_P+1)} \tag{1}$$

where the subscripts P and D stand for the proton and the deuteron. By using the facts that $I_D = 1$, $I_P = \frac{1}{2}$, $(\gamma_D/2\pi) = 6.535 \times 10^2$, $(\gamma_P/2\pi) = 42.57 \times 10^2$, we have $\alpha = 0.0236$. Thus, consider S_1, the second-moment contribution from nuclei *outside* the molecule. For $C_6H_3D_3$, any given lattice position is equally likely to have a proton or a deuteron. Therefore the proton contribution to the second moment is cut by a factor of two. If all the lattice sites were occupied by deuterons, the second moment would be cut by the factor α, but since only one-half the sites are occupied by deuterons, the deuterons contribute $\alpha S_1/2$. The total second moment, S_1', contributed by atoms outside the molecule is therefore

$$S_1' = \frac{S_1}{2} + \frac{\alpha S_1}{2} = \left(\frac{1+\alpha}{2}\right) S_1 \tag{2}$$

in which α is, of course, known.

The analysis for the contribution from atoms within the molecule proceeds in a similar way. Let S_2 and S_2' be the contribution for C_6H_6 and $C_6H_3D_3$, respectively. S_2' will be smaller than S_2, since the nuclei in positions 2, 4, and 6 will give

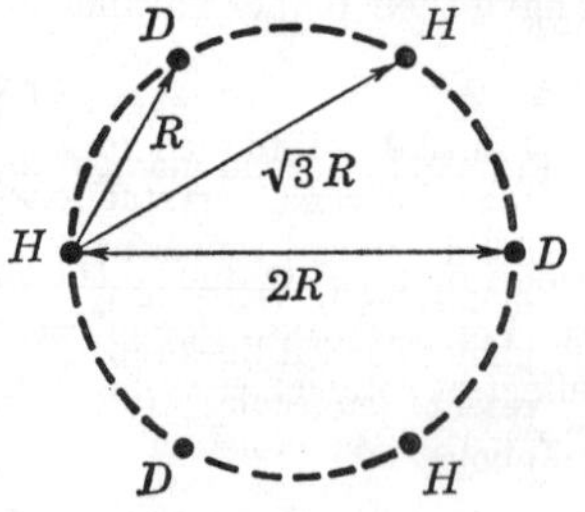

FIG. 3.10. Positions of protons and deuterons and the relative distances.

only α times as big a contribution for the deuterated compound. By referring to Fig. 3.10 and recognizing the $1/r^6$ dependence of the contribution to the second moment, we see that

$$\frac{S_2'}{S_2} = \frac{\alpha\left[1 \times 1 + \left(\frac{1}{2}\right)^6\right] + 2 \times \left(\frac{1}{\sqrt{3}}\right)^6}{2 + \left(\frac{1}{2}\right)^6 + 2\left(\frac{1}{\sqrt{3}}\right)^6} = \frac{\left(1 + \frac{1}{128}\right)\alpha + \frac{1}{27}}{1 + \frac{1}{27} + \frac{1}{128}} = \delta \tag{3}$$

Thus we have for the second moments of $C_6H_3D_3$ and C_6H_6, respectively,

$$S' = S'_1 + S'_2 = \left(\frac{1+\alpha}{2}\right) S_1 + \delta S_2 \qquad (4)$$
$$S = S_1 + S_2$$

where α and δ are known. Therefore, measurement of S and S' gives us S_1 and S_2, the separate contributions from outside and inside the molecule. The data for C_6H_5D provide an independent check.

On the basis of such studies, Andrew and Eades determined the distance R between adjacent protons in the ring to be 2.495 ± 0.018 Å, which is consistent with a prediction of 2.473 ± 0.025 Å based on the C—C spacing as determined by x-rays, and an estimated value for the C—H bond length. Of course one can combine the x-ray and resonance data to obtain the C—H bond distance. In principle, observation of the C^{13} resonance would even permit a determination of the C—H bond length directly.

The data we have mentioned were measured at temperatures below about 90° K. A second important result of Andrew and Eades was deduced by their studies of the temperature dependence of the second moment (Fig. 3.11). The rapid

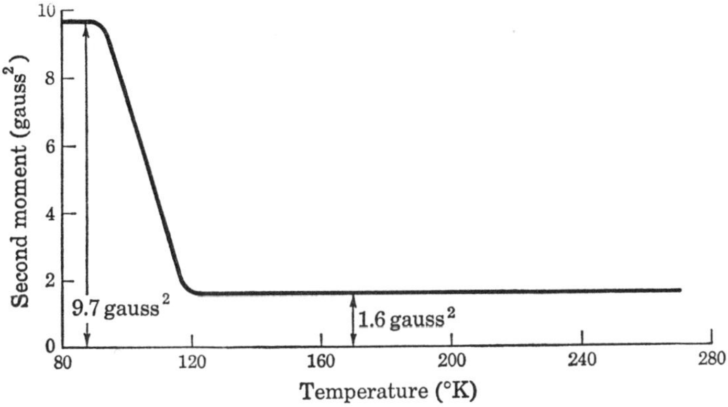

FIG. 3.11. Second moment in C_6H_6 as a function of temperature.

drop in second moment is due to the rotation of the benzene molecules about their hexad axis. Let us discuss this effect.

The effect of rotation may be expressed very simply in terms of the angles defined in Fig. 3.12. We consider a pair of nuclei j,k fixed in a molecule, the axis of

FIG. 3.12. Angles important in describing the rotation of a molecule.

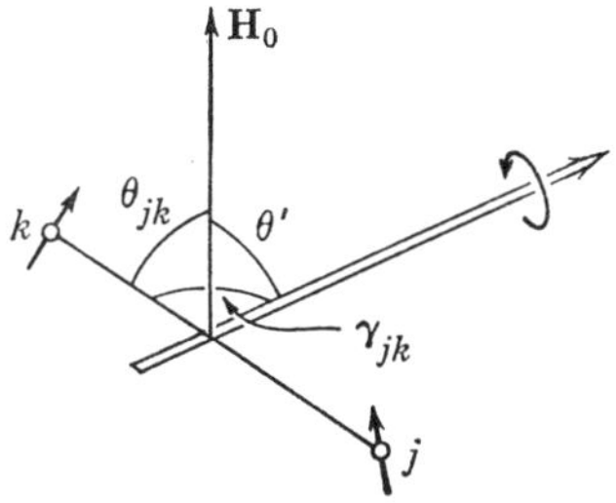

rotation of the molecule making an angle θ' with respect to the static field H_0. Let the radius vector from j to k make an angle γ_{jk} with the rotation axis. Then, as the molecule rotates, the angle θ_{jk} (between H_0 and the internuclear vector), which occurs in the factor $1 - 3\cos^2\theta_{jk}$ in the second moment, varies with time. Since the frequencies of rotation are high compared with the frequencies of interest in the resonance, it is the time average of $1 - 3\cos^2\theta_{jk}$ that affects the second moment. Assuming the motion is over a potential well of threefold or higher symmetry, this average can be shown to be independent of the details of the motion, and

$$\langle 1 - 3\cos^2\theta_{jk}\rangle_{\text{avg}} = (1 - 3\cos^2\theta')\frac{(3\cos^2\gamma_{jk} - 1)}{2} \tag{5}$$

Equation (5) shows that if the axis of rotation is parallel to the internuclear axis ($\gamma_{jk} = 0$), in which case the relative position of the two nuclei is unaffected by the rotation, the angular factor is unaffected by the rotation. On the other hand, if $\gamma_{jk} = \pi/2$,

$$\langle 1 - 3\cos^2\theta_{jk}\rangle_{\text{avg}} = \tfrac{1}{2}(1 - 3\cos^2\theta') \tag{6}$$

In a powder sample, we find all orientations of the crystal axes with respect to $\mathbf{H}_0$. For a rigid lattice, we must therefore average $(1 - 3\cos^2\theta_{jk})^2$ over the random crystal orientations. When motion sets in, we must first average $1 - 3\cos^2\theta_{jk}$ over the motion, to obtain the second moment for a given crystal orientation. Then we must average over crystal orientations.

For interacting pairs, the contribution to the second moment of the rigid lattice, $\langle\Delta\omega^2\rangle_{RL}$, then goes as

$$\langle\Delta\omega^2\rangle_{\text{RL}} \propto \overline{(1 - 3\cos^2\theta_{jk})^2} \tag{7}$$

where the bar indicates an average over random orientations of θ_{jk}.

When rotation sets in, we have a second moment from the pair $\langle\Delta\omega^2\rangle_{\text{rot}}$, given by

$$\langle\Delta\omega^2\rangle_{\text{rot}} \propto \overline{(\langle 1 - 3\cos^2\theta_{jk}\rangle_{\text{avg}})^2} \tag{8}$$

where the "avg" indicates an average over rotation, and the bar indicates an average of the orientation of the rotation axis with respect to $\mathbf{H}_0$. By using Eq. (5), we get

$$\langle\Delta\omega^2\rangle_{\text{rot}} \propto \overline{(1 - 3\cos^2\theta')^2}\left(\frac{3\cos^2\gamma_{jk} - 1}{2}\right)^2 \tag{9}$$

Since the crystal axes are randomly oriented with respect to H_0, so are the *rotation* axes, specified by θ'. As a result

$$\overline{(1 - 3\cos^2\theta_{jk})^2} = \overline{(1 - 3\cos^2\theta')^2}$$

and

$$\langle\Delta\omega^2\rangle_{\text{rot}} = \langle\Delta\omega^2\rangle_{\text{RL}}\left(\frac{3\cos^2\gamma_{jk} - 1}{2}\right)^2 \tag{10}$$

If $\gamma_{jk} = \pi/2$ (a pair rotating about an axis perpendicular to the internuclear axis), the contribution of the pair interaction to the second moment is reduced by a factor of 4.†

For the case of benzene, Andrew and Eades found that the second moment of C_6H_6 from protons within the molecule drops from 3.10 gauss^2 at low temperatures to 0.77 ± 0.05 gauss^2 at high temperatures. The assumption that the narrowing results from rotation about the hexad axis makes $\gamma_{jk} = \pi/2$, since all protons lie in a plane perpendicular to the hexad axis, and predicts that the second moment should drop to 3.10/4 = 0.78 gauss^2, in excellent agreement with the observed decrease.

† The justification for averaging $1 - 3\cos^2\theta_{jk}$ over the motion *before* squaring rather than averaging $(1 - 3\cos^2\theta_{jk})^2$ may be seen also by referring to the exact expression for $\chi''(\omega)$, which was proportional to

$$\sum_{a,b} e^{-E_a/kT}(a|\mu_x|b)(b|\mu_x|a)\,\delta(E_a - E_b - \hbar\omega)$$

The states $|a)$ and $|b)$ may be considered to involve both spin and rotational quantum numbers. But, since $E_a - E_b$ is chosen to be near the Larmor frequency, the states $|a)$ and $|b)$ must have the same rotational quantum numbers. Therefore, in computing the second moment, the trace will be over spin variables only, but the angular factor will be a diagonal matrix element in the "lattice" coordinates. But this means that we replace the classical $1 - 3\cos^2\theta_{jk}$ by $\int u_L^*(1 - 3\cos^2\theta_{jk})u_L\,d\tau$, where u_L is a lattice (in this case, rotation) state. This procedure amounts to "averaging" $1 - 3\cos^2\theta_{jk}$ over the motion prior to squaring.

CHAPTER 4

MAGNETIC INTERACTIONS OF NUCLEI WITH ELECTRONS

4·1 INTRODUCTION

So far we have ignored the fact that the nuclei are surrounded by electrons with which they can interact. In this chapter we shall consider the magnetic interactions, postponing until later the consideration of the strong electrostatic effects that may be found when a nucleus possesses an electrical quadrupole moment. The magnetic coupling of the electrons to the nucleus arises from magnetic fields originating either from the motion of the electrical charges or from the magnetic moment associated with the electron spin. The former gives rise to the so-called chemical shifts; the latter, to the Knight shifts in metals and to a coupling between nuclear spins.

Both the chemical shifts and the Knight shifts have certain features in common. The total Hamiltonian of the electrons and the nuclei may be written as a sum of four terms:

$$\mathcal{H}_{nz}(H) + \mathcal{H}_e(0) + \mathcal{H}_{ez}(H) + \mathcal{H}_{en}$$

where $\mathcal{H}_{nz}$ is the nuclear Zeeman coupling in the applied field H; $\mathcal{H}_e(0)$ is the Hamiltonian of the electrons (orbital and spin) in the absence of H; $\mathcal{H}_{ez}(H)$ is the electron Zeeman energy; and $\mathcal{H}_{en}$ is the interaction between the nuclear spins and the electron orbital and spin coordinates.

If $\mathcal{H}_{en}$ were zero, the nuclear spin system would be decoupled from the electrons, and the nuclear energy levels would be solely the Zeeman levels in the applied field H. The term $\mathcal{H}_{en}$ corresponds to the extra magnetic fields the nuclei experience owing to the electrons. In a diamagnetic or paramagnetic substance, the average field a nucleus experiences owing to the electrons vanishes when H vanishes. However, since the interaction $\mathcal{H}_{ez}(H)$ polarizes the electron system, the effect of the electron-nuclear coupling, $\mathcal{H}_{en}$, is no longer zero. We may say that the nuclei experience both a direct interaction with H through $\mathcal{H}_{nz}(H)$ and an indirect one through the interplay of $\mathcal{H}_{ez}(H)$ and $\mathcal{H}_{en}$. The problem is very similar to the calculation of the electric field in a dielectric, in which we must add to the applied electric field the field arising from induced dipole moments in the other atoms.

Systems such as ferromagnets possess electronic magnetization even with $H = 0$. For them, the contribution of $\mathcal{H}_{en}$ is non-zero even without an applied field.

We shall consider the orbital effects first, starting with a review of the major facts about chemical shifts.

4.2 EXPERIMENTAL FACTS ABOUT CHEMICAL SHIFTS

The most famous and most quoted example of chemical shifts is ethyl alcohol, CH_3CH_2OH (see references on "Chemical Shifts" in the Bibliography). The proton resonance consists of three lines whose intensities are in the ratios 3:2:1. If one possesses a highly homogeneous magnet, each of these lines is found to possess structure that (as we shall see) is due to effects of electron spin. The three lines are clearly due to the three "types" of protons, three in the CH_3 group, two in the CH_2 group, and one in the OH. Evidently the nuclei experience fields of local origin that are different for different molecular surroundings. A comparison of the spacing in magnetic field between the lines as a function of the frequency of the resonance apparatus shows that the splitting is proportional to the frequency. If we attribute the splitting to the fact that the nuclei must see a magnetic field ΔH in addition to the applied field H_0, we may say the resonance frequency ω obeys the equation

$$\omega = \gamma(H_0 + \Delta H) \tag{1}$$

where $\Delta H \propto H_0$. We may therefore define a quantity σ, which is independent of H, by the equation

$$\Delta H = -\sigma H_0 \tag{2}$$

If σ is positive, we must use a larger magnetic field to produce the resonance than would be necessary for the bare nucleus. Of course we never do experiments on a bare nucleus, so that what we measure are the differences in σ associated with different molecular environments. For protons, the entire range of σ's covers about one part in 10^5. For fluorine atoms, however, the range is about six parts in 10^4, two orders of magnitude larger. Because of the small size of the shifts, they are ordinarily studied in liquids where resonance lines are narrow. Since the shifts should in general depend upon the orientation of the molecule with respect to the static field, it would be interesting if single crystal orientation studies could be carried out.

As we have remarked, the chemical shifts are due to the orbital motion of electrons. It is important to contrast the orbital motion in solids or molecules with that in free atoms. We shall turn to this subject next.

4.3 QUENCHING OF ORBITAL MOTION

Classical electricity and magnetism tell us that a charge q moving with velocity $\mathbf{v}$ produces a magnetic field $\mathbf{H}$ at a point $\mathbf{r}'$ away, given by

$$\mathbf{H} = \frac{q}{c}\frac{\mathbf{v} \times \mathbf{r}'}{r'^3} \tag{1}$$

If we choose rather to ask for the field at the origin of a set of coordinates due to a charge at position $\mathbf{r}$, then $\mathbf{r}' = -\mathbf{r}$ and Eq. (1) becomes

$$\mathbf{H} = \frac{q}{c}\frac{\mathbf{r}\times\mathbf{v}}{r^3} = \frac{q}{mc}\frac{\mathbf{r}\times m\mathbf{v}}{r^3} = \frac{q}{mc}\frac{\mathbf{L}}{r^3} \tag{2}$$

where $\mathbf{L}$ is the angular momentum of the particle about the origin. Equation (2) has a quantum mechanical counterpart, as we shall discuss. We see immediately, however, that for s-states, $\mathbf{H} = 0$ at the position of a nucleus, since s-states have zero angular momentum, whereas $\mathbf{H} \neq 0$ for p,d, and other states of non-zero angular momentum. The magnitude of $\mathbf{H}$ is of order

$$H \simeq \frac{\beta}{r^3} \tag{3}$$

where β is the Bohr magneton (10^{-20} erg/gauss). For fluorine the average value of $1/r^3$ for the $2p$ electrons is

$$\left(\frac{1}{r^3}\right)_{2p} = \frac{8.9}{a_0^3} \tag{4}$$

where a_0 is the Bohr radius. In other words, $(\overline{1/r^3})$ corresponds to a typical distance of 1/4 Å; the magnetic fields, to about 600,000 gauss.

Such enormous fields would completely dominate the laboratory field H_0 for typical experiments, in contrast to the facts. (Of course, in atomic beam experiments such large couplings *can* be observed.) We must understand why the large fields of free atoms are not present in solids or molecules. The disappearance of these large fields is also closely associated with the fact that, in most substances, the atoms do not possess permanent electronic magnetic moments; that is, most substances are diamagnetic. The term *quenching of orbital angular momentum* is often applied to describe the phenomenon. Let us see how it comes about, by studying a particularly simple example.

We shall consider an atom with one electron outside closed shells in a p-state. We shall neglect spin, for convenience, although later in the book we shall return to the effect of spin in order to understand the so-called g-shifts in electron spin resonance. The three degenerate p-functions may be written in either of two ways:

$$\begin{matrix} xf(r) \\ yf(r) \\ zf(r) \end{matrix} \tag{5}$$

or

$$\begin{matrix} \dfrac{(x+iy)}{\sqrt{2}}f(r) \\ zf(r) \\ \dfrac{(x-iy)}{\sqrt{2}}f(r) \end{matrix} \tag{6}$$

where $f(r)$ is a spherically symmetric function. The three functions of Eq. (6) are eigenfunctions of L_z, the z-component of angular momentum and the m-values being, from top to bottom, 1, 0, and -1. The wave functions of Eq. (5) are simply linear combinations of those of Eq. (6). As long as the atom is free, either set of wave functions is equally good, but if a magnetic field is applied parallel to the z-direction, the set of Eq. (6) must be chosen.

If now we surround the atom by a set of charges in the manner of Fig. 4.1, and for the moment assume that no static magnetic field is present, the degeneracy

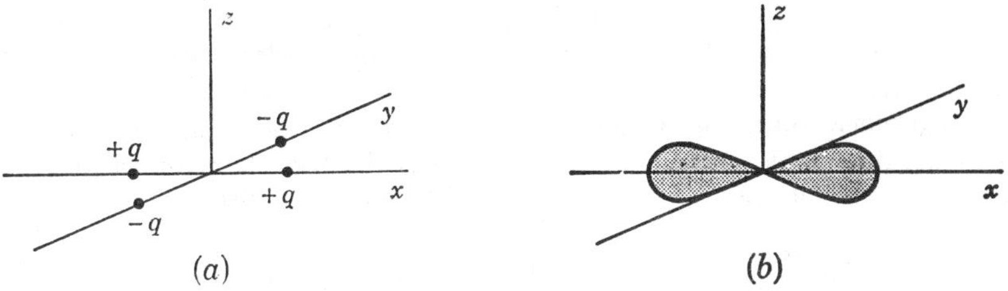

FIG. 4.1. (a) Four charges placed near an atom. The atom is assumed to be at the origin and the charges to be all equidistant from the origin. The charges $+q$ lie on the x-axis and $-q$ lies on the y-axis. (b) The wave function $xf(r)$ is largest along the x-axis for any given distance r from the origin.

is lifted. The proper eigenstates are then those of Eq. (5), since a symmetric potential such as that of Fig. 4.1 will have vanishing matrix elements between any pair of the functions of Eq. (5). On the other hand, the diagonal matrix elements will be different, since the state $xf(r)$ concentrates the electron on the x-axis, near to the positive charges, whereas the state $yf(r)$ concentrates the electron near the negative charge. Clearly, $xf(r)$ will lie lowest in energy, $yf(r)$ will be highest, and $zf(r)$ will be between (unshifted in fact in the first order). The resulting energy levels are shown in Fig. 4.2.

FIG. 4.2. Splitting of the three p-states by the charges of Fig. 4.1a.

The ground state $xf(r)$ may be written as

$$xf(r) = \frac{1}{\sqrt{2}}\left[\frac{(x+iy)}{\sqrt{2}}f(r) + \frac{(x-iy)}{\sqrt{2}}f(r)\right] \tag{7}$$

a linear combination of the $m = +1$ and $m = -1$ states. The states $m = +1$ and $m = -1$ correspond to electron circulation in opposite directions about the z-axis. Since they occur with *equal* weighting in Eq. (7), we see that $xf(r)$ corresponds to equal mixtures of the two senses of circulation, or to *zero* net circulation.

We can make a more precise statement by computing $\langle L_z \rangle$, the expectation value of the z-component of angular momentum. For generality, we shall make our proof for any wave function whose spatial part is real. The operator for L_z is

$$L_z = \frac{\hbar}{i}\left(x\frac{\partial}{\partial y} - y\frac{\partial}{\partial x}\right) \tag{8}$$

Therefore, for any wave function u_0,

$$(0|L_z|0) = \int u_0^* \frac{\hbar}{i}\left(x\frac{\partial}{\partial y} - y\frac{\partial}{\partial x}\right) u_0\, d\tau \tag{9}$$

which, since u_0 is real, may be written as

$$(0|L_z|0) = \frac{\hbar}{i}\int u_0 \left(x\frac{\partial}{\partial y} - y\frac{\partial}{\partial x}\right) u_0\, d\tau \tag{10}$$

Since all the quantities in the integral are real, Eq. (10) shows that $\langle L_z\rangle$ must be pure imaginary unless the integral vanishes. But the diagonal matrix elements of any Hermitian operator are real. Therefore the integral vanishes and

$$(0|L_z|0) = 0 \tag{11}$$

It is clear that this proof holds for any component of angular momentum.

We say that when

$$(0|L_x|0) = (0|L_y|0) = (0|L_z|0) = 0 \tag{12}$$

the angular momentum is quenched.

Under what circumstances will the angular momentum be quenched? Clearly, what is needed is the possibility of choosing the eigenfunctions as real. If the eigenfunctions are solutions of a Hamiltonian in the absence of a magnetic field (which means no spins are allowed!), the Hamiltonian is real. If, moreover, a state is non-degenerate, its eigenfunction is always real, since it is the solution of a real differential equation (apart from an arbitrary complex constant factor, which clearly does not affect the expectation value). Therefore $(0|L_x|0) = 0$ for such a state. We conclude that whenever the crystalline electric fields leave a state non-degenerate, the orbital angular momentum of that state is quenched. The physical basis of quenching is that the external charges exert torques on the electron orbit, causing the plane of the orbit to precess. When the plane has exactly turned over, the sense of circulation is reversed. Crudely stated, the electron path has been changed from lying in a plane to being much like the path of the string in a ball of twine.

Of course application of a magnetic field will change things. We can see intuitively that a magnetic field in the z-direction will cause one sense of circulation to be favored over the other. The wave functions will readjust so that the ground state has a slight circulation in the favorable sense (the $m = -1$ state will be favored). In terms of a small quantity, ϵ, this will make a new ground state:

$$\psi_0 = \frac{1}{\sqrt{2}}\left[(1-\epsilon)\frac{(x+iy)}{\sqrt{2}}f(r) + (1+\epsilon)\frac{(x-iy)}{\sqrt{2}}f(r)\right] \tag{13}$$

As we can see, this change results from the admixture of a small amount of the state $yf(r)$ into the ground state $xf(r)$. As we shall see, the amount ϵ, mixed in is proportional to H_0, giving rise to a circulation that is proportional to H_0.

We turn now to a closer look at the details of chemical shifts.

4·4 FORMAL THEORY OF CHEMICAL SHIFTS†

Chemical shifts arise because of the simultaneous interaction of a nucleus with an electron and that of the electron with the applied field H_0. A general theory has been given by Ramsey,†† but we shall present a somewhat different discussion, which breaks the calculation into two parts: (1) the determination of the electric currents produced in the molecule by the external field and (2) calculation of the magnetic field produced by these currents at the nucleus. We shall work out the theory for one electron. We start by considering the Hamiltonian of the electron. To treat the magnetic fields, we must introduce two vector potentials, $\mathbf{A}_0$ and $\mathbf{A}_n$, one associated with the magnetic field $\mathbf{H}_0$, the other with the magnetic field $\mathbf{H}_n$ due to the nucleus. In terms of $\mathbf{A}_0$ and $\mathbf{A}_n$ we have

$$\begin{aligned}\mathbf{H}_0 &= \nabla \times \mathbf{A}_0 \\ \mathbf{H}_n &= \nabla \times \mathbf{A}_n\end{aligned} \tag{1}$$

As is well known, there is more than one vector potential that will produce a given field. Thus, if $\mathbf{H} = \nabla \times \mathbf{A}$, a new vector potential, $\mathbf{A}' = \mathbf{A} + \nabla\phi$ (where ϕ is any scalar function), will give the same field, since the curl of the gradient of any function vanishes. A transformation from $\mathbf{A}$ to $\mathbf{A}'$ is called a *gauge transformation*. We must be sure that the physical results of any calculation are independent of the choice of gauge, that is, are gauge-invariant. The effect of a magnetic field is introduced into the Schrödinger equation by replacing the operator $(\hbar/i)\nabla$ by $(\hbar/i)\nabla - (q/c)\mathbf{A}$, where q is the charge of the particle (q is positive or negative, depending on the sign of the charge of the particle.)

The Hamiltonian then becomes

$$\mathcal{H} = \frac{1}{2m}\left(\mathbf{p} - \frac{q}{c}\mathbf{A}\right)^2 + V \tag{2}$$

where $\mathbf{p} = (\hbar/i)\nabla$. If one uses a different gauge, $\mathbf{A}' = \mathbf{A} + \nabla\phi(r)$, the new solution ψ' is related to the old one (ψ) by the (unitary) transformation

$$\psi' = \psi e^{+(iq/\hbar c)\phi(r)} \tag{3}$$

If we compare the expectation values of $(\hbar/i)\nabla$, $(\psi, (\hbar/i)\nabla\psi)$, and $(\psi', (\hbar/i)\nabla\psi')$, we find that they are not equal. Therefore, since any physical observable must be independent of the choice of gauge, we see that $(\hbar/i)\nabla$ cannot be the momentum operator $m\mathbf{v}$. The operator for $m\mathbf{v}$, rather, is $(\hbar/i)\nabla - (q/c)\mathbf{A}$, which is gauge-invariant. That is,

$$\left(\psi', \left[\frac{\hbar}{i}\nabla - \frac{q}{c}\mathbf{A}'\right]\psi'\right) = \left(\psi, \left[\frac{\hbar}{i}\nabla - \frac{q}{c}\mathbf{A}\right]\psi\right) \tag{4}$$

In a similar manner the operator for angular momentum, $\mathbf{r} \times m\mathbf{v}$ is

$$\mathbf{r} \times \left(\frac{\hbar}{i}\nabla - \frac{q}{c}\mathbf{A}\right)$$

† See references under "Chemical Shifts" in the Bibliography.
†† N. F. Ramsey, *Phys. Rev.*, **78**: 699 (1950); *Phys. Rev.*, **86**: 243 (1952).

The distinction between $m\mathbf{v}$ and $\mathbf{p}(=(\hbar/i)\nabla)$ is found in classical mechanics. Thus, in terms of the Lagrangian L, the definition of the canonical momentum p_x is $\partial L/\partial \dot{x}$, whereas the x-component of linear momentum is $m\dot{x}$. When a magnetic field is present, one finds $p_x = m\dot{x} + [(q/c)A_x]$.

A quantity that will be of great importance to us is something which we shall call the current density $\mathbf{j}(\mathbf{r})$. It is defined as follows:

$$\mathbf{j}(\mathbf{r}) = \frac{q}{2m}\frac{\hbar}{i}[\psi^*\nabla\psi - \psi\nabla\psi^*] - \frac{q^2}{mc}\mathbf{A}\psi^*\psi \tag{5}$$

We note that $\mathbf{j}(\mathbf{r})$ is a vector function of position, and it is real (that is, has zero imaginary part). We recognize it as being q times the quantum mechanical probability current. Explicit evaluation, first using ψ and $\mathbf{A}$ and then using ψ' and $\mathbf{A}'$, shows that $\mathbf{j}(\mathbf{r})$ is gauge-invariant. Moreover, by assuming that ψ is a solution of Schrödinger's time-dependent equation, one can show that

$$\operatorname{div}\mathbf{j} + \frac{\partial\rho}{\partial t} = 0 \qquad \text{with} \qquad \rho \equiv q\psi^*\psi \tag{6}$$

That is, $\mathbf{j}$ obeys the classical equation of continuity. For stationary states, $\psi^*\psi$ is independent of time and $\operatorname{div}\mathbf{j} = 0$. $\mathbf{j}$ acts much as a classical current density. As we shall see shortly, such an interpretation is very useful in considering chemical shifts.

The Hamiltonian for our electron acted on by two magnetic fields is therefore

$$\mathcal{H} = \frac{1}{2m}\left(\mathbf{p} - \frac{q}{c}\mathbf{A}_0 - \frac{q}{c}\mathbf{A}_n\right)^2 + V \tag{7}$$

where V represents all potential energy, including that due to fields that may quench the orbital angular momentum.

It is convenient to define a quantity $\boldsymbol{\pi}$ by the equation

$$\boldsymbol{\pi} = \mathbf{p} - \frac{q}{c}\mathbf{A}_0 \tag{8a}$$

Since both $\mathbf{p}$ and $\mathbf{A}_0$ are Hermitian operators, so is $\boldsymbol{\pi}$. Then Eq. (7) becomes

$$\mathcal{H} = \frac{1}{2m}\pi^2 - \frac{q}{2mc}(\boldsymbol{\pi}\cdot\mathbf{A}_n + \mathbf{A}_n\cdot\boldsymbol{\pi}) + \frac{q^2}{2mc^2}A_n^2 + V \tag{8b}$$

We shall choose $\mathbf{A}_n$ to be

$$\mathbf{A}_n = \frac{\boldsymbol{\mu}\times\mathbf{r}}{r^3} \tag{9}$$

where $\boldsymbol{\mu}$ is the nuclear moment, since this vector potential generates the field of a dipole. Since μ is very small compared with electron moments, we expect to be able to treat it as an expansion parameter, and accordingly we drop the A_n^2 term in comparison with the term linear in A_n. We then have

$$\mathcal{H} = \frac{1}{2m}\pi^2 + V - \frac{q}{2mc}(\boldsymbol{\pi}\cdot\mathbf{A}_n + \mathbf{A}_n\cdot\boldsymbol{\pi}) \tag{10}$$

In the absence of a nuclear coupling, $(1/2m)\pi^2 + V$ is simply the Hamiltonian of the electron in the presence of the static field. We shall treat the term involving $\mathbf{A}_n$ as a perturbation, computing the energy by using first-order perturbation theory.

Let us consider, then, the first-order change in energy of a state whose wave function ψ is the *exact* solution of the problem of an electron acted on by the potential V and the static field $\mathbf{H}_0$. The energy perturbation, E_{pert}, is then

$$E_{\text{pert}} = -\frac{q}{2mc}\int \psi^*(\boldsymbol{\pi}\cdot\mathbf{A}_n + \mathbf{A}_n\cdot\boldsymbol{\pi})\psi\, d\tau \tag{11}$$

where the integration is over electron coordinates. (Actually, $\mathbf{A}_n$ is a function of the nuclear moment $\boldsymbol{\mu}$, which must itself be considered an operator. Thus E_{pert} will be an operator as far as the nuclear spin is concerned. We simply add it into the nuclear spin Hamiltonian.)

By using the fact that $\boldsymbol{\pi}$ is a Hermitian operator, we rewrite Eq. (11) as

$$E_{\text{pert}} = -\frac{q}{2mc}\int \mathbf{A}_n\cdot[(\boldsymbol{\pi}\psi)^*\psi + \psi^*\boldsymbol{\pi}\psi]\, d\tau \tag{12}$$

But, by using the definition of $\boldsymbol{\pi}$ given in Eq. (8) and of the current density in Eq. (5), we can write

$$\begin{aligned}\frac{q}{2m}[\psi(\boldsymbol{\pi}\psi^*) + \psi^*\boldsymbol{\pi}\psi] &= \frac{q}{2m}\frac{\hbar}{i}[\psi^*\nabla\psi - \psi\nabla\psi^*] - \frac{q^2}{mc}\mathbf{A}_0\psi^*\psi \\ &= \mathbf{j}_0(\mathbf{r})\end{aligned} \tag{13}$$

$\mathbf{j}_0(\mathbf{r})$ is the current density flowing when the static field is on. That is, $\mathbf{j}_0$ is the current computed for the electron acted on by V and $\mathbf{H}_0$ (but not by the nucleus). Therefore

$$E_{\text{pert}} = -\frac{1}{c}\int \mathbf{A}_n\cdot\mathbf{j}_0(\mathbf{r})\, d\tau \tag{14}$$

[Parenthetically, this formula gives us a general expression for the change in energy, δE, resulting from a change in field associated with a change $\delta\mathbf{A}$ in vector potential, in terms of the current $\mathbf{j}(\mathbf{r})$ prior to the change $\delta\mathbf{A}$:

$$\delta E = -\frac{1}{c}\int \delta\mathbf{A}\cdot\mathbf{j}(\mathbf{r})\, d\tau] \tag{15}$$

If we now set

$$\mathbf{A}_n = \frac{\boldsymbol{\mu}\times\mathbf{r}}{r^3} \tag{16}$$

we get

$$\begin{aligned}E_{\text{pert}} &= -\frac{1}{c}\int \frac{\boldsymbol{\mu}\times\mathbf{r}}{r^3}\cdot\mathbf{j}_0(\mathbf{r})\, d\tau \\ &= -\boldsymbol{\mu}\cdot\left[\frac{1}{c}\int \frac{\mathbf{r}\times\mathbf{j}_0(\mathbf{r})}{r^3}\, d\tau\right]\end{aligned} \tag{17}$$

where, as we have remarked, $\boldsymbol{\mu}$ is really the operator $\gamma\hbar\mathbf{I}$, but $\mathbf{j}_0(\mathbf{r})$ is simply a vector function of position. It is important to bear in mind that $\mathbf{j}_0(\mathbf{r})$ is independent of the gauge of $\mathbf{A}_0$, the vector potential of the static field. Eq. (17) is identical in form to the classical interaction of a magnetic moment $\boldsymbol{\mu}$ with a current density $\mathbf{j}_0(\mathbf{r})$, since the quantity in the square bracket is the field $\mathbf{H}$ due to the current.

There is a good deal of similarity to the expression for the magnetic moment, $\mathbf{M}$, of the electrons:

$$\mathbf{M} = \frac{1}{2c} \int \mathbf{r} \times \mathbf{j}_0(\mathbf{r})\, d\tau \tag{18}$$

Equation (17) contains the facts of the chemical shift. If we knew $\mathbf{j}_0(\mathbf{r})$, we could compute the resultant field at the nucleus. We can see that there are really two parts to the theory of chemical shifts: (1) finding the current density $\mathbf{j}_0(\mathbf{r})$; (2) computing the integral of Eq. (17) once $\mathbf{j}_0(\mathbf{r})$ is known. The latter problem is entirely classical and immediately involves one in such things as multipole expansions. Thus the effect of currents on an atom distant from the nucleus in question can often be approximated by a magnetic dipole moment.

Since in general the current $\mathbf{j}_0(\mathbf{r})$ flows as a result of the presence of the static field $\mathbf{H}_0$, determination of $\mathbf{j}_0(\mathbf{r})$ from first principles involves the solution of the quantum mechanics problem of an electron acted on by electrostatic potentials and by a static field. On the other hand, in some instances one can guess the spatial form of $\mathbf{j}_0(\mathbf{r})$ and use measured magnetic susceptibilities to fix its magnitude, a technique that has been used to explain the chemical shifts of protons in various ring compounds such as benzene, in which the currents in the rings are computed to give agreement with experimental (or theoretical) magnetic moments. Alternatively, one can turn the problem around and use the measured chemical shifts to determine information about magnetic susceptibilities of atoms, molecules, or bonds. Moreover, we can see that in general the chemical shifts will be most sensitive to nearby currents because of the $1/r^3$ factor in the integral of Eq. (17), unless nearby currents are especially small. We shall see shortly that the small chemical shifts of protons compared, for example, to fluorine atoms results from the fact that the currents near the protons are relatively very small. In any event, Eqs. (17) and (18) give concise statements of what a chemical shift or susceptibility experiment measures about the currents induced in a molecule by the external field.

4·5 COMPUTATION OF CURRENT DENSITY

We turn now to computing $\mathbf{j}_0(r)$. To do so, we need the wave function ψ, which describes the electron when acted on by both the electrostatic potentials and the static field. We have, then,

$$\mathcal{H}\psi = E\psi \tag{1}$$

where

$$\mathcal{H} = \frac{1}{2m}\left(\mathbf{p} - \frac{q}{c}\mathbf{A}_0\right)^2 + V \tag{2}$$

By expanding the parentheses, we find

$$\mathcal{H} = \frac{p^2}{2m} + V - \frac{q}{2mc}(\mathbf{p}\cdot\mathbf{A}_0 + \mathbf{A}_0\cdot\mathbf{p}) + \frac{q^2}{2mc^2}A_0^2 \tag{3}$$

Let us assume that we know the wave functions that are the solution of the Hamiltonian $\mathcal{H}_0$ in the absence of the external field:

$$\begin{aligned} \mathcal{H}_0 &= \frac{p^2}{2m} + V \\ \mathcal{H}_0\psi_n &= E_n\psi_n \end{aligned} \tag{4}$$

Then we can look on the terms in Eq. (3) that involve $\mathbf{A}_0$ as perturbing the energies and wave functions. We shall compute perturbed wave functions so that we can compute the effect of the magnetic field on the current density. Of course $\mathbf{A}_0$ goes to zero when H_0 vanishes, being given typically by

$$\mathbf{A}_0 = \tfrac{1}{2}\mathbf{H}_0 \times \mathbf{r} \tag{5}$$

Although this involves a particular gauge, we can see that in any gauge, $\mathbf{A}_0$ will be proportional to H_0. In the expression for the current, $\mathbf{j}_0(\mathbf{r})$,

$$\mathbf{j}_0(\mathbf{r}) = \frac{\hbar q}{2mi}[\psi^*\nabla\psi - \psi\nabla\psi^*] - \frac{q^2}{mc}\mathbf{A}_0\psi^*\psi \tag{6}$$

we can compute $\mathbf{j}_0(\mathbf{r})$ correctly to terms linear in H_0 as a first approximation. To do this, we need ψ and ψ^* correct to terms linear in H_0 for that part of $\mathbf{j}_0(\mathbf{r})$ in the brackets, but for the last term, we can use for ψ the unperturbed function ψ_0. Since we always have

$$\psi_0' = \psi_0 + \sum_n \frac{(n|\mathcal{H}_{\text{pert}}|0)}{E_0 - E_n}\psi_n \tag{7}$$

we need keep only those parts of the perturbation that are linear in H_0, or by referring to Eqs. (3), (4), and (5), we take

$$\mathcal{H}_{\text{pert}} = -\frac{q}{2mc}(\mathbf{p}\cdot\mathbf{A}_0 + \mathbf{A}_0\cdot\mathbf{p}) \tag{8}$$

Let us define

$$\epsilon_{n0} = \frac{(n|\mathcal{H}_{\text{pert}}|0)}{E_0 - E_n} \tag{9}$$

Then

$$\psi_0' = \psi_0 + \sum_n \epsilon_{n0}\psi_n \tag{10}$$

which gives us for the current,

$$\begin{aligned} \mathbf{j}_0(\mathbf{r}) = \frac{\hbar q}{2mi}[\psi_0^*\nabla\psi_0 - \psi_0\nabla\psi_0^*] &+ \sum_n \frac{\hbar q}{2mi}[\psi_0^*\nabla\psi_n - \psi_n\nabla\psi_0^*]\epsilon_{n0} \\ &+ \sum_n \frac{\hbar q}{2mi}[\psi_n^*\nabla\psi_0 - \psi_0\nabla\psi_n^*]\epsilon_{n0}^* - \frac{q^2}{mc}\mathbf{A}_0\psi_0^*\psi_0 \end{aligned} \tag{11}$$

The term

$$\frac{\hbar}{2mi}q[\psi_0^*\nabla\psi_0 - \psi_0\nabla\psi_0^*] \equiv \mathbf{J}(\mathbf{r}) \tag{12}$$

is the current that would flow when $H_0 = 0$.

When the orbital angular momentum is quenched so that ψ_0 is real, we see that $\mathbf{J}(\mathbf{r}) = 0$, *and the current density vanishes at all points in the molecule in the absence of* $\mathbf{H}_0$.

It is the term $\mathbf{J}(\mathbf{r})$ that gives rise, however, to the magnetic fields at a nucleus originating in the bodily rotation of the molecule; that is, the so-called spin-rotation interactions that are observed in molecular beam experiments.

It is instructive to compute $\mathbf{j}_0(\mathbf{r})$ for a *free* atom in the $m = +1$ p-state, H_0 being zero. $\mathbf{j}_0(\mathbf{r})$ then equals $\mathbf{J}(\mathbf{r})$, so that

$$\mathbf{j}_0(\mathbf{r}) = \frac{\hbar q}{2mi}[\psi_0^* \nabla \psi_0 - \psi_0 \nabla \psi_0^*] \tag{13}$$

But

$$\begin{aligned} \psi_0 &= \left(\frac{x + iy}{\sqrt{2}}\right) f(r) \\ \nabla \psi_0 &= \left(\frac{\mathbf{i} + i\mathbf{j}}{\sqrt{2}}\right) f(r) + \left(\frac{x + iy}{\sqrt{2}}\right) \nabla f(r) \end{aligned} \tag{14}$$

giving

$$\begin{aligned} \mathbf{j}_0(\mathbf{r}) &= \frac{\hbar q}{2m}(x\mathbf{j} - y\mathbf{i}) f^2(r) \\ &= \frac{\hbar q}{2m} \mathbf{k} \times \mathbf{r} f^2(r) \end{aligned} \tag{15}$$

The current therefore flows in a circle whose plane is perpendicular to the z-axis. If we define a velocity $\mathbf{v}(\mathbf{r})$ by the equation

$$\mathbf{v}(\mathbf{r}) = \frac{\mathbf{j}_0(r)}{q\psi^*\psi} \tag{16}$$

where $q\psi^*\psi$ is the charge density, we find

$$\mathbf{v}(\mathbf{r}) = \frac{\hbar}{m} \frac{\mathbf{k} \times \mathbf{r}}{(x^2 + y^2)} \tag{17}$$

which is tangent to a circle whose plane is perpendicular to the z-axis, so that

$$|\mathbf{v}(\mathbf{r})| = \frac{\hbar}{m} \frac{1}{\sqrt{x^2 + y^2}} \tag{18}$$

This gives a z angular momentum of

$$mv\sqrt{x^2 + y^2} = \hbar \tag{19}$$

in accordance with our semiclassical picture of the electron in an $m = +1$ state possessing one quantum of angular momentum.

We see, therefore, the close relationship in this case of the current density, the "velocity," and our semiclassical picture of quantized orbits.

When the states ψ_0 and ψ_n may be taken as real (quenched orbital angular momentum), we have $\mathbf{J}(\mathbf{r}) = 0$, and

$$\mathbf{j}_0(\mathbf{r}) = \frac{\hbar}{2mi} q \sum_n (\epsilon_{n0} - \epsilon_{n0}^*)(\psi_0 \nabla \psi_n - \psi_n \nabla \psi_0) - \frac{q^2}{mc} \mathbf{A}_0 \psi_0^2 \tag{20}$$

For Eq. (20) to be valid, it is actually necessary only that the *ground* state possess quenched orbital angular momentum, but for excited states, we have assumed that the real form of the wave functions has been chosen.

Let us now proceed to look at some examples. We shall consider two cases, an *s*-state and a *p*-state. It will turn out that the chemical shifts for *s*-states are very small but that, for *p*-states, the effect of the magnetic field in unquenching the orbital angular momentum plays the dominant role, giving chemical shifts two orders of magnitude larger than those typically found for *s*-states.

To proceed, we must now choose a particular gauge for $\mathbf{A}_0$. It turns out, as we shall see, to be particularly convenient to take

$$\mathbf{A}_0 = \tfrac{1}{2}\mathbf{H}_0 \times \mathbf{r} = \tfrac{1}{2}H_0\mathbf{k} \times \mathbf{r} \tag{21}$$

although an equally correct one would be

$$\mathbf{A}_0 = \tfrac{1}{2}\mathbf{H}_0 \times (\mathbf{r} - \mathbf{R}) \tag{22a}$$

where $\mathbf{R}$ is a constant vector, or

$$\begin{aligned} A_{0z} &= 0 \\ A_{0x} &= H_0 y \\ A_{0y} &= 0 \end{aligned} \tag{22b}$$

In terms of the $\mathbf{A}_0$, Eq. (21), we have

$$\operatorname{div} \mathbf{A}_0 = 0 \tag{23}$$

Then we have, from Eq. (8),

$$\mathcal{H}_{\text{pert}} = -\frac{q}{2mc}\,[\mathbf{A}_0 \cdot \mathbf{p} + (\mathbf{p} \cdot \mathbf{A}_0) + \mathbf{A}_0 \cdot \mathbf{p}] \tag{24}$$

where $(\mathbf{p} \cdot \mathbf{A}_0)$ means $\mathbf{p}$ acts solely on $\mathbf{A}_0$. But since $\mathbf{p} = (\hbar/i)\nabla$,

$$(\mathbf{p} \cdot \mathbf{A}_0) = \frac{\hbar}{i}\,(\nabla \cdot \mathbf{A}_0) = 0 \tag{25}$$

Then, using Eq. (21), we have

$$\begin{aligned} \mathcal{H}_{\text{pert}} &= -\frac{q}{2mc}\,(\mathbf{H} \times \mathbf{r}) \cdot \mathbf{p} \\ &= -\frac{q}{2mc}\,\mathbf{H}_0 \cdot (\mathbf{r} \times \mathbf{p}) \end{aligned} \tag{26a}$$

We recognize that $\mathbf{r} \times \mathbf{p}$ is the operator for angular momentum in the absence of H_0. It is convenient in computing matrix elements to use the dimensionless operator $(1/i)\mathbf{r} \times \boldsymbol{\nabla}$ for angular momentum. Denoting this by the symbol $\mathbf{L}$, we can write Eq. (26a) alternatively as

$$\mathcal{H}_{\text{pert}} = -\frac{q\hbar}{2mc}\,H_0 L_z \tag{26b}$$

Had we chosen the gauge of Eq. (22a), we would have

$$\begin{aligned}\mathcal{H}_{\text{pert}} &= -\frac{q}{2mc}\mathbf{H}_0 \cdot (\mathbf{r} - \mathbf{R}) \times \mathbf{p} \\ &= -\frac{q\hbar}{2mc} H_0 L_z(\mathbf{R})\end{aligned} \tag{26c}$$

where $L_z(\mathbf{R})$ is the z-component of angular momentum about the point at $\mathbf{R}$. The choice of gauge therefore specifies the point about which angular momentum is measured in the perturbation. It is, of course, most natural to choose $\mathbf{R} = 0$, corresponding to measurement of angular momentum about the nucleus, since in general the electronic wave functions are classified as linear combinations of s, p, d (and so on) functions. When the electron orbit extends over several atoms, more than one force center enters the problem. The choice of the best gauge then becomes more complicated. A closely related problem in electron spin resonance involving the g-shift is discussed in Chapter 7.

Let us now consider an s-state. Then the wave function is spherically symmetric:

$$\psi_s(\mathbf{r}) = \psi_s(r) \tag{27}$$

It is clear that, since $L_z\psi_s = 0$,

$$(n|\mathcal{H}_{\text{pert}}|\psi_s) = 0 \tag{28}$$

Therefore ϵ_{n0} is zero for all excited states, and the entire current $\mathbf{j}_0(r)$ comes from the last term of Eq. (11):

$$\mathbf{j}_0(r) = -\frac{q^2}{mc}\mathbf{A}_0\psi_0^2 = -\frac{q^2}{2mc}H_0\mathbf{k} \times \mathbf{r}\psi_s^2(r) \tag{29}$$

The current therefore flows in circles centered on the z-axis. The direction is such as to produce a magnetic moment directed opposite to $\mathbf{H}_0$ so that it produces a diamagnetic moment. We see that the current direction will also produce a field opposed to H_0 at the nucleus (see Fig. 4.3).

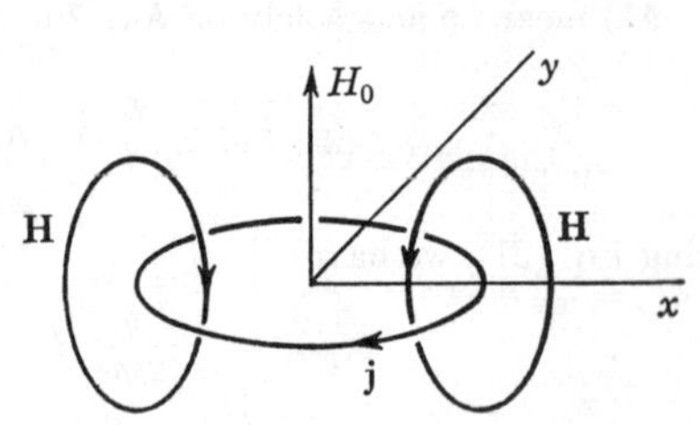

FIG. 4.3. Diamagnetic current flow in an s-state atom, and the magnetic fields produced by the current.

It is interesting to note that there is a current flowing in the s-state. There must certainly be an associated angular momentum, yet we customarily think of s-states as having zero angular momentum. We are confronted with the paradox: If s-states have zero angular momentum, how can there be electronic angular momentum in a *first*-order perturbation treatment if the first-order perturbation uses the *unperturbed* wave function? The answer is that the angular momentum operator has changed from $\mathbf{r} \times (\hbar/i)\nabla$ in the absence of a field to $\mathbf{r} \times [(\hbar/i)\nabla - (q/c)\mathbf{A}]$ when the field is present. By using the changed operator, the unchanged s-state has acquired angular momentum. The angular momentum is imparted to the electron by the electric field associated with turning on the magnetic field, since this electric field produces a torque about the nucleus. There is a corresponding back reaction on the magnet. We note that since **A** is continuously variable, we can make the angular momentum continuously variable. By using typical numbers for H_0 and r, one finds the angular momentum *much* smaller than $\hbar$. Does this fact violate the idea that angular momentum changes occur in units of $\hbar$? No, it does not, since the electron is not free but rather is coupled to the magnet. The *complete* system of magnet plus electron can only change angular momentum by $\hbar$, but the division of angular momentum between the parts of a coupled system does not have to be in integral units of $\hbar$.

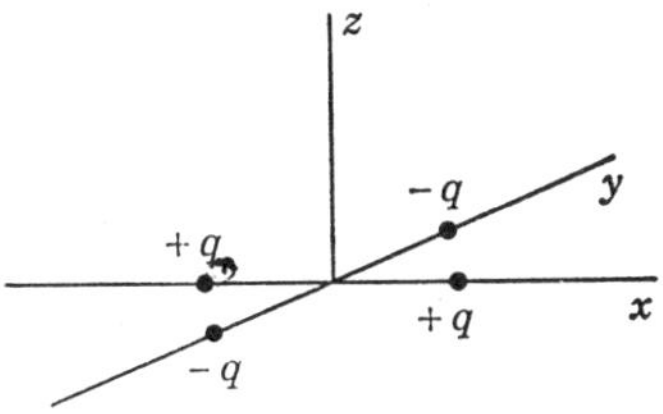

FIG. 4.4. Crystalline field due to charges $+q$ at $x = \pm a$, $y = z = 0$; $-q$ at $y = \pm a$, $x = z = 0$.

We turn now to a p-state, $xf(r)$, acted on by the crystalline field such as that discussed in Section 4.3. We duplicate the figures for the reader's convenience (Fig. 4.4).

The energy levels are then as in Fig. 4.5:

FIG. 4.5. Energy levels for a crystalline field such as shown in Fig. 4.4.

Let us consider H_0 to lie along the z-direction. In contrast to the s-state, the p-state has non-vanishing matrix elements to the excited states, corresponding to the tendency of the static field to unquench the angular momentum. For this orientation of H_0, the matrix element to $zf(r)$ vanishes. That to $yf(r)$ is

$$
\begin{aligned}
(n|\mathcal{H}_{\text{pert}}|0) &= -\frac{q}{2mc} H_0 \frac{\hbar}{i} \int yf(r) \left(x \frac{\partial}{\partial y} - y \frac{\partial}{\partial x} \right) xf(r)\, d\tau \\
&= +\frac{q}{2mc} H_0 \frac{\hbar}{i} \int (yf(r))^2\, d\tau \\
&= -\frac{iq\hbar H_0}{2mc}
\end{aligned}
\tag{30}
$$

where we have used the fact that the function $yf(r)$ is normalized.

By using Eq. (30) we find

$$
\epsilon_{n0} = \frac{(n|\mathcal{H}_{\text{pert}}|0)}{E_0 - E_n} = i \frac{q\hbar H_0}{2mc} \frac{1}{\Delta} \tag{31}
$$

The term $\psi_0 \nabla \psi_n - \psi_n \nabla \psi_0$ of Eq. (20) is readily shown to be

$$\psi_0 \nabla \psi_n - \psi_n \nabla \psi_0 = (x\mathbf{j} - y\mathbf{i})f^2(r) \tag{32}$$

It is convenient that the part of Eq. (11) associated with the excited states should be called the paramagnetic current, $\mathbf{j}_P$, since (as we shall see) it contributes a paramagnetic magnetic moment. We call the last term of Eq. (11) the diamagnetic current $\mathbf{j}_D$. Then, using Eqs. (11), (31), and (32), we get for our example

$$\mathbf{j}_P = \frac{\hbar^2}{2m} \frac{q^2}{mc} \frac{H_0}{\Delta} \mathbf{k} \times \mathbf{r} f^2(r) \tag{33}$$

and by using Eqs. (11) and (21),

$$\begin{aligned} \mathbf{j}_D &= -\frac{q^2}{mc} \frac{1}{2} H_0 \mathbf{k} \times \mathbf{r} |\psi|^2 \\ &= -\frac{q^2}{2mc} H_0 (\mathbf{k} \times \mathbf{r}) x^2 f^2(r) \end{aligned} \tag{34}$$

It is clear that both $\mathbf{j}_P$ and $\mathbf{j}_D$ flow in concentric circles but in opposite directions. However, although div $\mathbf{j}_P = 0$, the same is not true of $\mathbf{j}_D$. Since div $\mathbf{j} = 0$ for a stationary state ($\mathbf{j} = \mathbf{j}_P + \mathbf{j}_D$), there is clearly a discrepancy. It may be traced to the fact that the wave functions used to derive $\mathbf{j}_P$ and $\mathbf{j}_D$ are not exact solutions of the crystalline field, but are, rather, only zero-order functions. The charges that give rise to the crystalline splitting will also distort the functions. For example, $xf(r)$, which points towards the positive charges, will presumably be elongated somewhat, whereas $yf(r)$ will be somewhat compressed. This will result in current flow with a radial component that will, so to speak, supply the circular currents of the diamagnetic term. However, radial currents will affect neither the chemical shift (since they produce zero field at the origin) nor the atomic magnetic moment. Therefore we shall not search for better starting functions.

The division between diamagnetic and paramagnetic currents would change if we had chosen a different gauge for $\mathbf{A}_0$. However, if our solution for $\mathbf{j}_0(\mathbf{r})$ were exact (to order H_0), the *total* current $\mathbf{j}_0(\mathbf{r})$ would be gauge-invariant. It is for this reason that our expression in Eq. (17) of Section 4.4 is so useful, since it holds regardless of the gauge of $\mathbf{A}_0$ used to compute the currents or of the division of $\mathbf{j}_0$ between paramagnetic and diamagnetic terms.

It is important to compare the relative magnitudes of j_P and j_D. From Eqs. (33) and (34) we get

$$\begin{aligned} \mathbf{j}_D &= -\mathbf{j}_P \frac{m}{\hbar^2} x^2 \Delta \\ &= -\mathbf{j}_P \frac{\Delta}{(\hbar^2/mx^2)} \end{aligned} \tag{35}$$

where $\hbar^2/mx^2$ has the units of energy (comparable to the kinetic energy of an electron whose de Broglie wave length is x) By substituting numbers, we find

$$\mathbf{j}_D = -\mathbf{j}_P \frac{x^2 \Delta}{8 \text{ ev}} \tag{36}$$

where x is measured in angstroms. Thus, if $\Delta = 8$ ev (a fairly typical Δ for chemical shift problems), we see that j_P is larger for x less than 1 Å but that j_D is larger outside. As we shall see, the distance that is most important for typical chemical shifts is about $\frac{1}{4}$ Å, so the paramagnetic current dominates; however, for computing magnetic moments, a distance of 1 Å or greater is more typical, making it difficult to assess which factor is the more important.

We can now compute the chemical shift fields $\mathbf{H}_P$ and $\mathbf{H}_D$ due to $\mathbf{j}_P$ and $\mathbf{j}_D$:

$$\begin{aligned}\mathbf{H}_P &= \frac{1}{c}\int \frac{\mathbf{r}\times \mathbf{j}_P}{r^3}\,d\tau \\ &= \frac{\hbar^2}{2m}\frac{q^2}{mc^2}\frac{H_0}{\Delta}\int \frac{\mathbf{r}\times(\mathbf{k}\times\mathbf{r})}{r^3}f^2(r)\,d\tau\end{aligned} \tag{37}$$

Direct evaluation shows that the x and y components of $\mathbf{H}_P$ vanish, leaving only the z-component:

$$\mathbf{H}_P = \mathbf{k}\,\frac{\hbar^2}{2m}\frac{q^2}{mc^2}\frac{H_0}{\Delta}\int \frac{(x^2+y^2)}{r^3}f^2(r)\,d\tau \tag{38}$$

Now, for any wave function $\psi(r)$, the mean value of $1/r^3$ is given by

$$\overline{\left(\frac{1}{r^3}\right)} = \int \frac{1}{r^3}|\psi|^2\,d\tau \tag{39}$$

so that we see

$$\begin{aligned}\int \frac{x^2 f^2(r)\,d\tau}{r^3} &= \overline{\left(\frac{1}{r^3}\right)} \\ &= \int \frac{y^2 f^2(r)\,d\tau}{r^3}\end{aligned} \tag{40}$$

Therefore we find

$$\mathbf{H}_P = \mathbf{k}\,\frac{\hbar^2}{m}\frac{q^2}{mc^2}\frac{H_0}{\Delta}\overline{\left(\frac{1}{r^3}\right)} \tag{41}$$

We note that $\mathbf{H}_P$ aids the static field and is in fact proportional, in keeping with the experimental data.

The diamagnetic field, which is given by

$$\mathbf{H}_D = -\frac{q^2}{2mc^2}H_0\int \frac{\mathbf{r}\times(\mathbf{k}\times\mathbf{r})}{r^3}x^2f^2(r) \tag{42}$$

turns out also to be in the z-direction only:

$$\mathbf{H}_D = -\frac{\mathbf{k}q^2}{2mc^2}H_0\int \frac{(x^2+y^2)}{r^3}x^2f^2(r) \tag{43}$$

It is most convenient to average $\mathbf{H}_D$ over all orientations of H_0 with respect to the x-, y-, and z-axes. This can be shown to be equivalent to averaging H_D for H_0 parallel to the x-, y-, and z-axes, in turn giving

$$\begin{aligned}\mathbf{H}_D &= -\frac{1}{3}\frac{q^2}{2mc^2}H_0\int \frac{[(x^2+y^2)+(x^2+z^2)+(y^2+r^2)]}{r^3}x^2f(r) \\ &= -\frac{q^2}{3mc^2}H_0\overline{\left(\frac{1}{r}\right)}\end{aligned} \tag{44}$$

Since $H_D = -\sigma_D H_0$, where σ_D is the diamagnetic contribution to the chemical shielding parameter σ, we have

$$\sigma_D = \frac{q^2}{3mc^2}\overline{\left(\frac{1}{r}\right)} \tag{45}$$

an expression first derived by Lamb† to describe the shielding of closed atomic shells.

We can likewise average $\mathbf{H}_P$; however, we note here that $\mathbf{H}_P$ is zero when H_0 is parallel to the x-axis, since the perturbation gives zero when acting on the cylindrically symmetric function $xf(r)$. It is also convenient to assume that $yf(r)$ and $zf(r)$ are degenerate, both a distance Δ above $xf(r)$, since this corresponds to the typical case of a chemical bond. Then we have

$$H_P = \frac{2}{3}\frac{\hbar^2}{m}\frac{q^2}{mc^2}\frac{H_0}{\Delta}\overline{\left(\frac{1}{r^3}\right)} \tag{46}$$

and σ_P, the paramagnetic contribution to σ, is

$$\sigma_P = -\frac{2}{3}\frac{\hbar^2}{m}\frac{q^2}{mc^2}\frac{1}{\Delta}\overline{\left(\frac{1}{r^3}\right)} \tag{47}$$

If we take $\Delta = 4.3$ ev, and $(\overline{1/r^3}) = 8.89/a_0^3$, where a_0 is the Bohr radius (values appropriate to the $2p$ electrons of fluorine, with the energy chosen to be appropriate for the F_2 molecule), we find $\sigma_P = -20 \times 10^{-4}$. σ_D is typically 10^{-5}. We see that this value of σ_P is quite comparable to the changes in σ observed for fluorine compounds, whereas σ_D is much too small to account for the effects. It is clear also why the range of fluorine chemical shifts is so much larger than that of protons.

Physically, the large fluorine shifts come about because the magnetic field leads to an unquenching of the angular momentum. The smaller Δ, the more effectively H_0 can "unquench."

What can we say is the cause of the s-state shift? One simple picture is to note that an s-state is a radial standing wave. Since the magnetic force is transverse to the radial motion, it produces a slow rotation quite analogous to the manner in which the Coriolis force causes the direction of a Foucault pendulum to turn.

As we have seen, for any reasonable values of Δ, the paramagnetic shielding term will completely overwhelm the diamagnetic term. What can we say about $\mathbf{M}$, the electron contribution to the atomic magnetic moment?

$$\mathbf{M} = \frac{1}{2c}\int \mathbf{r} \times \mathbf{j}_0 \, d\tau \tag{48}$$

We contrast this with the shielding field

$$\mathbf{H} = \frac{1}{c}\int \frac{\mathbf{r} \times \mathbf{j}_0}{r^3} \, d\tau \tag{49}$$

Clearly, the $1/r^3$ factor makes $\mathbf{H}$ relatively much more sensitive to currents close to the nucleus. In fact we can quickly convert our formulas for shielding to for-

† W. Lamb, *Phys. Rev.*, **60**: 817 (1941).

mulas for average susceptibility χ by recognizing that only the radial averages differ. Thus the paramagnetic and diamagnetic currents contribute χ_P and χ_D, respectively, to the susceptibility χ, where

$$\begin{aligned} \chi &= \chi_P + \chi_D \\ \mathbf{M} &= \chi \mathbf{H}_0 \end{aligned} \tag{50}$$

We find (averaging over all orientations)

$$\chi_P = \frac{1}{3} \frac{\hbar^2}{m} \frac{q^2}{mc^2} \frac{1}{\Delta}$$

$$\chi_D = -\frac{1}{6} \frac{q^2}{mc^2} \overline{r^2}$$

There are anisotropies that, for both χ_P and χ_D, are a substantial fraction of the average value. If we compare χ_P and χ_D, we have

$$\begin{aligned} \chi_D &= -\chi_P \frac{\hbar^2}{m} \frac{\overline{r^2}}{2} \Delta \\ &= -\chi_P \frac{\overline{r^2}}{2} \frac{\Delta}{8 \text{ ev}} \end{aligned} \tag{51}$$

where r is measured in angstroms and Δ in electron volts. In general we must expect $\sqrt{\overline{r^2}} \sim 1$ Å, and $\Delta \sim 8$ ev. Therefore it is clear that $\chi_D \cong -\chi_P$. We cannot decide which term is the larger without specific examination. Note in particular that the mere fact that $\mathbf{j}_P$ is dominant in producing the chemical shift does *not* mean that it will be the major factor in determining the atomic susceptibility. The susceptibility, since it depends on currents *far* from the origin, is much more strongly influenced by the diamagnetic currents than is the chemical shift because the diamagnetic currents are the more prominent at large distances from the origin.

It is important to bear in mind that our particular choice of gauge has made $\mathcal{H}_{\text{pert}}$ dependent on the angular momentum about the origin. For an *exact* solution, this gauge is no better than any other gauge. However, we rarely deal with exact solutions. There may then be some physical preference in choosing a gauge that puts the perturbation in terms of angular momentum measured about the most prominent force center in the problem. Since our wave functions will be approximate, the approximations will then at least be so primarily because of failure to account for the small crystalline potential rather than for the much larger atomic (central) potential.

When we are dealing with chemical shifts in molecules, we find it very hard to deal with bonds, since two force centers, one at each nucleus (for a pair bond), are important. The only simple approximation is to treat the atoms as virtually isolated, taking the excitation energies as being those of excited bonds, and including such effects as ionic character by using non-normalized atomic wave functions. Pople† has discussed this problem, using a technique due to London. His results can also be obtained by using perturbation theory. A similar problem arises when calculating g-shifts, and this is discussed in Chapter 7.

† J. A. Pople, *Proc. Roy. Soc.*, **A239**: 541, 550 (1957).

When one has ring compounds such as benzene, the interatomic currents are important. Then one chooses a *molecular* force center; that is, a gauge in which L_z is the angular momentum about an axis around which the molecule has roughly cylindrical symmetry. For benzene, this is the hexad axis. About this axis only a diamagnetic current results. This current, which flows all around the benzene ring, produces chemical shifts at the proton positions. Of course, since the distance of the protons from the ring is comparable to the radius of the ring, the chemical shielding field is not accurately given by replacing the ring by a dipole.

On the other hand, when the currents, $\mathbf{j}(\mathbf{r})$ are well localized in an atom or in a single bond, the dimensions of which are small compared with the distance to the nucleus under study, we can represent the effect of the currents by a magnetic dipole. When we average the result over the random orientations of a molecule in a liquid, we find that the shift vanishes unless the atomic susceptibility is itself a function of the orientation of the magnetic field with respect to the molecule.

One important contribution to atomic currents, which vanishes in a liquid, is the contribution of currents in closed shells on atoms other than that containing the nucleus under study. The result in the liquid can be shown to follow simply because the current distribution in a closed shell is independent of the orientation of H_0 with respect to the molecular axes. We should emphasize that an attempt to compute the closed-shell contribution to shielding fields by *approximate* methods is dangerous, since one may find that the paramagnetic and diamagnetic contributions are large. Their algebraic sum (which is zero for an *exact* calculation in a liquid) may be non-zero unless a very accurate computation is made. It is therefore always safest (1) to judge the currents $\mathbf{j}_0(\mathbf{r})$ on physical grounds, (2) always to choose gauges for each atomic current that puts $\mathcal{H}_{\text{pert}}$ as proportional to the angular momentum about the most important atomic force center, and (3) to exclude from the calculation any currents that will give an exactly zero result.

Finally, we emphasize again the fact that the a priori judgment of whether a distant atom has a paramagnetic moment or a diamagnetic moment is not possible, but rather a detailed judgment of excitation energy and mean square atomic radius is essential. Moreover, for example, a *paramagnetic* moment on another atom can produce either diamagnetic or paramagnetic shielding fields, depending on whether the anisotropic moment is largest when the internuclear axis is perpendicular or parallel to the direction of H_0.

All the expressions given involve one electron only. If there are N electrons, we generalize by adding subscripts "$j = 1$ to N" to the electron position coordinate. Thus we define $\mathbf{A}_{0j}$ by the equation

$$\begin{aligned} \nabla_j \times \mathbf{A}_{0j} &= \mathbf{H}_0 \\ \nabla_j \times \mathbf{A}_{nj} &= \mathbf{H}_n \end{aligned} \tag{52}$$

Typically,

$$\begin{aligned} \mathbf{A}_{nj} &= \frac{\boldsymbol{\mu} \times \mathbf{r}_j}{r_j^3} \\ \mathbf{A}_{0j} &= \tfrac{1}{2}\mathbf{H}_0 \times (\mathbf{r}_j - \mathbf{R}) \end{aligned} \tag{53}$$

where $\mathbf{R}$ is a convenient origin. We then define

$$\boldsymbol{\pi}_j = \frac{\hbar}{i}\nabla_j - \frac{q}{c}\mathbf{A}_{0j} \tag{54}$$

so that the Hamiltonian, including both external magnetic field and the nuclear field, is

$$\mathcal{H} = \frac{1}{2m} \sum_{j=1}^{N} \left(\boldsymbol{\pi}_j - \frac{q}{c} \mathbf{A}_{nj}\right)^2 + V \tag{55}$$

If we define Ψ to be the exact solution of the N electron problem in the *absence* of the nuclear coupling, it obeys the equation

$$\left(\frac{1}{2m} \sum_j \boldsymbol{\pi}_j^2 + V\right) \Psi = E\Psi \tag{56}$$

Ψ is, of course, a function of the $\mathbf{r}_j$'s of all N electrons. Then we define the current associated with the jth electron as

$$\mathbf{J}_{0j}(\mathbf{r}_j) = \int \left\{\frac{\hbar q}{2mi} (\Psi^* \nabla_j \Psi - \Psi \nabla_j \Psi^*) - \frac{q}{mc} \mathbf{A}_{0j} \Psi^* \Psi\right\} d\tau_1 \cdots d\tau_{j-1}\, d\tau_{j+1} \cdots d\tau_N \tag{57}$$

where the integration leaves $\mathbf{J}_{0j}$ a function of $\mathbf{r}_j$ only. In terms of Eq. (57), the nuclear coupling E_{pert} is then

$$E_{\text{pert}} = -\boldsymbol{\mu} \cdot \frac{1}{c} \sum_j \int \frac{\mathbf{r}_j \times \mathbf{J}_{0j}(\mathbf{r}_j)}{r_j^3}\, d\tau_j \tag{58}$$

The wave function Ψ, which is needed to compute the currents, is then found by using perturbation theory. Defining the functions Ψ_0, Ψ_n to be solutions of the Hamiltonian $\mathcal{H}_0$ in the absence of the external field, with eigenvalues E_0 and E_n,

$$\begin{aligned} \left(\sum_j - \frac{\hbar \nabla_j^2}{2m} + V\right) \Psi_0 &= E_0 \Psi_0 \\ \left(\sum_j - \frac{\hbar \nabla_j^2}{2m} + V\right) \Psi_n &= E_n \Psi_n \end{aligned} \tag{59}$$

We express Ψ correct to first order in H_0 as

$$\Psi = \Psi_0 + \sum_n \frac{(n|\mathcal{H}_{\text{pert}}|0)}{E_0 - E_n} \Psi_n \tag{60}$$

where

$$\mathcal{H}_{\text{pert}} = -\frac{q}{2mc} \sum_j (\mathbf{p}_j \cdot \mathbf{A}_{0j} + \mathbf{A}_{0j} \cdot \mathbf{p}_j) \tag{61}$$

$\mathbf{p}_j$ being $(\hbar/i)\nabla_j$.

To obtain explicit solutions, one must now assume reasonable N electron wave functions for Ψ_0 and Ψ_n. Ordinarily one will choose the functions to be products of one electron functions, or perhaps pair functions to represent a covalent bond. Although j labels electrons, one can often rewrite Eq. (58) so that the sum over electron numbers is replaced by a sum over *orbits,* and in this way one can distinguish closed shell electrons from valence electrons.

The formalism we have discussed is useful for obtaining a physical understanding of chemical shifts. The final result can be expressed more compactly in a single formula such as has been given by Ramsey. To do this, we express the magnetic field, using Eq. (58), as

$$\mathbf{H} = \frac{1}{c}\sum_j \int \frac{\mathbf{r}_j \times \mathbf{J}_{0j}(\mathbf{r}_j)}{r_j^3}\, d\tau_j \tag{62}$$

Expressing $\mathbf{J}_{0j}$ by means of Eq. (57), Ψ by means of Eqs. (60) and (61), and taking $\text{div}_j\,\mathbf{A}_{0j} = 0$, straightforward manipulations give the result:

$$\mathbf{H} = \frac{q^2\hbar}{m^2c^2}\sum_n \frac{\left(0\left|\sum_j \frac{\mathbf{L}_j}{r_j^3}\right|n\right)\left(n\left|\sum_k \mathbf{A}_{0k}\cdot\mathbf{p}_k\right|0\right) + \left(0\left|\sum_k \mathbf{A}_{0k}\cdot\mathbf{p}_k\right|n\right)\left(n\left|\sum_j \frac{\mathbf{L}_j}{r_j^3}\right|0\right)}{E_n - E_0} - \frac{q^2}{mc^2}\left(0\left|\sum_j \mathbf{r}_j \times \mathbf{A}_{0j}\right|0\right) \tag{63}$$

If we further assume that $\mathbf{A}_{0k} = \frac{1}{2}\mathbf{H}_0 \times \mathbf{r}_k$ and that $\mathbf{H}_0 = H_0\mathbf{k}$, we get

$$\mathbf{H} = H_0\frac{q^2\hbar^2}{2m^2c^2}\sum_n \frac{\left(0\left|\sum_j \frac{\mathbf{L}_j}{r_j^3}\right|n\right)\left(n\left|\sum_k L_{zk}\right|0\right) + \left(0\left|\sum_k L_{zk}\right|n\right)\left(n\left|\sum_j \frac{\mathbf{L}_j}{r_j^3}\right|0\right)}{E_n - E_0} - \frac{q^2}{2mc^2}H_0\left(0\left|\sum_j\left[\frac{\mathbf{k}(x_j^2+y_j^2)}{r_j^3} - \frac{\mathbf{i}x_jz_j}{r_j^3} - \frac{\mathbf{j}y_jz_j}{r_j^3}\right]\right|0\right) \tag{64}$$

One can proceed to evaluate this expression directly rather than to compute the current density as an explicit function of position, as we did in our examples.

4·6 ELECTRON SPIN INTERACTION

The coupling to electron spins produces effects using first-order perturbation theory when the electron spin moment is non-zero, as in paramagnetic or ferromagnetic materials. The Knight shifts (shift of the resonance frequency in metals relative to their positions in insulators) are an example.† For diamagnetic materials, one must go to second-order perturbation theory to obtain non-vanishing spin couplings. One important class of phenomena that then results is the coupling of one nucleus with another via the electrons. These couplings give rise to fine structure of resonances in liquids and to either *narrowing* or *broadening* of resonance lines in solids. For example, the indirect couplings make the pure quadrupole resonance in indium metal be about ten times broader than that computed from

† See references to "Nuclear Magnetic Resonance in Metals" in the Bibliography.

the direct nuclear dipolar coupling alone. However, there is no chemical shift associated with electron spin for diamagnetic substances. We shall discuss this point at the end of Section 4.8.

We start by discussing the form of the magnetic coupling between an electron and a nucleus. As long as the nuclear and electron moments $\boldsymbol{\mu}_n$ and $\boldsymbol{\mu}_e$ are far enough apart, we expect their interaction to be that of a pair of magnetic dipoles, the Hamiltonian being

$$\mathcal{H} = \frac{\boldsymbol{\mu}_e \cdot \boldsymbol{\mu}_n}{r^3} - \frac{3(\boldsymbol{\mu}_e \cdot \mathbf{r})(\boldsymbol{\mu}_n \cdot \mathbf{r})}{r^5} \tag{1}$$

where $\mathbf{r}$ is the radius vector from the nucleus to the electron. As long as the electronic wave function is a p-state, d-state, or other state of non-zero angular momentum, we expect Eq. (1) to be a good approximation. For s-states, however, the electron wave function is non-zero at the nucleus. For these close distances, the dipole approximation is suspect. A closer examination emphasizes the troubles. Suppose we average $\mathcal{H}$ over an s-state electron wave function $u(r)$, as we would do to perform a first-order perturbation calculation of the coupling. There are a number of terms to Eq. (1), similar to the terms A, B, C, D, E, and F when computing the rigid lattice line breadth (see p. 47). Let us pick out a term A, which depends on angle and distance as $(1 - 3\cos^2\theta)/r^3$. Then, apart from a multiplicative constant, the average of such a term will be

$$\int \frac{u^2(r)}{r^3}(1 - 3\cos^2\theta)r^2\, dr\, d\Omega \tag{2}$$

where $d\Omega$ is an element of solid angle. If we do the angular integral first, it vanishes, giving us a result of zero for Eq. (2).

On the other hand, if we were to integrate first over r, we would encounter trouble near $r \cong 0$, where $u^2(r) = u^2(0) \neq 0$, giving a logarithmic infinity. Since we can get either zero or infinity, depending on our method of calculation, it is clear that we cannot simply ignore the contributions when r is small.

From what we have said, it is evident that the dipole approximation has broken down. There are two effects that come in and which have been neglected. First of all, we know the nucleus has a finite size. To the extent that the nuclear magnetic moment results from the bodily rotation of the nucleus, the currents are distributed over the nuclear volume. From the electron viewpoint the spin moments of the nuclear particles are also spread over a comparable region, since the nuclear particles effectively possess much higher frequencies of motion than does the electron (the nuclear energy levels are widely spaced in energy compared with those of electrons). A second effect is that the electronic coupling to the nucleus, when computed by using a relativistic theory (the Dirac equation), shows a marked change when the electron is within a distance e^2/mc^2 of the nucleus; e^2/mc^2 is the classical radius of the electron, r_0, and is about 3×10^{-13} cm. The electron is effectively smeared out over r_0. Since the radii of nuclei are given approximately by the formula

$$r = 1.5 \times 10^{-13} A^{1/3} \text{ cm} \tag{3}$$

we see that the nuclear size is comparable to the electron radius r_0.

Of course, completely aside from all these remarks, the fact that the electronic potential energy is of order mc^2 near the nucleus shows us that a relativistic theory is advisable.

We shall first give a simple classical derivation of the interaction for s-states, and then we shall discuss briefly how the Dirac theory exhibits the same features. The theorems on the relation between magnetic fields and currents, which we developed in discussing chemical shifts, will show us that our result is really rigorous for the contribution to the coupling resulting from bodily motion of nuclear charges. Finally, since a volume distribution of magnetic moment (as produced by the spin moments of the nuclear particles) is equivalent to a current distribution, our result will also include the contributions of intrinsic spin. Thus, although simple, our calculation is in fact rigorous in the non-relativistic case.

We shall represent the nucleus by a charge q going in a circular path of radius a with velocity $\mathbf{v}$. This, effectively, is a current loop of current $(q/c)(1/T)$, where T is the period of the motion. We can express $\overline{H}_z$—the magnetic field in the z-direction, due to the nucleus averaged over the electron orbital probability density $|u(r)|^2$—as

$$\overline{H}_z = \int H_z(\mathbf{r})|u(r)|^2\, d\tau \tag{4}$$

where $H_z(\mathbf{r})$ is the field of the current loop. We shall take z to be normal to the loop. The other components of H can be shown to vanish when averaged, since $|u(r)|^2$ is spherically symmetric for an s-state. If we draw a sphere of radius a about the origin, we can express $H_z(\mathbf{r})$ by means of a scalar magnetic potential either for $r < a$ or $r > a$. It is straightforward to show that the contribution from regions outside the sphere vanishes from the angular integrations. If we express the scalar potential inside the sphere as a sum of products of spherical harmonics with radial functions, all contributions except the first term (the term that corresponds to a uniform field within $r < a$) vanish. We can evaluate this term simply, since it is the only one that does not vanish at $r = 0$. Therefore Eq. (4) may be rewritten as

$$\overline{H}_z = \int_0^a H_c u^2(r)\, d\tau \tag{5}$$

where H_c is the field at the center of the sphere. We may approximate Eq. (5) by recognizing that $u(r)$ varies little over the nucleus as

$$\overline{H}_z = H_c u^2(0) \frac{4\pi}{3} a^3 \tag{6}$$

The field at the center of the loop is simply

$$\mathbf{H}_c = \frac{q}{c}\frac{\mathbf{r} \times \mathbf{v}}{r^3} = \frac{q}{c}\frac{v}{a^2}\mathbf{k} \tag{7}$$

But the magnetic moment μ_n of the nucleus is $i\pi a^2$, where i is the "current" or

$$\boldsymbol{\mu}_n = \frac{q}{c}\frac{1}{T}\pi a^2\mathbf{k} = \mathbf{k}\frac{q\,av}{2c} \tag{8}$$

Thus

$$\mathbf{H}_c = \frac{2\boldsymbol{\mu}_n}{a^3} \tag{9}$$

By substituting into Eq. (6) we find

$$\mathbf{k}\overline{H}_z = \frac{8\pi}{3}\boldsymbol{\mu}_n u^2(0) \tag{10}$$

The effective interaction energy, E, with an electron moment $\boldsymbol{\mu}_e$ is then

$$E = -\frac{8\pi}{3}\boldsymbol{\mu}_e \cdot \boldsymbol{\mu}_n u^2(0) \tag{11}$$

It is convenient to express the coupling as a term in the Hamiltonian that will give this interaction. This is readily done by means of the Dirac δ-function:

$$\mathcal{H} = -\frac{8\pi}{3}\boldsymbol{\mu}_e \cdot \boldsymbol{\mu}_n\, \delta(\mathbf{r}) \tag{12}$$

where $\mathbf{r}$ is now the position of the electron relative to the nucleus. It is convenient also to re-express Eq. (12) in terms of the nuclear and electron spins $\mathbf{I}$ and $\mathbf{S}$. For the electron we shall use a gyromagnetic ratio γ_e, which is positive, but for the nucleus γ_n is to have an algebraic significance, being either positive or negative. Then we have

$$\begin{aligned}\boldsymbol{\mu}_e &= -\gamma_e\hbar\mathbf{S}\\ \boldsymbol{\mu}_n &= \gamma_n\hbar\mathbf{I}\end{aligned} \tag{13}$$

which give

$$\mathcal{H} = \frac{8\pi}{3}\gamma_e\gamma_n\hbar^2\mathbf{I}\cdot\mathbf{S}\,\delta(\mathbf{r}) \tag{14}$$

We notice that in Eq. (11), the radius of the nucleon orbit has dropped out. Clearly, we should get the same answer for a volume distribution of circular currents. Moreover, since the smeared nucleon spin moment is equivalent to a volume distribution of current, we have also included the intrinsic spin of the nucleons if we use, for γ_n and $\mathbf{I}$, the experimental values. Equation (14) is therefore quite general. We see also that if we may *not* neglect the variations in $u(r)$ over the nucleus, the answer will be a bit different. Two isotopes that have different current distributions will then have couplings which are *not* simply in the ratio of the nuclear moments. This phenomenon is the source of the so-called hyperfine anomalies.

The treatment of the interaction by the Dirac equation is somewhat more involved. We shall sketch the important steps but leave the details to the reader. The Dirac Hamiltonian for an electron (charge $-e$) is

$$\mathcal{H} = -\boldsymbol{\alpha}\cdot(c\mathbf{p} + e\mathbf{A}) - \beta mc^2 + V \tag{15}$$

where $\boldsymbol{\alpha}$ and β are 4 by 4 matrices, V is the electron potential energy, and $\mathbf{A}$ is the vector potential. We can express $\boldsymbol{\alpha}$ and β in terms of the two by two Pauli matrices, $\boldsymbol{\sigma}$, and the two by two identity matrix $\mathbf{1}$ as

$$\boldsymbol{\alpha} = \begin{pmatrix} 0 & \boldsymbol{\sigma} \\ \boldsymbol{\sigma} & 0 \end{pmatrix} \qquad \beta = \begin{pmatrix} 1 & 0 \\ 0 & -1 \end{pmatrix} \tag{16}$$

The wave functions Ψ, which are solutions of Eq. (15), are represented by a column matrix of four functions, but these are most conveniently expressed in terms of the functions Ψ_1 and Ψ_2, each of which are column matrices with two elements:

$$\Psi = \begin{pmatrix} \Psi_1 \\ \Psi_2 \end{pmatrix} \tag{17}$$

The eigenvalues E of $\mathcal{H}$ may be written as

$$E = E' + mc^2 \tag{18}$$

where E' is the energy measured above mc^2, so that for a free particle at rest, $E' = 0$.

If we define

$$\boldsymbol{\pi} = c\mathbf{p} + e\mathbf{A} \tag{19}$$

and define ϕ as V/e, we have

$$\begin{aligned}(E' + e\phi + 2mc^2)\Psi_1 + \boldsymbol{\sigma} \cdot \boldsymbol{\pi}\Psi_2 &= 0 \\ (E' + e\phi)\Psi_2 + \boldsymbol{\sigma} \cdot \boldsymbol{\pi}\Psi_1 &= 0\end{aligned} \tag{20}$$

where $\phi = e/r$ is the potential due to the nucleus. As is well known, Ψ_1 is much smaller than Ψ_2 in the non-relativistic region. One customarily calls Ψ_2 the "large component." For s-states in hydrogen, Ψ_2 is also much larger than Ψ_1, even at the nucleus. One can eliminate Ψ_1 (still with no approximations) to obtain a Hamiltonian for Ψ_2, $\mathcal{H}'$ such that

$$\mathcal{H}'\Psi_2 = E'\Psi_2 \tag{21}$$

By tedious manipulation one finds that

$$\begin{aligned}\mathcal{H}' = \frac{1}{E' + e\phi + 2mc^2} &[c^2p^2 + e^2A^2 + 2ec\mathbf{A} \cdot \mathbf{p} - iec \operatorname{div} \mathbf{A} + e\hbar c\boldsymbol{\sigma} \cdot \nabla \times \mathbf{A}] \\ + \frac{e\hbar c}{(E' + e\phi + 2mc^2)^2} &[ie\mathbf{E} \cdot \mathbf{A} + ic\mathbf{E} \cdot \mathbf{p} - c\boldsymbol{\sigma} \cdot \mathbf{E} \times \mathbf{p} - e\boldsymbol{\sigma} \cdot \mathbf{E} \times \mathbf{A}]\end{aligned} \tag{22}$$

where $\mathbf{E}$ is the electric field due to the nucleus. For our present needs, we focus on two terms only:

$$\frac{1}{E' + e\phi + 2mc^2} e\hbar c\boldsymbol{\sigma} \cdot \nabla \times \mathbf{A} \tag{23a}$$

and

$$\frac{1}{(E' + e\phi + 2mc^2)^2} e^2\hbar c\boldsymbol{\sigma} \cdot \mathbf{E} \times \mathbf{A} \tag{24a}$$

For our problem, the nuclear coupling is given by introducing the vector potential $\mathbf{A} = \boldsymbol{\mu}_n \times \mathbf{r}/r^3$. Therefore $\nabla \times \mathbf{A}$ is simply the magnetic field of the nucleus computed by using the dipole approximation. As long as $e\phi \ll 2mc^2$, Eq. (23a) is exactly the same as Eq. (1) and goes as $1/r^3$. If, however, r is so small that $e\phi \sim 2mc^2$, the answer is modified. By writing $e\phi = e^2/r$, multiplying Eq. (23a) by r on top and bottom, using $e^2/mc^2 = r_0$ (the classical electron radius), and neglecting E', we get for Eq. (23a):

$$\left(\frac{2r}{2r + r_0}\right) \frac{e\hbar}{2mc} \boldsymbol{\sigma} \cdot \nabla \times \mathbf{A} \tag{23b}$$

Now we no longer have an infinity from the radial integral in computing $\mathbf{H}_z$, and it is clear that the angular average makes Eq. (23b) to be zero.

The term, Eq. (24a) can be rewritten as

$$\left(\frac{2r}{2r + r_0}\right)^2 \frac{e^3\hbar c}{(2mc^2)^2} \boldsymbol{\sigma} \cdot \left[\frac{\mathbf{r}}{r^3} \times \left(\frac{\boldsymbol{\mu}_n \times \mathbf{r}}{r^3}\right)\right] \tag{24b}$$

The term in the square brackets goes as $1/r^4$. For $r \gg r_0$, Eq. (24b) can be shown to be of order r_0/r times Eq. (23b); therefore, much smaller. However, when $r \leq r_0$, the radial dependence becomes less strong, going over to the harmless $1/r^2$ near $r = 0$. The term is therefore well behaved. It also has the feature that it does not average to zero over angle for s-states. It gives the answer of Eq. (11) for the magnetic interaction energy.

We see that these two terms are very similar to taking a δ-function for s-states and asserting that a finite size of the electron prevents the radial catastrophe of the conventional dipolar coupling of Eq. (1). For computational convenience we may consider that the dipolar interaction of Eq. (1) should be multiplied by the function $2r/(2r + r_0)$, to provide convergence.

We shall now turn to the study of some of the important manifestations of the coupling between nuclei and electron spins, considering first the effects that are first order in the interaction and then effects that arise in second order. Further discussion of first-order effects will be found in Chapter 8 on electron spin resonance.

4·7 KNIGHT SHIFT†

The Knight shift is named after Professor Walter Knight, who first observed the phenomenon. What he found was that the resonance frequency of Cu^{63} in metallic copper occurred at a frequency 0.23 percent higher than in diamagnetic CuCl, provided both resonances were performed at the same value of static field. Since this fractional shift is an order of magnitude larger than the chemical shifts among different diamagnetic compounds, it is reasonable to attribute it to an effect in the metal. Further studies revealed that the phenomenon was common to all metals, the principal experimental facts being four in number. By writing ω_m for the resonance frequency in the metal, ω_d for the resonance frequency in a diamagnetic reference, all at a single value of static field, there is a frequency displacement $\Delta\omega$ defined by

$$\omega_m = \omega_d + \Delta\omega \tag{1}$$

The four facts are

1. $\Delta\omega$ is positive (exceptional cases have been found, but we ignore them for the moment).
2. If one varies ω_d by choosing different values of static field, the *fractional* shift $\Delta\omega/\omega_d$ is unaffected.
3. The fractional shift is very nearly independent of temperature.
4. The fractional shift increases in general with increasing nuclear charge Z.

The fact that metals have a weak spin paramagnetism suggests that the shift may simply represent the pulling of the magnetic flux lines into the piece of metal. However, the susceptibilities are too small (10^{-6} cgs units/unit volume) to account for an effect of this size. As we shall see, however, the ordinary computation of internal fields in a solid that involves a spatial average of the local field is not what is wanted, since the nuclear moment occupies a very special place in the lattice—in fact a place at which the electron spends, so to speak, a large amount of time

† See references to "Nuclear Magnetic Resonance in Metals" in the Bibliography.

in response to the deep, attractive potential of the nuclear charge. As we shall see, the correct explanation of the Knight shift involves considering the field the nucleus experiences as a result of the interaction with conduction electrons through the *s*-state hyperfine coupling. If we think of the electrons in a metal as jumping rapidly from atom to atom, we see that a given nucleus experiences a magnetic coupling with many electrons. Therefore the coupling to the electron spins must be averaged over the electron spin orientations of many electrons. In the absence of an external field, there is no preferential orientation for the electron spins, and thus there is zero average magnetic coupling to the nuclei. On the other hand, the application of a static field, H_0, polarizes the electron spins, giving a non-vanishing coupling. Since the *s*-state interaction corresponds to the nucleus experiencing a magnetic field parallel to the electron magnetic moment,† and since the electron moment is preferentially parallel to H_0, the effective field at the nucleus will be increased. Since the shift in frequency is proportional to the degree of electron spin polarization, it will also be proportional to H_0 or ω_d. Moreover, since the electron polarization is temperature independent (the spin paramagnetism of a highly degenerate electron gas is independent of temperature), the shift will be temperature independent. And lastly, the Z-dependence will follow, since the wave function is larger at the position of a higher Z-nucleus, as is well known from the study of free atom hyperfine splittings. We can see from these considerations that the hyperfine coupling possesses the properties needed to explain the major facts. Let us now look into the details.

We consider a system of nuclear moments and of electrons coupled together by the hyperfine interaction. The relative weakness of the hyperfine coupling enables us to treat it by a perturbation theory in terms of the states of the electrons and the nuclear spins. We shall actually be able to avoid specifying the nuclear states, since we shall show that the effect of the interaction is simply to add an effective magnetic field parallel to the applied field. However, it is necessary to specify the electron wave function, which is, of course, a formidable task from a rigorous viewpoint, one that has not in fact been carried out because electrons couple to each other so strongly via the long range Coulomb interaction. Therefore we are forced to an approximation. We shall consider the electrons as being non-interacting—or at least only weakly so. Bohm and Pines†† have shown that this approximation has considerable theoretical justification. By means of a canonical transformation, they show that the principal effect of the Coulomb interaction is to give rise to a set of collective modes of oscillation, the plasma modes. The basic frequency of excitation of the plasma is so high that we may ordinarily consider the system to be in the ground plasma state. There still remain individual particle motions. The residual interaction between particles, however, is very weak and falls off nearly exponentially with distance. For low energy processes that do not excite the plasma modes, we may therefore treat the electrons as weakly interacting.

We shall describe the system, therefore, with a Hamiltonian:

$$\mathcal{H} = \mathcal{H}_e + \mathcal{H}_n + \mathcal{H}_{en} \tag{2}$$

where $\mathcal{H}_e$ describes a group of weakly interacting electrons, $\mathcal{H}_n$ is the nuclear

† The dependence of the interaction on the relative orientation of nuclear and electron moments is most readily seen by replacing the nucleus by a current loop.

†† D. Pines, *Solid State Physics*, Vol. 1, F. Seitz and D. Turnbull, eds. New York: Academic Press, 1955, p. 38.

Hamiltonian and includes the Zeeman energy of the nuclei in the static field H_0 as well as the magnetic dipolar coupling among the nuclei, and where $\mathcal{H}_{en}$ is the magnetic interaction between the nuclei and the electron spins. We omit the coupling of the nuclei to the electron orbital motion because it gives effects comparable to the chemical shifts. (Of course the electrons in the metal are free, so that the orbital effect is a bit different from that in an insulator.) It can be shown that the conventional dipolar coupling between nuclear and electron spins, Eq. (1) of Section 4.6, contributes nothing in a cubic metal. For non-cubic metals it gives rise to Knight shifts which depend on the orientation of H_0 with respect to the crystalline axes. Since resonance in metals is usually performed on powders (to permit adequate penetration of the alternating field into the material, a problem that we may call the "skin depth" problem), the anisotropy manifests itself through a line broadening. In the interest of simplicity, we shall confine our attention to the δ-function coupling:

$$\mathcal{H}_{en} = \frac{8\pi}{3}\gamma_e\gamma_n\hbar^2 \sum_{j,l} \mathbf{I}_j \cdot \mathbf{S}_l\, \delta(\mathbf{r}_l - \mathbf{R}_j) \tag{3}$$

where $\mathbf{r}_l$ is the radius vector to the position of the lth electron, and $\mathbf{R}_j$ that to the position of the jth nucleus. Since we treat the nuclei and electrons as only weakly interacting, we may write the complete wave function ψ as a product of the (many particle) wave functions ψ_e and ψ_n of the electrons and nuclei:

$$\psi = \psi_e\psi_n \tag{4}$$

(Of course this wave function would be exact if $\mathcal{H}_{en}$ were zero.) We shall then perform a perturbation calculation of the energy E_{en}:

$$E_{en} = \int \psi^*\mathcal{H}_{en}\psi\, d\tau_e\, d\tau_n \tag{5}$$

where $d\tau_e$ and $d\tau_n$ indicate integration over electron and nuclear coordinates (spatial and spin). Of course we shall wish to see the effect of Eq. (5) on *transitions* of the nuclear system from one nuclear state ψ_n to another $\psi_{n'}$. Since the transitions are in the nuclear system, they leave the electron state ψ_e unchanged. In computing the energy of the nuclear transition $E_{en} - E_{en'}$, we have to compute both E_{en} and $E_{en'}$. Both energies involve the integral over the electron coordinates. It is convenient for us to postpone a specification of the nuclear states and to compute therefore, the electronic integral

$$\mathcal{H}'_{en} = \int \psi_e^*\mathcal{H}_{en}\psi_e\, d\tau_e \tag{6}$$

which is simply the first step in computing Eq. (5) on the assumption of a product function, $\psi = \psi_e\psi_n$ or $\psi' = \psi_e\psi_{n'}$. We denote Eq. (6) by $\mathcal{H}'_{en}$ to emphasize that the nuclear coordinates still appear as operators.

The function ψ_e will itself be a simple product of one electron function if we assume that the electrons do not interact among themselves—or at least interact weakly. For the individual electrons we shall take the so-called Bloch functions. We remind ourselves of what these are: If the electrons were thought of as moving in a one-dimensional box of length a (Eig. 4.6), the position coordinate being x, the wave functions would be $\sin kx$ or $\cos kx$, where only those values of k are allowed that satisfy the proper boundary conditions at $x = 0$ and $x = a$. In order to describe a situation in which a current can flow, it is customary to consider instead solutions e^{ikx}, where now the allowed values of k are those that make the

FIG. 4.6. Metal represented by a box, with a potential depth V_0.

wave function the same at $x = a$ as it is at $x = 0$. The periodic boundary conditions for a three-dimensional box give solutions of the form

$$\psi = e^{i\mathbf{k}\cdot\mathbf{r}} \tag{7}$$

These solutions are modified in a very simple way to take account of the fact that the real potential is very deep in the vicinity of the nuclei. The wave functions, called *Bloch functions*, are then of the form

$$\psi_{\mathbf{k}} = u_{\mathbf{k}}(\mathbf{r})e^{i\mathbf{k}\cdot\mathbf{r}} \tag{8}$$

That is, there is still a quantity $\mathbf{k}$, the allowed values of which are given by requiring periodicity of the wave function on the walls of a box, but the plane wave $e^{i\mathbf{k}\cdot\mathbf{r}}$ is multiplied by a modulating function $u_{\mathbf{k}}(\mathbf{r})$, which is a function possessing the lattice periodicity. A typical $u_{\mathbf{k}}(\mathbf{r})$ peaks up strongly near a nucleus. The fact that we explicitly label u with a subscript $\mathbf{k}$ points out that u will in general vary with $\mathbf{k}$.

We shall need to add a spin coordinate as well, giving us finally a function

$$\psi_{\mathbf{k}s} = u_{\mathbf{k}}e^{i\mathbf{k}\cdot\mathbf{r}}\psi_s \tag{9}$$

where ψ_s is a spin function. The wave function for the N-electrons, ψ_e, will then be a product of $\psi_{\mathbf{k}s}$'s, properly antisymmetrized to take account of the Pauli exclusion principle. We can do this readily in terms of the permutation operator P:†

$$\psi_e = \frac{1}{\sqrt{N!}}\sum_P (-1)^P P\psi_{\mathbf{k}s}(1)\psi_{\mathbf{k}'s'}(2)\psi_{\mathbf{k}''s''}(3)\cdots\psi_{\mathbf{k}_N s_N}(N) \tag{10}$$

where the symbol $(-1)^P$ means to take a plus or minus sign, depending on whether or not the permutation involves an even or an odd number of interchanges. The factor $1/\sqrt{N!}$ is, of course, simply normalization.

Let us compute $\mathcal{H}'_{enj}$, the contribution to Eq. (6) of the jth nuclear spin, and choose the origin of coordinates at that nuclear site ($\mathbf{R}_j = 0$). Then we have

$$\mathcal{H}'_{enj} = \frac{8\pi}{3}\gamma_e\gamma_n\hbar^2\mathbf{I}_j\cdot\int\psi_e^*\sum_l \mathbf{S}_l\,\delta(\mathbf{r}_l)\psi_e\,d\tau_e \tag{11}$$

Since the operator $\mathbf{S}_l\,\delta(\mathbf{r}_l)$ involves only one electron, there are no contributions to Eq. (11) from terms in which electrons are exchanged, and therefore we get

$$\frac{8\pi}{3}\gamma_e\gamma_n\hbar^2\mathbf{I}_j\cdot\sum_l\int[\psi_{\mathbf{k}s}(1)\psi_{\mathbf{k}'s'}(2)\cdots]^*\mathbf{S}_l\,\delta(\mathbf{r}_l)[\psi_{\mathbf{k}s}(1)\psi_{\mathbf{k}'s'}(2)\cdots]\,d\tau_1\,d\tau_2\cdots \tag{12}$$

† L. Pauling and E. B. Wilson, Jr., *Introduction to Quantum Mechanics.* New York: McGraw-Hill Book Co., Inc., 1935, p. 232.

We now assume the electrons are quantized along the z-direction by the external static field H_0. Then the only contribution to Eq. (12) comes from S_{zl}. (We could alternatively have kept just that part proportional to I_{zj}, assuming the nuclear spins to be quantized along H_0, the result being the same.) We can write the results of Eq. (12) as

$$\frac{8\pi}{3}\gamma_e\gamma_n\hbar^2 I_{zj}\sum_{\mathbf{k},s}|u_{\mathbf{k},s}(0)|^2 m_s p(\mathbf{k}, s) \tag{13}$$

where the sum is over-all values of $\mathbf{k}$, s, and where $p(\mathbf{k}, s)$ is a factor that is 1 if $\mathbf{k}$, s are occupied by an electron, zero otherwise. The factor m_s is the m value of the state $\psi_{\mathbf{k},s}$; hence it is $+\frac{1}{2}$ or $-\frac{1}{2}$, and of course $u_{\mathbf{k},s}(0)$ is the wave function evaluated at the position of nucleus j.

If we average this expression over a set of occupations $p(\mathbf{k}, s)$, which are representative of the temperature of the electrons, we can write for the effective interaction with jth nucleus,

$$\frac{8\pi}{3}\gamma_e\gamma_n\hbar^2 I_{zj}\sum_{\mathbf{k},s}|u_{\mathbf{k},s}(0)|^2 m_s f(\mathbf{k}, s) \tag{14}$$

where $f(\mathbf{k}, s)$ is the Fermi function. For the electrons at absolute zero, $f(\mathbf{k}, s)$ is 1 for all $\mathbf{k}$, s, which make the total (that is, spin plus spatial) electron energy less

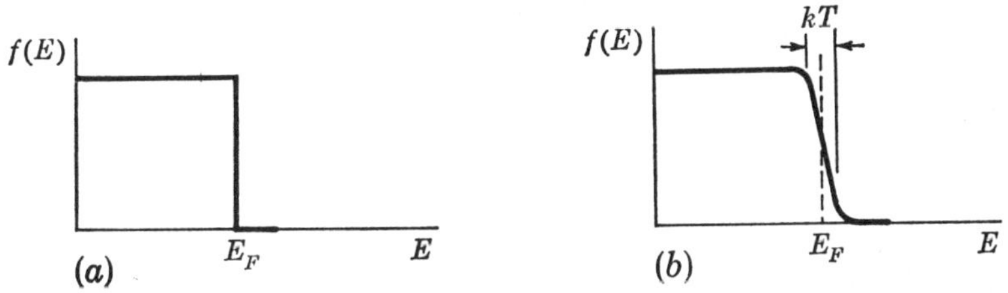

FIG. 4.7. (a) Fermi function $f(E)$ at absolute zero. (b) Fermi function at a temperature T above absolute zero.

than the Fermi energy E_F and is zero for energies greater than E_F. At temperatures above absolute zero, $f(\mathbf{k}, s)$ is modified within about kT of E_F (Fig. 4.7). Of course $f(E)$ is

$$f(E) = \frac{1}{1 + \exp[(E - E_F)/kT} \tag{15}$$

The notation $f(\mathbf{k}, s)$ means $f(E)$, of course, where E is the energy of an electron with wave vector $\mathbf{k}$ and spin coordinate s. Typically, $E = E_{\mathbf{k}} + E_{\text{spin}}$, where E_{spin} is the energy associated with the spin orientation and $E_{\mathbf{k}}$ is the sum of the kinetic and potential energies of an electron of wave vector $\mathbf{k}$. (We shall call $E_{\mathbf{k}}$ the *translational energy* of the electron.) For example, E_{spin} is the Zeeman energy of the electron spin in the static field H_0. There may be other contributions to E_{spin}, however, from the electrostatic coupling between electrons, which depends on their relative spin orientation. If we consider a typical term in the sum of

Eq. (14) corresponding to a single value of **k**, there are two values of m_s, giving us

$$\frac{8\pi}{3}\gamma_n\hbar I_{zj}[\gamma_e\hbar(\tfrac{1}{2})f(\mathbf{k},\tfrac{1}{2}) + \gamma_e\hbar(-\tfrac{1}{2})f(\mathbf{k},-\tfrac{1}{2})]|u_{\mathbf{k}}(0)|^2 \tag{16}$$

As we can see, the quantity in the bracket is (apart from a minus sign, since $\boldsymbol{\mu}_e = -\gamma_e\hbar\mathbf{S}$) the average contribution of state **k** to the z-component of electron magnetization of the sample. We shall denote it by $\overline{\mu_{z\mathbf{k}}}$. The *total* z-magnetization of the electrons, $\overline{\mu_z}$, is then

$$\overline{\mu_z} = \sum_{\mathbf{k}} \overline{\mu_{z\mathbf{k}}} \tag{17}$$

If we define the total spin susceptibility of the electrons, χ_e^s, by

$$\overline{\mu_z} = \chi_e^s H_0 \tag{18}$$

and define a quantity $\chi_{\mathbf{k}}^s$ by

$$\overline{\mu_{z\mathbf{k}}} = \chi_{\mathbf{k}}^s H_0 \tag{19}$$

then Eq. (17) is equivalent to

$$\chi_e^s = \sum_{\mathbf{k}} \chi_{\mathbf{k}}^s \tag{20}$$

We can therefore write Eq. (16) as

$$-\frac{8\pi}{3}\gamma_n\hbar I_{zj}|u_{\mathbf{k}}(0)|^2\chi_{\mathbf{k}}^s H_0 \tag{21}$$

so that the total effective interaction for spin j is

$$-\frac{8\pi}{3}\gamma_n\hbar I_{zj}\left[\sum_{k}|u_{\mathbf{k}}(0)|^2\chi_{\mathbf{k}}^s\right]H_0 \tag{22}$$

Our problem now is to evaluate the summation. It would be simple to make the assumption of completely free electrons, but it is actually no harder to treat the case of a material with a more complicated band structure. We shall do the latter, since the resulting expression will enable us to make some important comparisons between experiment and theory.

We assume, therefore, that the energy of the electrons, apart from spin effects, is determined by its **k** vector. For free electrons, the dependence would be

$$E_k = \frac{\hbar^2k^2}{2m} \tag{23}$$

so that in **k**-space, all electrons on a sphere of given k would have the same energy. That is, the points of constant energy form a surface, in this case a sphere (Fig. 4.8). In general the effect of the lattice potential is to distort the surfaces from spheres. We shall assume that the function $|u_{\mathbf{k}}(0)|^2\chi_{\mathbf{k}}^s$ varies slowly as one moves the point **k** in **k**-space from one allowed **k**-value to the next, so that we can define a density function to describe the number of allowed **k**-values in any region. Let us define $g(E_{\mathbf{k}}, A)\,dE_{\mathbf{k}}\,dA$ as the number of allowed **k**-values lying within a certain region of k-space, defined as follows: It is a small cylinder lying between the energy surfaces $E_{\mathbf{k}}$ and $E_{\mathbf{k}} + dE_{\mathbf{k}}$ (Fig. 4.9). Its surface area on the top or bottom surface is

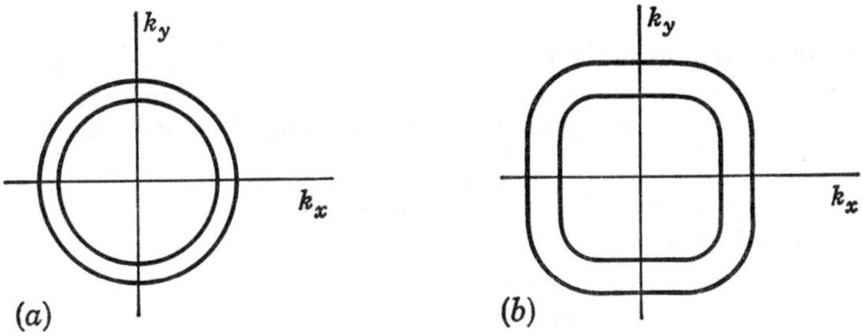

FIG. 4.8. Intersection of two surfaces of constant energy with the $k_z = 0$ plane. (a) Circular section of a free electron. (b) A less symmetric section for a hypothetical "real" substance.

an element of dA of the constant energy surface. We denote the particular coordinates on the surface also by the symbol A in $g(E, A)$. The *total* number of states dN

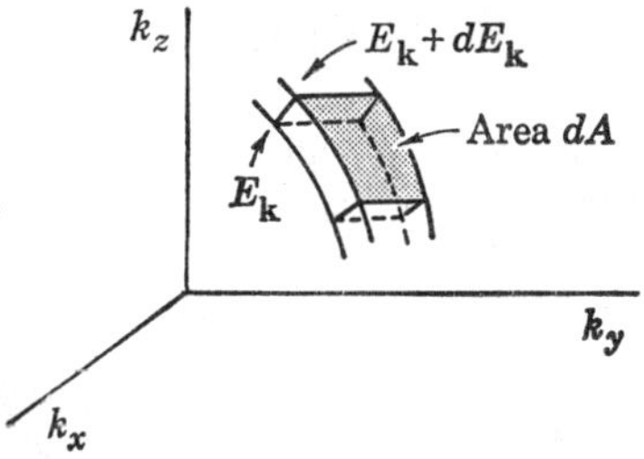

FIG. 4.9. Volume in **k**-space associated with $dE\,dA$.

between $E_{\mathbf{k}}$ and $E_{\mathbf{k}} + dE_{\mathbf{k}}$ is found by summing the contributions over the entire surface:

$$\begin{aligned} dN &= dE_{\mathbf{k}} \int_{E_{\mathbf{k}}=\text{const}} g(E_{\mathbf{k}}, A)\, dA \\ &\equiv \rho(E_{\mathbf{k}})\, dE_{\mathbf{k}} \end{aligned} \tag{24}$$

We can use these functions to evaluate the summation by replacing it with an integral:

$$\sum_{\mathbf{k}} |u_{\mathbf{k}}(0)|^2 \chi_{\mathbf{k}}^s = \int |u_{\mathbf{k}}(0)|^2 \chi_{\mathbf{k}}^s g(E_{\mathbf{k}}, A)\, dE_{\mathbf{k}}\, dA \tag{25}$$

Now $\chi_{\mathbf{k}}^s$ depends on the Fermi functions $f(\mathbf{k}, \frac{1}{2})$ and $f(\mathbf{k}, -\frac{1}{2})$ and thus on the energy $E_{\mathbf{k}}$ *and* on the difference in energy of a spin in state $\mathbf{k}$ with spin up versus that with spin down ($\gamma_e \hbar H_0$ for free electrons). Therefore, $\chi_{\mathbf{k}}^s$ would be the same for any states $\mathbf{k}$ having the same value of translational energy $E_{\mathbf{k}}$. Even when we allow the electrostatic coupling between the electrons to affect the energy to turn over a spin, it may be reasonable to assume that this modification depends at most on $E_{\mathbf{k}}$. We therefore assume that $\chi_{\mathbf{k}}^s$ is a function only of the energy $E_{\mathbf{k}}$.

$$\chi_{\mathbf{k}}^s = \chi^s(E_{\mathbf{k}}) \tag{26}$$

We can therefore rewrite Eq. (25) as

$$\sum_{\mathbf{k}} |u_{\mathbf{k}}(0)|^2 \chi_{\mathbf{k}}^s = \int |u_{\mathbf{k}}(0)|^2 \chi^s(E_{\mathbf{k}}) g(E_{\mathbf{k}}, A)\, dA\, dE_{\mathbf{k}} \tag{27}$$

If we have any function F of E, we define its average value over the surface of constant translational energy $E_{\mathbf{k}}$, $\langle F(\mathbf{k})\rangle_{E_{\mathbf{k}}}$, as

$$\langle F(\mathbf{k})\rangle_{E_{\mathbf{k}}} = \frac{\int F(\mathbf{k}) g(E_{\mathbf{k}}, A)\, dA}{\int g(E_{\mathbf{k}}, A)\, dA} = \frac{1}{\rho(E_{\mathbf{k}})} \int F(\mathbf{k}) g(E_{\mathbf{k}}, A)\, dA \tag{28}$$

Then we can set the integral over dA in Eq. (27) equal to

$$\int |u_{\mathbf{k}}(0)|^2 g(E_{\mathbf{k}}, A)\, dA = \rho(E_{\mathbf{k}}) \langle |u_{\mathbf{k}}(0)|^2 \rangle_{E_{\mathbf{k}}} \tag{29}$$

giving

$$\sum_{k} |u_{\mathbf{k}}(0)|^2 \chi_{\mathbf{k}}^s = \int \langle |u_{\mathbf{k}}(0)|^2 \rangle_{E_{\mathbf{k}}} \chi^s(E_{\mathbf{k}}) \rho(E_{\mathbf{k}})\, dE_{\mathbf{k}} \tag{30}$$

Now $\chi^s(E_{\mathbf{k}})$ is zero for all values of $E_{\mathbf{k}}$ that are not rather near to the Fermi energy, since for small values of $E_{\mathbf{k}}$ the two spin states are 100 percent populated, whereas

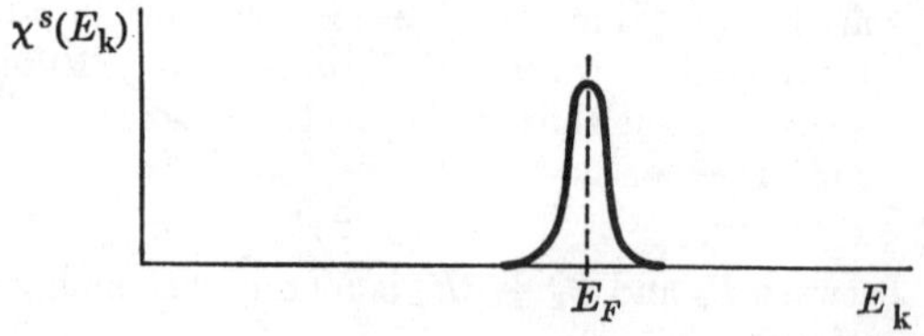

FIG. 4.10. Function $\chi^s(E_{\mathbf{k}})$ versus $E_{\mathbf{k}}$.

for large $E_{\mathbf{k}}$, *neither* spin state is occupied. $\chi^s(E_{\mathbf{k}})$ must look much like Fig. 4.10. $\chi^s(E_{\mathbf{k}})$ will be non-zero for a region of width about kT around the Fermi energy E_F.

We are therefore justified in assuming $\langle |u_{\mathbf{k}}(0)|^2 \rangle_{E_{\mathbf{k}}}$ varies sufficiently slowly to be evaluated at the Fermi energy and taken outside of the integral.

$$\sum_{\mathbf{k}} |u_{\mathbf{k}}(0)|^2 \chi_{\mathbf{k}}^s = \langle |u_{\mathbf{k}}(0)|^2 \rangle_{E_F} \int \chi^s(E_{\mathbf{k}}) \rho(E_{\mathbf{k}})\, dE_{\mathbf{k}} \tag{31}$$

The integral remaining in Eq. (31) is readily evaluated in terms of Eq. (20), since

$$\begin{aligned} \chi_e^s = \sum_{\mathbf{k}} \chi_{\mathbf{k}}^s &= \int \chi_{\mathbf{k}}^s\, g(E_{\mathbf{k}}, A)\, dE_{\mathbf{k}}\, dA \\ &= \int \chi^s(E_{\mathbf{k}}) g(E_{\mathbf{k}}, A)\, dE_{\mathbf{k}}\, dA \end{aligned} \tag{32a}$$

which, performing the integral over A, becomes

$$\chi_e^s = \int \chi^s(E_{\mathbf{k}})\rho(E_{\mathbf{k}})\, dE_{\mathbf{k}} \tag{32b}$$

Therefore, using Eqs. (22), (31), and (32), we may say that the interaction with jth nuclear spin is

$$-\gamma_n \hbar I_{zj}\left[\frac{8\pi}{3}\langle|u_{\mathbf{k}}(0)|^2\rangle_{E_F}\chi_e^s H_0\right] \tag{33}$$

This is entirely equivalent to the interaction with an *extra* magnetic field ΔH, which aids the applied field H_0, and is given in magnitude by the equation

$$\frac{\Delta H}{H_0} = \frac{8\pi}{3}\langle|u_{\mathbf{k}}(0)|^2\rangle_{E_F}\chi_e^s \tag{34}$$

We see that this formula has all the correct properties to explain the experimental results, since

1. It predicts that a higher frequency is needed for the metal than in the diamagnetic reference.
2. The fractional shift is independent of ω.
3. Since both $\langle|u_{\mathbf{k}}(0)|^2\rangle_{E_F}$ and χ^s are independent of temperature, $\Delta H/H_0$ is as well. Since the larger Z-atoms will have a larger value of $\langle|u_{\mathbf{k}}(0)|^2\rangle_{E_F}$ corresponding to the pulling in of their wave function by the larger nuclear charge, the increase of Knight shift with Z is explained.

The Knight shift formula can be checked if one can measure independently $\Delta H/H_0$, $\langle|u_{\mathbf{k}}(0)|^2\rangle_{E_F}$, and χ_e^s. There is only one case for which all three quantities are known (Li metal). The spin susceptibility has been measured by Schumacher† by a method we will describe shortly. Ryter†† has measured $\langle|u_{\mathbf{k}}(0)|^2\rangle_{E_F}$ by measuring the shift of the electron resonance by the nuclear moments. This shift, ΔH_e, is given by

$$\frac{\Delta H_e}{H_0} = \frac{8\pi}{3}\langle|u_{\mathbf{k}}(0)|^2\rangle_{E_F}\chi_n^s \tag{35}$$

where χ_n^s is the nuclear susceptibility of the Li^7 nuclei. Denoting the number of nuclei per unit volume by N, we have

$$\chi_n^s = \frac{N\gamma_n^2\hbar^2 I(I+1)}{3kT} \tag{36}$$

Thus, since χ_n^s is known, measurement of ΔH_e gives $\langle|u_k(0)|\rangle_{E_F}^2$. In order to enhance the size of the shift, Ryter polarized the nuclei, using the so-called Overhauser effect. It is necessary then to modify the formulas slightly, but the principle remains the same.

For comparison with experiment it is convenient to compute $\langle|u_{\mathbf{k}}(0)|^2\rangle_{E_F}$, using wave functions normalized to the atomic volume. We shall denote $\langle|u_{\mathbf{k}}(0)|^2\rangle_{E_F}$ in this case by P_F. We shall use P_A to denote the wave function density at the

† R. T. Schumacher and C. P. Slichter, *Phys. Rev.*, **101**: 58 (1956).
†† Ch. Ryter, *Phys. Rev. Letters*, **5**: 10 (1960).

nucleus for a free atom. It is then convenient to discuss the ratio P_F/P_A for Li and Na. A comparison of Ryter's values, theoretical values, and values deduced from combining Schumacher's measurement of χ_e^s with measured Knight shifts is given in Table 4.1.

TABLE 4.1.

	P_F/P_A in Li
Kohn and Kjeldaas theoretical	0.49 ± 0.05
Experimental (χ_e^s plus Knight shift)	0.45 ± 0.03
Ryter (experimental)	0.442 ± 0.015

There is excellent agreement among all three values. For Na, Kohn and Kjeldaas† find $P_F/P_A = 0.80 \pm 0.03$. We can combine this value with the measured Knight shift to obtain a quasi-experimental value of χ_e^s. Before presenting these results, we shall describe Schumacher's direct measurement of χ_e^s.

The fundamental problem in measuring χ_e^s is how to distinguish it from the other contributions to the total susceptibility, which (in a metal) are quite comparable in size. The method employed by Schumacher is to isolate the spin contribution by use of magnetic resonance. From the Kramers-Kronig relations we have for the electron spin susceptibility χ_e^s:

$$\chi_e^s = \frac{2}{\pi}\int_0^\infty \frac{\chi_e'' \, d\omega}{\omega} \tag{37}$$

where χ_e'' is the imaginary part of the conduction electron spin susceptibility. For a sufficiently narrow resonance, we may neglect the variation in ω across the absorption line, taking it out of the integral. We can then change the integration from one over frequency to one over field, using $\omega = \gamma H$:

$$\begin{aligned} \chi_e^s &= \frac{2}{\pi}\frac{1}{\omega_0}\int_0^\infty \chi_e'' \, d\omega \\ &= \frac{2}{\pi}\frac{\gamma_e}{\omega_0}\int_0^\infty \chi_e'' \, dH \end{aligned} \tag{38}$$

An absolute measurement of the area under the resonance curve will therefore enable one to determine χ_e^s. (Actually, the approximation of a narrow resonance is not well fulfilled in Schumacher's case; however, the final formula can be shown still to be correct. For a discussion of these points the reader is referred to Schumacher's paper. We may also note that the resonant absorption of energy at the cyclotron frequency occurs degenerate with that of the spin. However, the rapid electron collisions broaden it so much as to render it unobservable. One may be confident that it is only χ_e'' that is being measured.)

† W. Kohn, *Phys. Rev.*, **96**: 590 (1954); T. Kjeldaas, Jr., and W. Kohn, *Phys. Rev.*, **101**: 66 (1956).

Absolute measurements of absorption are always very difficult. Schumacher circumvented them by making use of the nuclear resonance of the Li^7 or Na^{23} nuclei in the same sample for which he measured the conduction electron resonance. For the nuclei, one has a spin susceptibility χ_n^s, given by Eq. (36) and for which

$$\chi_n^s = \frac{2}{\pi} \frac{\gamma_n}{\omega_0} \int_0^\infty \chi_n'' \, dH \tag{39}$$

By choosing $\omega_0/2\pi \cong 10$ Mc/sec, Schumacher could observe either the electron or nuclear resonances simply by changing H_0, the remainder of the apparatus being left unchanged. The nuclear resonance occurred at about 10,000 gauss, whereas the electron resonance was at only a few gauss. Then, if we denote the area under the electron or nuclear resonances by A_e or A_n, respectively, we have

$$\frac{\chi_e^s}{\chi_n^s} = \frac{\gamma_e}{\gamma_n} \frac{A_e}{A_n} \tag{40}$$

Since χ_n^s can be computed, we are thus able to determine χ_e^s. Note that we can measure the "area" in any units we wish (such as square centimeters on the face of an oscilloscope) as long as they are the same for both resonances. We do not even need to know how much sample we have, since it is the same for both electrons and nuclei.

The experimental values obtained are listed in Table 4.2 together with various

TABLE 4.2.

χ_e^s (all values are 10^6 cgs volume units)

	Free Electrons	Sampson and Seitz	Bohm-Pines	Knight Shift and Theoretical P_F/P_A	Schumacher
Li	1.17	2.92	1.87	1.85 ± 0.20	2.08 ± 0.10
Na	0.64	1.21	0.85	0.83 ± 0.03	0.95 ± 0.10

theoretical values. The first column† gives theoretical values based on non-interacting electrons, but an effective mass has been introduced to take account of the lattice potential. The effective masses are computed by Harvey Brooks, using the quantum defect method. The second column shows the theoretical values obtained by Sampson and Seitz, who took into account the electron-electron coupling by means of an interpolation formula of Wigner. The next column shows theoretical values due to Pines, based upon the Bohm-Pines collective description. Next we give values obtained by using the Knight shift and the Kohn-Kjeldaas theoretical values of P_F/P_A. The last column shows Schumacher's results.

We point out that if Ryter's value of P_F/P_A is used, the Knight shift value is raised, providing excellent agreement with that of Schumacher.

† The various experimental and theoretical numbers quoted here are discussed by D. Pines, *Solid State Physics*, Vol. 1, Seitz and Turnbull, eds. New York: Academic Press, Inc.

The Knight shift calculation is closely related to the problem of the nuclear resonance in samples in which the electron magnetization does not vanish when $H_0 = 0$, as with ferromagnets or antiferromagnets. Let us discuss the case of ferromagnetism briefly.†

Once again the electron-nuclear interaction will consist of the sum of the conventional dipolar coupling $\mathcal{H}_d$ and the s-state interaction $\mathcal{H}_s$:

$$\mathcal{H}_{en} = \mathcal{H}_d + \mathcal{H}_s \tag{41}$$

We shall average this over the electron wave function ψ_e, as with the Knight shift, to get an effective nuclear Hamiltonian $\mathcal{H}'_{en}$, which will contain the nuclear spins as operators:

$$\mathcal{H}'_{en} = \int_G \psi_e^*(\mathcal{H}_d + \mathcal{H}_s)\psi_e \, d\tau_e \tag{42}$$

where $d\tau_e$ stands for integration over all electron coordinates (spin and spatial), and where the symbol G signifies that the spatial integration goes over the entire physical volume of the sample. By breaking G into the atomic cells $G_1, G_2, \cdots G_N$ of the N atoms of the crystal, we may formally interpret the contribution of $\mathcal{H}_d$ to Eq. (42) as arising from the summation of the dipolar fields of the electrons on the various atoms. The wave function ψ_e will provide a detailed picture of the spatial distribution of the electron magnetization in each atomic cell. Evaluation of this term is identical to computing the local field due to a volume distribution of electron magnetization. Suppose the magnetization is uniform throughout the sample. If the lattice has cubic symmetry, $\mathcal{H}_d$ will contribute an effective field given by the Lorentz local field:

$$\frac{4\pi}{3}\mathbf{M} - \boldsymbol{\alpha} \cdot \mathbf{M} \tag{43}$$

where $\mathbf{M}$ is the magnetic dipole moment per unit volume and $\boldsymbol{\alpha}$ is a demagnetizing factor (in general a tensor) that expresses the effect of the "magnetic poles" on the outer surface of the sample. For example, $\boldsymbol{\alpha} = 4\pi/3(\mathbf{ii} + \mathbf{jj} + \mathbf{kk})$ for a sphere.

The s-state term may be interpreted as contributing a magnetic field $\mathbf{H}_{sj}$ at the jth nucleus.

$$\mathbf{H}_{sj} = -\frac{8\pi}{3}\gamma_e\hbar \sum_l \int \psi_e^* \mathbf{S}_l \, \delta(\mathbf{r}_l - \mathbf{R}_j)\psi_e \, d\tau_e \tag{44}$$

If we took the wave function to be a product of one electron states $|\beta)$ of a set of quantum numbers β, we would have, then,

$$\mathbf{H}_{sj} = -\frac{8\pi}{3}\gamma_e\hbar \sum_{\substack{\beta \\ \text{occupied}}} (\beta|\mathbf{S}\,\delta(\mathbf{r} - \mathbf{R}_j)|\beta) \tag{45}$$

where "occupied" means that we include in the sum only those states $|\beta)$ containing an electron and we have omitted the subscript l from $\mathbf{S}$ and $\mathbf{r}$. By using the fact that $\boldsymbol{\mu}_e = -\gamma_e\hbar\mathbf{S}$, we have

$$\mathbf{H}_{sj} = \frac{8\pi}{3} \sum_{\substack{\beta \\ \text{occupied}}} (\beta|\boldsymbol{\mu}_e\,\delta(\mathbf{r} - \mathbf{R}_j)|\beta) \tag{46}$$

† See the references listed under "Nuclear Resonance in Ferromagnets and Antiferromagnets" in the Bibliography.

Since the matrix element involves coordinates of only one electron, the various values of l now appear as the values of β that are occupied. In a substance such as iron, we may think of some values of β as corresponding to closed shells, some to the $3d$ band, and some to the $4s$ band. We shall discuss these contributions shortly.

The contribution of the term $\mathcal{H}_d$ is somewhat different for a ferromagnet than for a paramagnet. For the latter, the magnetization is uniform in both magnitude and direction for ellipsoidal samples, and the simple demagnetizing arguments follow. For a ferromagnet the magnetization within a domain is uniform, but the various domains have differing magnetization vectors. Thus, for a soft ferromagnet in zero applied field, the magnetization averaged over a volume large compared with the domain size is zero. The density of magnetic poles on the outer surface therefore vanishes. Within the body of the ferromagnet, div $\mathbf{M} = 0$ even at domain boundaries. If, then, we calculate the dipolar contribution to the magnetic field at a nucleus, we may proceed as follows:

We draw a small sphere about the nucleus, of radius small enough to lie within one domain. We compute the field due to magnetization on atoms within the sphere by a direct sum. The atoms outside the sphere are treated in the continuum approximation. For cubic symmetry, the atoms within the sphere give zero total contribution. The atoms outside the sphere contribute as a result of the surface pole density on the inner sphere and the outer sample surface. The former is the contribution $4\pi\mathbf{M}/3$, where $\mathbf{M}$ is the magnetization within the domain containing the nucleus. The latter contributes $-\boldsymbol{\alpha}\cdot\mathbf{M}'$, where $\mathbf{M}'$ is the magnetization averaged over a volume large compared with a domain size. The total field seen by the jth nucleus, $\mathbf{H}_{Tj}$, is therefore given by

$$\mathbf{H}_{Tj} = \mathbf{H}_0 + \frac{4\pi}{3}\mathbf{M} - \boldsymbol{\alpha}\cdot\mathbf{M}' + \mathbf{H}_{Sj} \tag{47}$$

where $\mathbf{H}_0$ is an externally applied field. Although $\mathbf{H}_0$ and $\mathbf{M}'$ vanish in zero-applied field, $\mathbf{H}_{Tj}$ does not. Therefore we have a "zero field" resonance. Such a resonance was first observed by Gossard and Portis† in the face-centered cubic form of cobalt. Using the Co^{59} resonance, the measured $H_{Sj} = 213{,}400$ gauss. In iron, H_{Sj} is 330,000 gauss. H_{Sj} has also been observed by means of the Mössbauer effect. It was discovered there that application of a static field, $\mathbf{H}_0$ *lowered* the resonance frequency, showing the $\mathbf{H}_{Sj}$ points opposed to the magnetization $\mathbf{M}$.

The contribution from the $4d$ and $4s$ shells in iron is expected by Marshall†† to give a field of 100,000 to 200,000 gauss *parallel* to the local magnetization. Therefore the inner electrons must give a field of about 400,000 gauss opposed to the local magnetization.§

This phenomenon, called *core polarization*, was actually already known from electron magnetic resonance of paramagnetic ions for which the $4s$ electrons are missing. In principle the $3d$ electrons are incapable of giving an isotropic hyperfine coupling, since d-states vanish at the nucleus. However, the d-electrons are coupled to inner shell electrons electrostatically, the coupling for an inner electron of spin parallel to the d-electron spin being different from that of an electron whose spin is opposed to that of the d-electron. Consequently the spatial part of two wave

† A. C. Gossard and A. M. Portis, *Phys. Rev. Letters*, **3**: 164 (1959); J. A. P. Suppl., **31**: 2055 (1960).

†† W. Marshall, *Phys. Rev.*, **110**: 1280 (1958).

§ See also R. Watson and A. Freeman, *Phys. Rev.*, **123**: 2027 (1961).

functions such as the 3s are different for the two spin states. The spin magnetization of the two electrons does *not* add to zero at all points of the electron cloud. We can see from Eq. (46) that if the 3s electron densities at the nucleus differ, there will be a non-zero contribution from the 3s electrons to $\mathbf{H}_{Sj}$, even though their spins are opposed.

4·8 SECOND-ORDER SPIN EFFECTS—INDIRECT NUCLEAR COUPLING

We have discussed the role of electron spin coupling to nuclei in paramagnetic or ferromagnetic materials. Since, in a diamagnetic substance, the total spin of the electrons vanishes, the nuclei experience zero coupling to the electron spins in first order. Effects are found if one considers the coupling in second order†, however. The coupling is manifested through an apparent coupling of nuclei among themselves, the so-called indirect coupling.

The indirect coupling was discovered independently by Hahn and Maxwell and by Gutowsky and McCall. The phenomena they observed are illustrated by the case of PF_3, a molecule in which all nuclei have spin $\frac{1}{2}$. In liquid PF_3, the rapid tumbling narrows the line. It is found that both the P^{31} or F^{19} resonances consist of several lines, as illustrated in Fig. 4.11. Since all the fluorine nuclei are chemi-

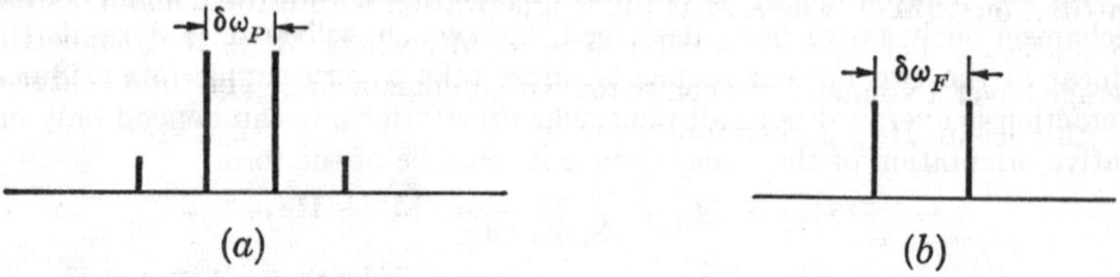

FIG. 4.11. (a) The P^{31} resonance in PF_3. The lines are equally spaced an amount $\delta\omega_p$, and the intensities are 1:3:3:1. (b) The F^{19} resonance in PF_3.

cally equivalent, the splittings cannot be due to chemical shifts. (Furthermore there is only one phosphorus atom per molecule but four phosphorus frequencies.) The fact that the individual lines themselves are narrow shows that the motion is sufficiently rapid to narrow the direct dipolar coupling. Moreover, the splittings are found to be independent both of temperature and static field. The number and relative intensity of lines are as though each nuclear species experienced a magnetic field proportional to the z-component of the total spin of the other species. It was found that $\delta\omega_F = \delta\omega_P\gamma_F/\gamma_P$ (see Fig. 4.11), where $\delta\omega_P$ and $\delta\omega_F$ are the frequency separations of adjacent lines in the phosphorus and fluorine spectra, respectively. These facts indicated the coupling was somehow related to the nuclear magnetic moments.

The original explanation proposed was that one nucleus induced currents in the electron cloud, which then coupled to the other nucleus. In a simple picture, the induced currents are represented by an induced electron magnetic moment. If this moment were *isotropic* (as one changes the orientation of the molecule with respect to the nuclear moment), the coupling to a second nucleus would average

† See references to "$\mathbf{I}_1 \cdot \mathbf{I}_2$ Coupling" in the Bibliography.

to zero in a liquid, owing to the rapid random tumbling of the molecules. However, as we observed in connection with the chemical shifts, the induced moment is in general not isotropic. We can estimate the size of the coupling between the two nuclei from second-order perturbation theory. The first nucleus exerts a magnetic field $\gamma_1\hbar(\overline{1/r^3})$ where $(\overline{1/r^3})$ is the average of the inverse cube of the distance between the electron and the first nucleus that partially unquenches the orbital angular momentum, producing a fractional admixture of excited state of $\gamma_1\gamma_e\hbar^2(\overline{1/r^3})/\Delta E$, where ΔE is the energy to the excited state. A complete unquenching would produce a magnetic field at the second nucleus of $\gamma_e\hbar/R^3$, where R is the distance between the nuclei (we treat the electron orbital magnetization as equivalent to a magnetic dipole). Therefore the order of magnitude of the nuclear-nuclear interaction energy, E_{12}, on this model is

$$E_{12} \cong \frac{\gamma_1\gamma_e\hbar^2(\overline{1/r^3})}{\Delta E}\,\frac{\gamma_e\hbar}{R^3}\,\gamma_2\hbar \tag{1}$$

This formula fails by an order of magnitude or more of accounting for the facts. However, it has the virtue of making it seem reasonable that the splittings in PF_3 were an order of magnitude larger than those in PH_3, since clearly this mechanism is closely related to chemical shifts that are always smaller for hydrogen than for fluorine.

As was pointed out by Hahn and Maxwell, and Gutowsky and McCall, any mechanism such as we have described, and which will lead to a result that is bilinear in the two nuclear moments, must take a very simple form. Since the interaction is averaged over all molecular orientations, it can depend only on the relative orientation of the nuclei; hence it must be of the form

$$A_{12}\boldsymbol{\mu}_1 \cdot \boldsymbol{\mu}_2 \tag{2}$$

where A_{12} is independent of temperature and field. These workers also pointed out that this particular form would also explain the puzzling fact that, for example, there were apparently no splittings of fluorines by fluorines in PF_3. We shall not give the proof here, but physically the explanation is based on the idea that the interaction energy, Eq. (2), which depends on the relative orientation of spins, is unchanged if *both* spins are rotated through the same angle. For equivalent nuclei such as the three fluorines in PF_3, one cannot rotate one fluorine spin without rotating the others by an equal amount, since the alternating and static fields are identical at all three fluorines. Therefore the coupling between equivalent nuclei does not affect the resonance frequency.

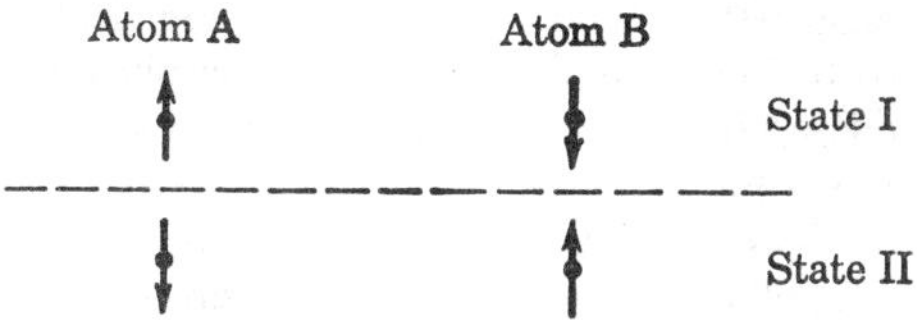

FIG. 4.12. Because of the bonds between atoms A and B, the electron wave function is formed by an equal mixture of the state I, in which the electron moment on atom A points up (that on B, down), and state II, in which the spin orientation is reversed.

Ramsey and Purcell proposed another mechanism, utilizing the electron spins, which was substantially larger because, as we shall explain, it allowed the *two* nuclei to interact with nearby electrons, in contrast with the orbital mechanism where only one nucleus is on the same atom as the electron that is polarized. We may schematize their mechanism as shown in Fig. 4.12.

In the absence of a nuclear moment the electron bond will consist of an equal mixture of the states I and II, shown in Fig. 4.12. If now we put a nucleus on atom A with its magnetic moment pointing up, state I will be slightly favored over state II. The electronic spin magnetic moment of atom A will have a slight polarization up; that on atom B, down. Therefore a nucleus on atom B will find a non-zero field owing to its own electron. Since this field would reverse if the nucleus on atom A were reversed, an effective nuclear-nuclear coupling results. We can easily estimate the size of the coupling. The fractional excess of state I over state II will be

$$\frac{\frac{8\pi}{3}\gamma_1\gamma_e\hbar^2|u(0)|_A^2}{\Delta E} = \frac{\text{hyperfine energy}}{\text{electrostatic energy}} \tag{3}$$

where $|u(0)|_A^2$ is the wave-function density of the electron at atom A, and ΔE is the energy to an appropriate excited state. The coupling of the electrons on atom B to nucleus 2 are thus given by the product of the electron spin coupling if the electron spin is in one orientation only, $(8\pi/3)\gamma_2\gamma_e\hbar^2|u(0)|_B^2$, times the excess fraction of the time the electron is in the favored orientation. Thus the coupling is

$$\frac{\left(\frac{8\pi}{3}\gamma_1\gamma_e\hbar^2|u(0)|_A^2\right)\left(\frac{8\pi}{3}\gamma_2\gamma_e\hbar^2|u(0)|_B^2\right)}{\Delta E} \tag{4}$$

This coupling turns out to have the correct order of magnitude. If the electron functions do not contain an *s*-part, we should instead use the ordinary dipolar coupling between the electron and nuclear spins.

The extension of these ideas to solids was made independently by Bloembergen and Rowland and by Ruderman and Kittel. We shall discuss the situation for metals, confining our attention to the coupling via the *s*-state hyperfine coupling. Since the metal is not diamagnetic, we should concern ourselves with the possibility of a first-order effect—related, therefore, to the Knight shift. This mechanism of coupling was originally proposed by Fröhlich and Nabarro.† As Yosida has explained, however, the Fröhlich-Nabarro effect is actually included in the second-order calculation. We shall discuss the physical reason shortly, but for the present, we shall simply ignore any first-order effect.††

The effect of the magnetic moment of a nucleus at any lattice site is to make that site a region favorable for an electron of parallel magnetic moment but unfavorable for an electron of antiparallel moment. In order to take advantage of the magnetic interaction, an electron of parallel moment will distort its wave function to be larger in the vicinity of the nucleus. The distortion is brought about by mixing in other states **k** of the same spin orientation. As we shall see, the result is as though only states above the Fermi surface were added. The wave functions of the Bloch states are added so as to be in phase with the unperturbed function (Fig. 4.13) at the nucleus in order to interfere constructively at that point, but because of the spread in wave lengths, they rapidly get out of step as one moves away from the nucleus.

† F. Fröhlich and F. R. N. Nabarro, *Proc. Roy. Soc.* (London), **A175**: 382 (1940).
†† See also J. H. Van Vleck, *Rev. Mod. Phys.* **34**, 681 (1962).

As a result of the beats between the unperturbed and perturbed functions, the original uniform distribution of spin-up charge density (we neglect the variations

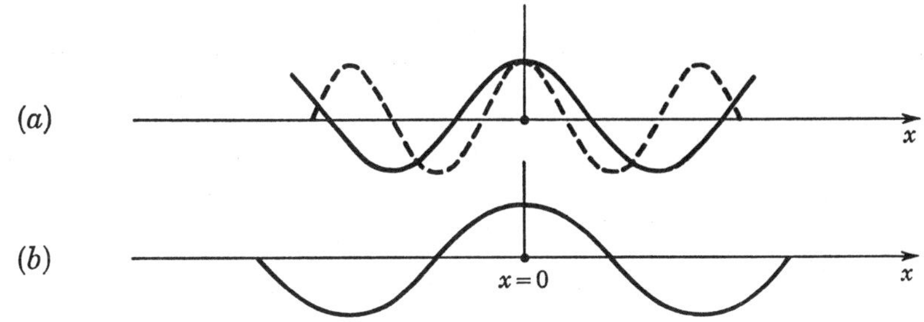

FIG. 4.13. The unperturbed function and two of the higher states mixed in. The nucleus is at $x = 0$, which guarantees that the waves be in phase at $x = 0$. Note that the admixed waves beat with one another. (a) Two of the waves mixed in by the perturbation. (b) Unperturbed function.

due to the lattice charge) is changed to have an oscillatory behavior, which dies out as one goes away from the nucleus. The characteristic length describing the attentuation is the wave length of electrons at the Fermi surface. The resulting charge density of electrons whose moment is parallel to the nucleus is shown in Fig. 4.14.

FIG. 4.14. The charge density of electrons whose magnetic moments are parallel to the nuclear moment. The nucleus is located at $x = 0$. ρ_0 is the charge density in the absence of a nuclear moment. At $x = x_1$, the electron charge is deficient, so that the net electron moment there is opposed to the nuclear moment.

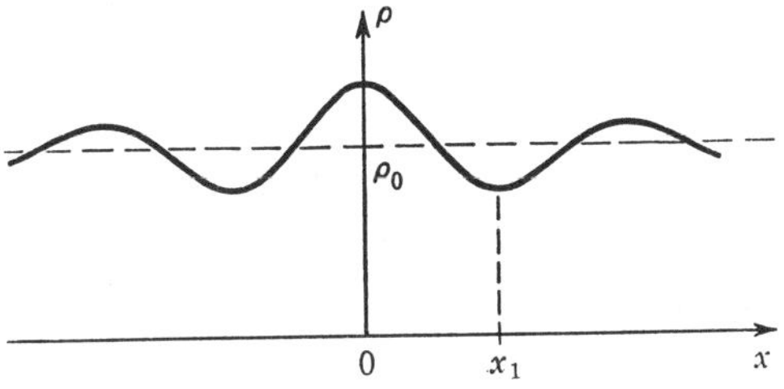

We now turn to the actual calculation of these effects. For simplicity we shall calculate the interaction between the two nuclei directly rather than compute the changes in the spatial distribution of electron spin. However, the oscillatory nature of the charge will be apparent from the answer.

We consider, therefore, an electron-nuclear coupling $\mathcal{H}_{en}$ involving only two nuclei of spins $\mathbf{I}_1$ and $\mathbf{I}_2$, and for simplicity, treat only the effect of the s-state coupling. We have, then,

$$\begin{aligned}\mathcal{H}_{en} &= \gamma_1\gamma_e\hbar^2\mathbf{I}_1 \cdot \sum_l \mathbf{S}_l\, \delta(\mathbf{r}_l - \mathbf{R}_1) + \gamma_2\gamma_e\hbar^2\mathbf{I}_2 \cdot \sum_l \mathbf{S}_l\, \delta(\mathbf{r}_l - \mathbf{R}_2) \\ &= \mathcal{H}_1 + \mathcal{H}_2 \qquad (5)\end{aligned}$$

where we have allowed the nuclei to be different by using two values of gyromagnetic ratio γ_1 and γ_2 and spins $\mathbf{I}_1$ and $\mathbf{I}_2$.

We must take into account the exclusion principle for the electrons. Two methods are available. We could use Eq. (5) to find perturbed one-electron functions and then fill these functions in accordance with the exclusion principle. Or, we could do perturbation theory in which we used the many electron functions as the unperturbed states. It is this latter procedure that we shall utilize, since it emphasizes that basically we are dealing with a many-electron problem and that the states we use are but one approximation.

Let us therefore consider a many-electron state $|0)$ with energy E_0 and excited states $|n)$ with energy E_n, and compute the second-order energy shift due to $\mathcal{H}_{en}$. We shall as usual assume the total wave function of the system to be a product of the electron and nuclear functions. Denoting the latter by ψ_α with energy E_α, where α represents the nuclear spin quantum numbers, we shall wish to compute the second-order energy shift of states $|0)\psi_\alpha$.

Therefore, for the second-order shift, we have $\Delta E_{0\alpha}^{(2)}$ of the state $|0)\psi_\alpha$:

$$\Delta E_{0\alpha}^{(2)} = \sum_{n,\alpha'} \frac{(0\alpha|\mathcal{H}_{en}|n\alpha')(n\alpha'|\mathcal{H}_{en}|0\alpha)}{(E_0 + E_\alpha) - (E_n + E_{\alpha'})} \tag{6}$$

Since the electronic energy differences are generally much greater than the differences in nuclear energy, we can neglect E_α and $E_{\alpha'}$ in the denominator.†

Writing $\mathcal{H}_{en}$ as $\mathcal{H}_1 + \mathcal{H}_2$, we find

$$\begin{aligned} \Delta E_{0\alpha}^{(2)} = \sum_{n,\alpha'} \frac{1}{E_0 - E_n} \{ & (0\alpha|\mathcal{H}_1|n\alpha')(n\alpha'|\mathcal{H}_1|0\alpha) \\ & + (0\alpha|\mathcal{H}_2|n\alpha')(n\alpha'|\mathcal{H}_2|0\alpha) \\ & + (0\alpha|\mathcal{H}_1|n\alpha')(n\alpha'|\mathcal{H}_2|0\alpha) \\ & + (0\alpha|\mathcal{H}_2|n\alpha')(n\alpha'|\mathcal{H}_1|0\alpha)\} \end{aligned} \tag{7}$$

The first two terms in the brace represent the changes in energy we should have were one or the other of the nuclei the only one. The last two terms represent the extra energy when both are simultaneously present, and are thus an interaction energy. Since it is only the interaction that we wish to calculate, we shall consider the last two terms only. We have, then,

$$\Delta E_{0\alpha}^{(2)} = \sum_{n,\alpha'} \frac{(0\alpha|\mathcal{H}_1|n\alpha')(n\alpha'|\mathcal{H}_2|0\alpha)}{E_0 - E_n} + \text{complex conjugate} \tag{8}$$

Now, from the form of $\mathcal{H}_1$ and $\mathcal{H}_2$, we can write them as

$$\begin{aligned} \mathcal{H}_1 &= \mathbf{I}_1 \cdot \mathbf{G}_1 = \sum_{\beta=x,y,z} I_{1\beta} G_{1\beta} \\ \mathcal{H}_2 &= \mathbf{I}_2 \cdot \mathbf{G}_2 = \sum_{\beta=x,y,z} I_{2\beta} G_{2\beta} \end{aligned} \tag{9}$$

† One can think of this as being, therefore, basically a calculation of the coupling between nuclei in zero external field. However, it turns out that the field dependence is very small. This results from the fact that the states E_n have a continuous distribution in energy starting from E_0. Neglecting $E_\alpha - E_{\alpha'}$ does not seriously perturb the spectra of excited states or the matrix elements. A further discussion of these points is given immediately following Eq. (23).

where $\mathbf{G}_1$ and $\mathbf{G}_2$ do not involve the nuclear spin coordinates. By using these relations,

$$\begin{aligned}\Delta E_{0\alpha}^{(2)} &= \sum_{\beta,\beta'}\sum_{n} \frac{(0|G_{1\beta}|n)(n|G_{2\beta'}|0)}{E_0 - E_n} \sum_{\alpha'} (\alpha|I_{1\beta}|\alpha')(\alpha'|I_{2\beta'}|\alpha) + \text{c.c.} \\ &= \sum_{\beta,\beta'}\sum_{n} \frac{(0|G_{1\beta}|n)(n|G_{2\beta'}|0)}{E_0 - E_n} (\alpha|I_{1\beta}I_{2\beta'}|\alpha) + \text{c.c.}\end{aligned} \tag{10}$$

To evaluate the energy of Eq. (10), we should need to specify the nuclear states $|\alpha)$. Just what they would be would depend on the total nuclear Hamiltonian, which would include such things as the coupling of the nuclei to the external static field H_0, the dipolar coupling between nuclei, and so forth. It is convenient to note that whatever the states $|\alpha)$ may be, the energy $\Delta E_{0\alpha}^{(2)}$ is just what we should find as the first-order perturbation contribution of an extra term in the nuclear Hamiltonian, $\mathcal{H}_{\text{eff}}$, given by

$$\mathcal{H}_{\text{eff}} = \sum_{\beta,\beta'} I_{1\beta}I_{2\beta'} \left\{\sum_{n} \frac{(0|G_{1\beta}|n)(n|G_{2\beta'}|0)}{E_0 - E_n}\right\} + \text{c.c.} \tag{11}$$

By expressing the couplings G_1 and G_2 explicitly, we obtain

$$\mathcal{H}_{\text{eff}} = C\sum_{n} \mathbf{I}_1 \cdot \frac{\left(0\left|\sum_{l} \mathbf{S}_l\,\delta(\mathbf{r}_l - \mathbf{R}_1)\right|n\right)\left(n\left|\sum_{l} \mathbf{S}_l\,\delta(\mathbf{r}_l - \mathbf{R}_2)\right|0\right)}{E_0 - E_n} \cdot \mathbf{I}_2 + \text{c.c.}$$

where

$$C = \frac{64\pi^2}{9}\gamma_1\gamma_2\gamma_e^2\hbar^4 \tag{12b}$$

We shall now take the states $|0)$ to be products of Bloch functions. Denoting the product of a Bloch function and a spin function by letters A, and so on,

$$\begin{aligned}|0) &= \frac{1}{\sqrt{N!}}\sum_{P}(-1)^P P[A(1)B(2)C(3)\cdots] \\ |n) &= \frac{1}{\sqrt{N!}}\sum_{P}(-1)^P P[A'(1)B'(2)C'(3)\cdots]\end{aligned} \tag{13}$$

Of course the permutation causes any function to vanish if any two functions such as A and B are identical. Consider the matrix element of a perturbation V, which is symmetric among all the electrons; that is, it is unchanged by interchanging the electron numbering.

$$(n|V|0) = \frac{1}{N!}\sum_{P,P'}(-1)^{P+P'}\int P'[A'(1)B'(2)\cdots]^* V P[A(1)B(2)C(3)\cdots]\,d\tau \tag{14}$$

Since V is symmetric, it is only the *relative* ordering of the states that counts. We can express this fact by defining the permutation P''. P'' is the permutation that, following P, gives the same ordering of electrons as P' alone. That is, $P''P = P'$ By making this substitution into Eq. (14), we get

$$\begin{aligned}(n|V|0) &= \frac{1}{N!}\sum_{P,P''}(-1)^{(2P+P'')}\int P''P[A'(1)B'(2)\cdots]^* VP[A(1)B(2)C(3)\cdots]\,d\tau \\ &= \frac{1}{N!}\sum_{P,P''}(-1)^{P''}\int P''P[A'(1)B'(2)\cdots]^* VP[A(1)B(2)\cdots]\,d\tau \\ &= \sum_{P''}(-1)^{P''}\int P''[A'(1)B'(2)\cdots]^* V[A(1)B(2)\cdots]\,d\tau \end{aligned} \tag{15}$$

where the last step follows because V is unchanged by relabeling the electrons. Let us now consider V to be a sum of one-electron operators:

$$V = \sum_l V(l) \tag{16}$$

where $V(l)$ depends only on the coordinates of the lth particle. Consider, for example, the contribution from $l = 1$:

$$(n|V_1|0) = \sum_{P''}(-1)^{P''}\int P''[A'(1)B'(2)\cdots]^* V_1[A(1)B(2)C(3)\cdots]\,d\tau \tag{17}$$

This will vanish unless the state $|n)$ contains $B(2)C(3)\cdots$. Let us therefore write such an excited state as

$$|n) = \frac{1}{\sqrt{N!}}\sum_P(-1)^P P[A'(1)B(2)C(3)\cdots] \tag{18}$$

This makes

$$\begin{aligned}(n|V_1|0) &= \sum_{P''}(-1)^{P''}\int P''[A'(1)B(2)C(3)\cdots]^* V_1[A(1)B(2)C(3)\cdots]\,d\tau \\ &= 0 \qquad \text{if } A' \text{ is identical to any of the functions } B, C, D, \text{etc.} \\ &= (A'|V_1|A) \qquad \text{otherwise}\end{aligned} \tag{19}$$

It is clear that the various values of l in Eq. (16) will simply pick out the various states A, B, C in $|0)$, and the sum over excited states $|n)$ will pick out the states A', B', and so on, which are *not* occupied in $|0)$. We can therefore write Eq. (12) as

$$\mathcal{H}_{\text{eff}} = C \sum_{\substack{\mathbf{k},s \text{ occupied} \\ \mathbf{k}',s' \text{ unoccupied}}} \mathbf{I}_1 \cdot \frac{(\mathbf{k}s|\mathbf{S}\,\delta(\mathbf{r}-\mathbf{R}_1)|\mathbf{k}'s')(\mathbf{k}'s'|\mathbf{S}\,\delta(\mathbf{r}-\mathbf{R}_2)|\mathbf{k}s)}{E_{\mathbf{k}s} - E_{\mathbf{k}'s'}} \cdot \mathbf{I}_2 + \text{c.c.} \tag{20}$$

where we have replaced $E_0 - E_n$ by $E_{\mathbf{k}s} - E_{\mathbf{k}'s'}$, since the states E_0 and E_n differ in energy solely by the transfer of one electron from the state $|\mathbf{k}, s)$ to $|\mathbf{k}', s')$. The terms "**k**, s occupied," "**k**$'$,s' unoccupied," refer to whether or not these states are occupied by electrons in the wave function $|0)$.

If we define the functions $p(\mathbf{k}, s)$ by

$$p(\mathbf{k}, s) = 1 \quad \text{if } \mathbf{k}, s \text{ is occupied in state } |0) \qquad = 0 \quad \text{if } \mathbf{k}, s \text{ is unoccupied in state } |0) \tag{21}$$

we can easily remove the restrictions on $\mathbf{k}$, s from the summation:

$$\mathcal{H}_{\text{eff}} = C \sum_{\substack{\mathbf{k},s\\ \mathbf{k}',s'}} \mathbf{I}_1 \cdot \frac{(\mathbf{k}s|\mathbf{S}\,\delta(\mathbf{r}-\mathbf{R}_1)|\mathbf{k}'s')(\mathbf{k}'s'|\mathbf{S}\,\delta(\mathbf{r}-\mathbf{R}_2)|\mathbf{k}s) \times p(\mathbf{k}, s)[1-p(\mathbf{k}', s')]}{E_{\mathbf{k}s} - E_{\mathbf{k}'s'}} \cdot \mathbf{I}_2 + \text{c.c.} \tag{22}$$

In order to express the variation of $\mathcal{H}_{\text{eff}}$ with the temperature of the electrons, we must average $\mathcal{H}_{\text{eff}}$ over an ensemble. This will simply replace $p(\mathbf{k}, s)$ by $f(\mathbf{k}, s)$, the Fermi function. We have, then,

$$\begin{aligned}\mathcal{H}_{\text{eff}} &= C \sum_{\substack{\mathbf{k},s\\ \mathbf{k}'s'}} \mathbf{I}_1 \cdot \frac{(\mathbf{k}s|\mathbf{S}\,\delta(\mathbf{r}-\mathbf{R}_1)|\mathbf{k}'s')(\mathbf{k}'s'|\mathbf{S}\,\delta(\mathbf{r}-\mathbf{R}_2)|\mathbf{k}s) \times f(\mathbf{k}, s)[1-f(\mathbf{k}', s')]}{E_{\mathbf{k}s} - E_{\mathbf{k}'s'}} \cdot \mathbf{I}_2 + \text{c.c.} \\ &= C \sum_{\substack{\mathbf{k},s\\ \mathbf{k}'s'}} \mathbf{I}_1 \cdot (s|\mathbf{S}|s')(s'|\mathbf{S}|s) \cdot \mathbf{I}_2 \\ &\quad \times \frac{(\mathbf{k}|\,\delta(\mathbf{r}-\mathbf{R}_1)|\mathbf{k}')(\mathbf{k}'|\,\delta(\mathbf{r}-\mathbf{R}_2)|\mathbf{k})f(\mathbf{k}, s)[1-f(\mathbf{k}', s')]}{E_{\mathbf{k}s} - E_{\mathbf{k}'s'}} + \text{c.c.}\end{aligned} \tag{23}$$

Now, the Fermi functions as well as the energies $E_{\mathbf{k}s}$ depend on the energy associated with the electron spin quantum number. For example, the electron spin Zeeman energy changes with s. However, the Fermi levels of the spin-up and spin-down distributions coincide. Thus, at absolute zero, there is a continuous range of $E_{\mathbf{k}s}$ up to the Fermi energy and a continuous range of $E_{\mathbf{k}'s'}$ from the Fermi energy on up. The matrix elements of the δ-functions vary slowly with energy. Therefore the variation of $\mathcal{H}_{\text{eff}}$ with the electron spin energy is very small, and we may forget about the energy of the electron spin coordinate, writing to a good approximation Eq. (23) in the form it would have in zero magnetic field:

$$\mathcal{H}_{\text{eff}} = C \sum_{\substack{\mathbf{k},\mathbf{k}'\\ s,s'}} \frac{\mathbf{I}_1 \cdot (s|\mathbf{S}|s')(s'|\mathbf{S}|s) \cdot \mathbf{I}_2 \times (\mathbf{k}|\,\delta(\mathbf{r}-\mathbf{R}_1)|\mathbf{k}')(\mathbf{k}'|\,\delta(\mathbf{r}-\mathbf{R}_2)|\mathbf{k})f(\mathbf{k})[1-f(\mathbf{k}')]}{E_{\mathbf{k}} - E_{\mathbf{k}'}} + \text{c.c.} \tag{24}$$

We can now perform the sums over s and s':

$$\begin{aligned}\sum_{s,s'} \mathbf{I}_1 \cdot (s|\mathbf{S}|s')(s'|\mathbf{S}|s) \cdot \mathbf{I}_2 &= \sum_{\substack{\beta,\beta'=x,y,z\\ s,s'}} I_{1\beta}(s|S_\beta|s')(s'|S_{\beta'}|s)I_{2\beta'} \\ &= \sum_{\beta,\beta'} I_{1\beta}I_{2\beta'}\operatorname{Tr}(S_\beta S_{\beta'})\end{aligned} \tag{25}$$

But, as we saw in Chapter 3,

$$\begin{aligned} \mathrm{Tr} S_\beta S_{\beta'} &= \tfrac{1}{3} S(S+1)(2S+1)\,\delta_{\beta\beta'} \\ &= \frac{\delta_{\beta\beta'}}{2} \qquad \text{since } S = \tfrac{1}{2}. \end{aligned} \tag{26}$$

which gives, finally,

$$\begin{aligned} \mathcal{H}_{\text{eff}} &= \mathbf{I}_1 \cdot \mathbf{I}_2 \frac{C}{2} \left\{ \sum_{\mathbf{k},\mathbf{k}'} \frac{(\mathbf{k}|\,\delta(\mathbf{r}-\mathbf{R}_1)|\mathbf{k}')(\mathbf{k}'|\,\delta(\mathbf{r}-\mathbf{R}_2)|\mathbf{k}) f(\mathbf{k})[1-f(\mathbf{k}')]}{E_{\mathbf{k}} - E_{\mathbf{k}'}} + \text{c.c.} \right\} \\ &= A_{12} \mathbf{I}_1 \cdot \mathbf{I}_2 \end{aligned} \tag{27}$$

where A_{12} is a constant independent of spin. We now evaluate the matrix elements in terms of the Bloch functions:

$$\psi_{\mathbf{k}} = u_{\mathbf{k}}(\mathbf{r}) e^{i\mathbf{k}\cdot\mathbf{r}} \tag{28}$$

where, as before, $u_{\mathbf{k}}(\mathbf{r})$ has the periodicity of the lattice. We have, then,

$$(\mathbf{k}'|\,\delta(\mathbf{r}-\mathbf{R}_2|\mathbf{k}) = u_{\mathbf{k}'}^*(\mathbf{R}_2) u_{\mathbf{k}}(\mathbf{R}_2) e^{i(\mathbf{k}-\mathbf{k}')\cdot\mathbf{R}_2} \tag{29}$$

so that

$$(\mathbf{k}|\,\delta(\mathbf{r}-\mathbf{R}_1|\mathbf{k}')(\mathbf{k}'|\,\delta(\mathbf{r}-\mathbf{R}_2)|\mathbf{k}) = u_{\mathbf{k}'}^*(\mathbf{R}_2) u_{\mathbf{k}'}(\mathbf{R}_1) u_{\mathbf{k}}^*(\mathbf{R}_1) u_{\mathbf{k}}(\mathbf{R}_2) e^{i(\mathbf{k}-\mathbf{k}')\cdot(\mathbf{R}_2-\mathbf{R}_1)} \tag{30}$$

If we assume that $\mathbf{R}_1$ and $\mathbf{R}_2$ are equivalent sites (as, for example, in a simple metal), and define

$$\mathbf{R}_{12} = \mathbf{R}_2 - \mathbf{R}_1 \tag{31}$$

we have

$$\begin{aligned} \mathcal{H}_{\text{eff}} &= \frac{C}{2} \mathbf{I}_1 \cdot \mathbf{I}_2 \sum_{\mathbf{k},\mathbf{k}'} \frac{|u_{\mathbf{k}'}(0)|^2 |u_{\mathbf{k}}(0)|^2 2 \cos[(\mathbf{k}-\mathbf{k}')\cdot\mathbf{R}_{12})]}{E_{\mathbf{k}} - E_{\mathbf{k}'}} f(\mathbf{k})[1-f(\mathbf{k}')] \\ &= \mathbf{I}_1 \cdot \mathbf{I}_2 \frac{64}{9} \pi^2 \gamma_e^2 \gamma_1 \gamma_2 \hbar^4 \sum_{\mathbf{k},\mathbf{k}'} \frac{|u_{\mathbf{k}'}(0)|^2 |u_{\mathbf{k}}(0)|^2 \cos[(\mathbf{k}-\mathbf{k}')\cdot\mathbf{R}_{12}] f(\mathbf{k})[1-f(\mathbf{k}')]}{E_{\mathbf{k}} - E_{\mathbf{k}'}} \end{aligned} \tag{32}$$

It is not possible to evaluate the summation without either some further approximations or some explicit information on the $\mathbf{k}$ dependence of wave functions and energy. If one assumes spherical energy surfaces, an effective mass m^*, and that $|u_{\mathbf{k}'}(0)|^2$ and $|u_{\mathbf{k}}(0)|^2$ may be replaced by a value appropriate to $\mathbf{k}$ and $\mathbf{k}'$ near the Fermi energy, one can evaluate the sums. In these terms,

$$E_{\mathbf{k}} = \frac{\hbar^2}{2m^*} k^2 \tag{33}$$

This gives us

$$\mathcal{H}_{\text{eff}} = \mathbf{I}_1 \cdot \mathbf{I}_2 \frac{64}{9} \pi^2 \gamma_e^2 \gamma_1 \gamma_2 \hbar^4 |u_{k_F}(0)|^4 \frac{2m^*}{\hbar^2} \sum_{\mathbf{k},\mathbf{k}'} \frac{\cos[(\mathbf{k}-\mathbf{k}')\cdot\mathbf{R}_{12}]}{k^2 - k'^2} f(\mathbf{k})[1-f(\mathbf{k}')] \tag{34}$$

The number dN of states in k-space within a solid angle $d\Omega$, and between two spherical shells of radii k and dk, is

$$dN = \frac{d\Omega}{4\pi}\frac{k^2\,dk}{2\pi^2} \tag{35}$$

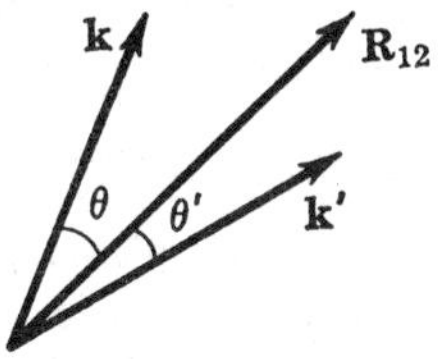

FIG. 4.15. Relative orientations of **k**, **k**′, and $\mathbf{R}_{12}$.

Denoting the angle between **k** and $\mathbf{R}_{12}$ as θ, that between **k**′ and $\mathbf{R}_{12}$ as θ' (see Fig. 4.15), and using R for $|\mathbf{R}_{12}|$, we have

$$\sum_{\mathbf{k},\mathbf{k}'} \frac{\cos[(\mathbf{k}-\mathbf{k}')\cdot\mathbf{R}_{12}]f(\mathbf{k})[1-f(\mathbf{k}')]}{k^2-k'^2}$$
$$= \left(\frac{1}{2\pi}\right)^6 \iint \frac{\begin{array}{c}[\cos(kR\cos\theta)\cos(k'R\cos\theta')\\ +\sin(kR\cos\theta)\sin(k'R\cos\theta')]\end{array}}{k^2-k'^2}\cdot$$
$$f(\mathbf{k})[1-f(\mathbf{k}')]k^2k'^2\,d\Omega\,d\Omega'\,dk\,dk' \tag{36}$$

The integrals over $d\Omega = -2\pi\,d(\cos\theta)$ and $d\Omega' = -2\pi\,d(\cos\theta')$ are readily performed to give, for the summation of Eq. (36),

$$\frac{4}{(2\pi)^4}\frac{1}{R^2}\iint \frac{\sin kR\sin k'R}{k^2-k'^2}kk'f(\mathbf{k})[1-f(\mathbf{k}')]\,dk\,dk' \tag{37}$$

This integral may be evaluated at absolute zero by noting that the limits on k' can go from 0 to ∞, not just k_F to ∞, since if $k' < k_F$ for each $k = k_1$, $k' = k_2$, there is a $k = k_2$, $k' = k_1$ which has the opposite sign for the integrand. The range of k' is then extended to cover $-\infty$ to $+\infty$, and the integral is evaluated by a contour integral. The infinity at $k = k'$ is avoided by taking a principal part. The final result is

$$\mathcal{H}_{\text{eff}} = -\frac{2}{9\pi}\gamma_e^2\gamma_1\gamma_2\hbar^2m^*|u_{k_F}(0)|^4\frac{[\sin 2k_FR - 2k_FR\cos 2k_FR]}{R^4}\mathbf{I}_1\cdot\mathbf{I}_2 \tag{38}$$

We note that this expression indeed corresponds to an oscillatory behavior as one varies R. For large distances the coupling goes as

$$+\frac{\cos 2k_FR}{R^3} \tag{39}$$

We see that the dependence on $|u(0)|^4$ will cause the coupling to be large for large Z-atoms. In fact the coupling for the heavier elements is substantially larger than the direct dipolar coupling.

Had we used the conventional dipolar form of coupling between the nuclear and electron spins appropriate to "non" s-states, we should have obtained

$$\mathcal{H}_{\text{eff}} = \left[\mathbf{I}_1\cdot\mathbf{I}_2 - \frac{3(\mathbf{I}_1\cdot\mathbf{R}_{12})(\mathbf{I}_2\cdot\mathbf{R}_{12})}{R_{12}^2}\right]B_{12} \tag{40}$$

where B_{12} is a complicated function. It vanishes if there is no "non" *s*-character to the wave function as seen by a single nucleus; for large distances, B_{12} typically falls off as $1/R_{12}^3$. For a discussion of B_{12} the reader is referred to the paper by Bloembergen and Rowland, listed in the Bibliography. In the case of molecules such as PF_3, Gutowsky *et al.* show that the assumption of *p*-type wave functions on *both* P and F, together with the "non" *s*-state coupling gives a coupling of the form

$$A_{12}\mathbf{I}_1 \cdot \mathbf{I}_2 \tag{41}$$

when averaged over all orientations of the molecule in the external field. The coupling does not vanish when averaged over molecular orientations, since the induced spin magnetization itself depends on the orientation of the molecule with respect to the nuclear spins.

Couplings such as Eq. (40) have the same spin dependence as that of the direct dipolar coupling. To emphasize this similarity, the coupling is often referred to as the "pseudo-dipolar" coupling. On the other hand, a coupling such as $A_{12}\mathbf{I}_1 \cdot \mathbf{I}_2$ has the same form as the electrostatic exchange coupling. Since in our case the physical origin is not an exchange integral, the term is referred to as the "pseudo-exchange" coupling.

The effect of pseudo-exchange or pseudo-dipolar coupling on the width and shape of resonance lines can be analyzed by simply adding these terms to the dipolar terms. The number of situations that arise are very numerous. In liquids, the pseudo-dipolar coupling averages to zero, but the pseudo-exchange does not, giving rise to resolved splittings.

For solids, both terms have effects. The pseudo-exchange term, since it commutes with $I_x = I_{1x} + I_{2x}$, has no effect on the second moment of the resonance but does increase the fourth moment. As Van Vleck discusses, this must mean that the *central* portion of the resonance is narrowed, but the wings are enhanced (see Fig. 4.16), since the fourth moment is more affected by the wings than is the second

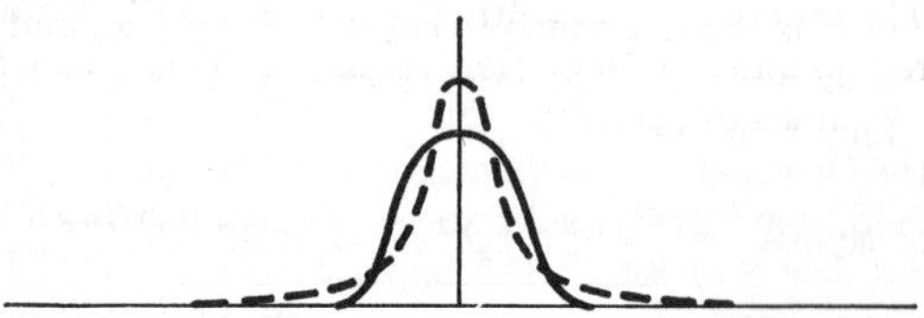

FIG. 4.16. Solid curve, the resonance shape with vanishing pseudo-exchange coupling. The dashed curve shows the shape when pseudo-exchange is included.

moment. The fact that the central portion appears sharper gives rise to the terms *exchange narrowing* or *pseudo-exchange narrowing.* Where a real exchange interaction exists, as in electron resonances, the exchange narrowing may be very dramatic.

If the two nuclei are *not* identical, one can approximate the pseudo-exchange coupling as $A_{12}I_{1z}I_{2z}$. Since this interaction does not commute with $I_{1x} + I_{2x}$, it increases the second moment. The resonance curve then appears broadened, and one speaks of "exchange broadening." If there is a quadrupole interaction that makes the various *m*-states unequally spaced, the exchange coupling can lead to a broadening, even when the nuclei are identical.

We conclude by remarking on the Fröhlich-Nabarro effect that the presence of one nucleus causes the electrons to repopulate their spin states, producing a magnetic field at other nuclei in much the same way as the static field produces a Knight shift. Yosida has analyzed the problem by performing a spatial Fourier analysis of the electron-nuclear interaction. Denoting the wave vector of a Fourier component by $\mathbf{q}$, Yosida points out that the Fröhlich-Nabarro effect is the $\mathbf{q} = 0$ term (infinite wave length). In the second-order perturbation, a component $\mathbf{q} \neq 0$ joins two electron states, $\mathbf{k}$ and $\mathbf{k}'$, that satisfy the relation

$$\mathbf{k}' = \mathbf{k} + \mathbf{q} \tag{42}$$

Since in a proper second-order calculation the excited and ground states must differ, we see from Eq. (42) that we must exclude $\mathbf{q} = 0$. Yosida treats $\mathbf{q} = 0$ by first-order theory, but $\mathbf{q} \neq 0$ by second order, adding the results. The answer he obtains in this way is identical to that of Bloembergen-Rowland and Ruderman-Kittel taking a principal part as mentioned on p. 111. The simplest way to see that the answers will be the same is to consider instead the Knight shift.

There are two ways one can calculate the Knight shift. The first method is to assume a uniform static field and to compute the first-order nuclear-electron coupling of the *polarized* electron state. The second method is more complicated. We assume a static field but one that is oscillating spatially with wave vector $\mathbf{q}$. For such a spatial oscillatory field there is no net spin polarization, since the field points up in some regions of space as much as it points down in others.

The usual first-order interaction vanishes. If one now goes to second-order perturbation in which one matrix element is the electron-nuclear coupling, the other the electron-applied field interaction, a non-zero result is found. That is, the static field induces a spatially varying spin polarization. Let us choose the maximum of the static field to be at the position of the nucleus. When $\mathbf{q}$ gets very small (long wave length), we expect that the result must be the same as if the field were strictly uniform. Therefore the limit of the second-order answer as $\mathbf{q} \to 0$ must be the usual Knight shift. This result can in fact be verified.

In evaluating Eq. (38) using principal parts, one takes the limit as $\mathbf{k}' \to \mathbf{k}$. This procedure, as with the Knight shift, includes the first-order perturbation repopulation contribution, or the Fröhlich-Nabarro effect.

Before concluding this chapter, we should consider the role of electron spin in the chemical shift of diamagnetic substances. In the absence of an applied magnetic field, diamagnetic substances are characterized by a total electron-spin quantum number S of zero. The application of a field H_0 in, say, the z-direction adds a term $\mathcal{H}_{sz}$, the spin Zeeman interaction, to the Hamiltonian:

$$\begin{aligned} \mathcal{H}_{sz} &= \gamma_e \hbar H_0 \sum_{j=1}^{N} S_{zj} \\ &= \gamma_e \hbar H_0 S_z \end{aligned} \tag{43}$$

where j labels the electrons, and where

$$S_z \equiv \sum_{j=1}^{N} S_{zj} \tag{44}$$

Since the ground-state wave function $|0)$ is a spin zero function, we have that

$$S_z|0) = 0 \tag{45}$$

so that all matrix elements of $\mathcal{H}_{sz}$ to excited states $|n)$ vanish:

$$(n|\mathcal{H}_{sz}|0) = \gamma_e \hbar H_0 (n|S_z|0) = 0 \tag{46}$$

The ground state is therefore strictly decoupled from all other states as far as the spin Zeeman coupling is concerned. The applied field is therefore unable to induce any net spin, and there is no phenomenon analogous to the unquenching of the orbital angular momentum.

The fact that the spins actually couple to a magnetic field makes this result seem strange. Intuitively we expect that, given a strong enough magnetic field, the spins *must* be polarized. The paradox is resolved by considering an example, the hydrogen molecule. The ground state is the singlet bonding state, but there is a triplet antibonding state. In the presence of an applied field, the states split, as shown in Fig. 4.17.

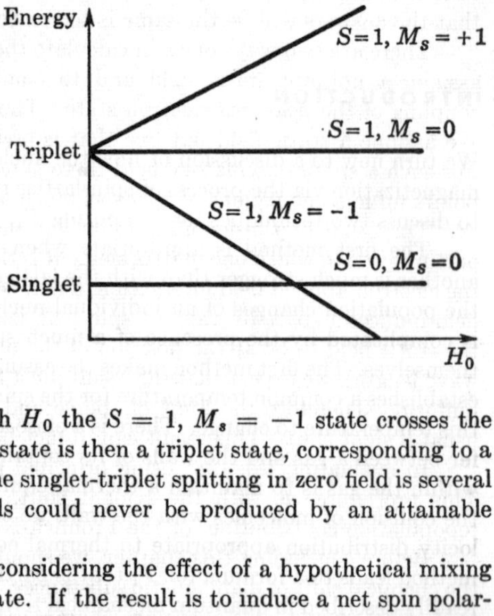

FIG. 4.17. Effect of the applied field H_0 on the singlet- and triplet-spin states of a hydrogen molecule. If H_0 were large enough, a triplet state would be lowest and the ground state would possess a magnetic moment.

As we can see, for large enough H_0 the $S = 1$, $M_s = -1$ state crosses the $S = 0$, $M_s = 0$ state. The ground state is then a triplet state, corresponding to a spin polarization. However, since the singlet-triplet splitting in zero field is several electron volts, the crossing of levels could never be produced by an attainable laboratory field.

Further insight is obtained by considering the effect of a hypothetical mixing of a triplet state into the ground state. If the result is to induce a net spin polarization in the positive z-direction on one atom, it induces an equal and opposite spin polarization in the negative z-direction on the other atom. Clearly there is zero net spin Zeeman interaction with an applied field in the z-direction. Since such a spin polarization gives no net lowering of energy, it is not in fact induced.

Note, however, that if the two atoms are dissimilar, there may be a different induced orbital moment which, through the spin-orbit coupling could then induce such a spin polarization. Thus, in a molecule such as HI, the iodine orbital magnetization could induce a spin polarization into the bond, giving a spin contribution to the chemical shift on the hydrogen as well as on the iodine.

CHAPTER 5

PIN-LATTICE RELAXATION ND MOTIONAL ARROWING OF ESONANCE LINES

5·1 INTRODUCTION

We turn now to a discussion of how the nuclei arrive at their thermal equilibrium magnetization via the process of spin-lattice relaxation. We shall find it convenient to discuss two techniques for computing T_1.

The first method is appropriate when the coupling of the nuclei with one another is much stronger than with the lattice. In this case an attempt to compute the population changes of an individual nucleus due to the coupling to the lattice is complicated by the presence of a much stronger coupling of the nuclei among themselves. The first method makes the assumption that the strong coupling simply establishes a common temperature for the spins and that the lattice coupling causes this temperature to change. There is a close analogy with the process of heat transfer between a gas and the walls of its container, in which the role of the collisions within the gas is to maintain a thermal equilibrium among the gas molecules. In the collision of molecules with the wall, we consider the molecules to have the velocity distribution appropriate to thermal equilibrium. As we shall see, the first method leads to a formula for T_1 that is particularly convenient when the lattice is readily described in quantum mechanical terms. For example, relaxation in a metal involves the transfer of energy to the conduction electrons, which are readily thought of in terms of Bloch functions and the exclusion principle.

The second method is that of the so-called density matrix. Although this is a completely general method, it finds its greatest utility for systems in which the lattice is naturally described classically and in which the resonance width is substantially narrowed by the motion of the nuclei. Moreover, when motion takes place, the relaxation time T_2, which describes coupling between the nuclei, becomes long, and it may be a very poor approximation to assume that a spin temperature is achieved rapidly as compared to T_1. Thus the second method is useful when the first one fails. Because of their large mass, the motion of the nuclei is often given very well in classical terms. In fact an attempt to describe the motion of molecules in a liquid quantum mechanically would be quite cumbersome. Consequently the density matrix method is well suited to discussing cases in which motional narrowing takes place. An added feature is that both T_1 and T_2 processes (relaxation of I_z and I_x or I_y) can be treated by the density matrix method, provided there is motional narrowing.

The density matrix method is very closely related to the conventional time-dependent perturbation theory. Actually the two are entirely equivalent. The density matrix method, however, gives results in a particularly useful form. It is ideal for treating problems in which phase coherence is important, and in fact the density matrix or a mathematical equivalent is necessary to treat such problems. In any event, much of the formalism of this chapter applies equally well to systems other than spins. For example, dielectric relaxation can be treated by these methods.

As we see, the two approaches complement one another, one applying to the broad resonances of a rigid lattice and the other being most useful when the resonance has been narrowed by nuclear motion.

5·2 RELAXATION OF A SYSTEM DESCRIBED BY A SPIN TEMPERATURE†

A system with a set of energies E_a, E_b, and so on, which is in thermal equilibrium with a reservoir of temperature T, occupies the levels with probabilities $p(E_a)$, $p(E_b)$, and so forth, which are given by

$$\frac{p(E_a)}{p(E_b)} = \frac{e^{-E_a/kT}}{e^{-E_b/kT}} \tag{1}$$

so that, since

$$\sum_{E_a} p(E_a) = 1 \tag{2}$$

we have

$$p(E_a) = \frac{e^{-E_a/kT}}{\sum_c e^{-E_c/kT}} = \frac{e^{-E_a/kT}}{Z} \tag{3}$$

where

$$Z = \sum_c e^{-E_c/kT} \tag{4}$$

is the partition function or "sum of states."

These equations may actually have two interpretations, which we might illustrate by considering N identical spins. The first interpretation considers the spins as isolated from one another. The "system" consists then of a single spin, and the energies E_a represent the possible energies of the single spin. The second interpretation considers the system to be formed by all N spins. In this case, E_a represents the total energy of all N spins. We shall find it convenient to use both interpretations. We should perhaps note that the first interpretation is only correct if the spins can be considered to obey Maxwell-Boltzmann statistics, but the second interpretation holds true whether or not the individual particles obey Maxwell-Boltzmann, Fermi-Dirac, or Bose-Einstein statistics. The statistics would enter only when we tried to express the wave function of the total system in terms of the wave functions of individual spins.

† See references to "Spin Temperature" in the Bibliography.

We shall say that any system whose population obeys Eq. (1) is described by a temperature T, even when the system is not in equilibrium with a reservoir. Equation (3) enables us to make a simple plot to schematize the populations. We

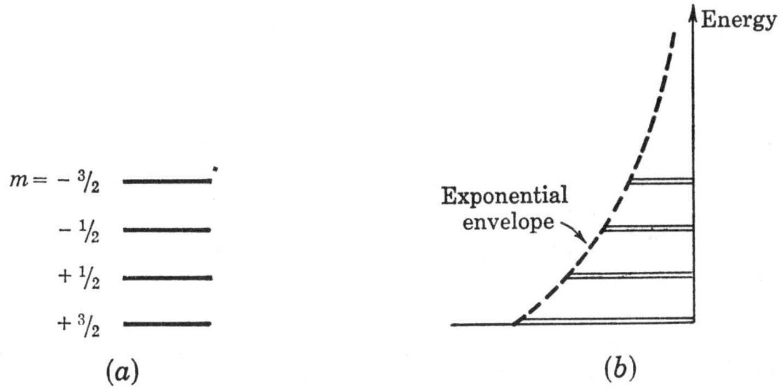

FIG. 5.1. (a) Energy levels of a spin 3/2 nucleus. (b) Bar graph of population versus energy. The lengths of the bars are determined by the exponential envelope.

illustrate in Fig. 5.1 for a case based on our first interpretation: we consider the population of the various energy states of a single spin of $I = \frac{3}{2}$ acted on by a static magnetic field.

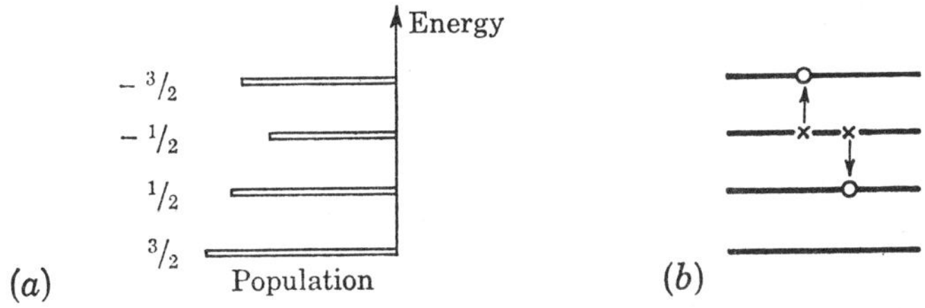

FIG. 5.2. (a) Population distribution not describable by a temperature. (b) A possible transition of a pair of spins from the states designated by crosses to those designated by circles.

A system such as shown in Fig. 5.2 clearly does not correspond to thermal equilibrium, since the bar graph envelope is not an exponential.

In Fig. 5.2b we indicate a transition that could take place, conserving the total energy of the spins. Two spins designated by crosses couple together, inducing transitions to the states designated by circles, one spin going up in energy and the other down. (Such a transition would be induced by the $I_1^+ I_2^-$ terms of the dipolar coupling.) The number of transitions per second from cross to circle, $dN/dt)_{x \to 0}$, will be the product of the probabilities of finding two spins in the initial state times the probability of transition, $W_{x \to 0}$, *if* the spins are in the initial state. Thus,

$$\left.\frac{dN}{dt}\right)_{x \to 0} = p_{-1/2} p_{-1/2} W_{x \to 0} \tag{5}$$

The inverse reaction from the circle to the cross will have a rate $dN/dt)_{0\to x}$, given by

$$\left.\frac{dN}{dt}\right)_{0\to x} = p_{-3/2}p_{1/2}W_{0\to x} \tag{6}$$

If we equate these rates, we guarantee equilibrium. This is the assumption that equilibrium is obtained by detailed balance. Since $W_{0\to x} = W_{x\to 0}$, we find

$$p_{-1/2}p_{-1/2} = p_{-3/2}p_{1/2} \quad \text{or} \quad \frac{p_{-3/2}}{p_{-1/2}} = \frac{p_{-1/2}}{p_{+1/2}} \tag{7}$$

But this is just the condition of thermal equilibrium among the states, since they are equally spaced in energy.

We see, therefore, that thermal equilibrium is reached by processes such as we have indicated in Fig. 5.2b. The typical rate for such a process is of the order of the inverse of the rigid lattice line breadth, or between 10 to 100 μsec for typical nuclei. Therefore, if T_1 is milliseconds to seconds, we should consider the nuclear populations to be given by a Boltzmann distribution.

We shall now proceed to consider the relaxation of a system of nuclear spins whose Hamiltonian $\mathcal{H}$ has eigenvalues E_n, and in which the fractional occupation of state n is p_n. (*Thus n designates a state of the total system, rather than the energy of a single spin.*) Normalization requires that

$$\sum_n p_n = 1 \tag{8}$$

The average energy of the system, $\bar{E}$, is then

$$\bar{E} = \sum_n p_n E_n \tag{9}$$

We shall assume further that the energies E_n are measured from a reference such that

$$\sum_n E_n = \text{Tr}\mathcal{H} = 0 \tag{10}$$

a condition that is fulfilled for both the Zeeman and dipolar energies.

To compute the relaxation, we shall consider changes in the average energy. If we define $\beta = 1/kT$ to represent the spin temperature, we have that

$$\frac{d\bar{E}}{dt} = \frac{d\bar{E}}{d\beta}\frac{d\beta}{dt} \tag{11}$$

But since $\bar{E} = \sum_n p_n E_n$, we have also that

$$\frac{d\bar{E}}{dt} = \frac{d}{dt}\sum_n p_n E_n = \sum_n E_n \frac{dp_n}{dt} \tag{12}$$

We shall assume that the p_n's obey simple linear rate equations. Introducing W_{mn} as the probability per second that the lattices induce a transition of the system from m to n if the system is in state m, the rate equation is

$$\frac{dp_n}{dt} = \sum_m (p_m W_{mn} - p_n W_{nm}) \tag{13}$$

This equation is frequently called the "master" equation.

By substituting into Eq. (12) we have, then, that

$$\frac{d\bar{E}}{dt} = \sum_{m,n} (p_m W_{mn} - p_n W_{nm}) E_n$$

$$= \frac{1}{2} \sum_{m,n} (p_m W_{mn} - p_n W_{nm})(E_n - E_m) \tag{14}$$

where the second form is introduced because it treats the labels m and n more symmetrically. By equating Eqs. (11) and (14), we obtain a differential equation for the changes in spin temperature. We have two problems: (1) finding $d\bar{E}/d\beta$ and (2) seeing what becomes of Eq. (14) when we introduce the requirement that at all times a spin temperature apply.

We turn first to evaluating $d\bar{E}/d\beta$:

$$p_n = \frac{e^{-\beta E_n}}{Z} \tag{15}$$

and

$$\frac{d\bar{E}}{d\beta} = \frac{d}{d\beta} \sum_n p_n(\beta) E_n \tag{16}$$

We first seek an approximate expression for Z. Once again, assuming the temperature to be high enough so that $\beta E_n \ll 1$ for the majority of states, we expand $e^{-\beta E_n}$ in a power series and keep only the leading terms:

$$Z = \sum_n \left(1 - \beta E_n + \frac{\beta^2 E_n^2}{2!} + \cdots\right) \tag{17}$$

Approximating such a power series expansion by the leading terms clearly has validity if $|E_n| \ll kT$ for the significant energies. However, the approximation proves legitimate under less stringent conditions using an argument similar to that in Appendix E both here and in Eqs. (19) through (26) below.

By utilizing Eq. (10), the second term on the right vanishes. We then neglect the β^2 term, and Z becomes equal to the total number of states. Since this is also Z for infinite temperature, Z_∞, we may say that

$$Z = Z_\infty \tag{18}$$

By utilizing this fact and Eq. (15), Eq. (16) becomes

$$\frac{d\bar{E}}{d\beta} = -\frac{1}{Z_\infty} \sum_n E_n^2 e^{-\beta E_n} \tag{19}$$

$$= -\frac{1}{Z_\infty} \sum_n E_n^2 (1 - \beta E_n + \cdots)$$

$$\cong -\frac{1}{Z_\infty} \sum_n E_n^2$$

again in the high-temperature limit. Thus

$$\frac{d\overline{E}}{dt} = -\frac{d\beta}{dt}\frac{\sum_n E_n^2}{Z_\infty} \tag{20}$$

We now turn to evaluation of Eq. (14). Since the system is always describable by a temperature, we have

$$p_n = p_m e^{(E_m - E_n)\beta} \tag{21}$$

We shall furthermore assume that when the system is in thermal equilibrium with the lattice, the transitions between every pair of levels are in equilibrium. This is the so-called principle of detailed balance. Denoting by p_n^L the value of p_n when the spins are in thermal equilibrium with the lattice, the principle of detailed balance says that

$$p_m^L W_{mn} = p_n^L W_{nm} \tag{22}$$

or that

$$W_{mn} = W_{nm}\frac{p_n^L}{p_m^L} \tag{23}$$

$$= W_{nm} e^{(E_m - E_n)\beta_L}$$

where $\beta_L = 1/(kT_L)$.

By substituting Eqs. (21) and (23) into Eq. (14), we find

$$\frac{d\overline{E}}{dt} = \frac{1}{2}\sum_{m,n} p_m W_{mn}[1 - e^{(E_m - E_n)(\beta - \beta_L)}](E_n - E_m) \tag{24}$$

Now, expanding the exponential, we find

$$\frac{d\overline{E}}{dt} \cong \frac{1}{2}\sum_{m,n} p_m W_{mn}(E_n - E_m)^2(\beta - \beta_L) \tag{25}$$

Now

$$p_m \cong \frac{e^{-\beta E_m}}{Z_\infty} \cong \frac{1 - \beta E_m + \dfrac{\beta^2 E_m^2}{2!}}{Z_\infty} \tag{26}$$

$$\cong \frac{1}{Z_\infty}$$

Thus, combining Eq. (26) with Eq. (25) and equating the resultant $d\overline{E}/dt$ to that of Eq. (20), we find

$$\frac{d\beta}{dt} = (\beta_L - \beta)\left[\frac{1}{2}\frac{\sum_{m,n} W_{mn}(E_m - E_n)^2}{\sum_n E_n^2}\right] \tag{27}$$

$$= \frac{\beta_L - \beta}{T_1}$$

where

$$\frac{1}{T_1} = \frac{1}{2}\frac{\sum_{m,n} W_{mn}(E_m - E_n)^2}{\sum_n E_n^2} \tag{28}$$

Equation (28) was first derived by Gorter on the assumption that $|\beta - \beta_L| \ll \beta$.† As we can see, this restriction is not necessary.

The great advantage of Eq. (28) is that, by postulating a temperature, it has taken into account the spin-spin couplings. The rate equations, Eq. (14), would by themselves imply that there are multiple time constants that describe the spin-lattice relaxation, but the assumption of a temperature forces the whole system to relax with a single exponential.

We may get added insight by viewing our states n as being *nearly* exact solutions of the nuclear spin Hamiltonian, between which (since they are not *exact* states) transitions take place rapidly to guarantee a thermal equilibrium, but between which the lattice also makes much slower transitions. After each lattice transition, which disturbs the nuclear distribution, the nuclei readjust among their approximate levels so that the lattice once again finds the spins distributed according to a temperature when it induces the next spin transition. Our formalism implies that treating the states n as being exact makes a negligible difference in the answer.

5·3 RELAXATION OF NUCLEI IN A METAL

We now turn to an example of the application of Eq. (28) of Section 5.2. We shall consider the relaxation of nuclei in a metal by their coupling to the spin magnetic moments of the conduction electrons. This is the dominant relaxation mechanism.

In a T_1 process, the nucleus undergoes a transition in which it either absorbs or gives up energy. In order to conserve energy, the lattice must undergo a compensating change. For coupling to the conduction electrons, we may think of the nuclear transition as involving a simultaneous electron transition from some state of wave vector $\mathbf{k}$ and spin orientation s, to a state $\mathbf{k}'$, s'. We may think of this as a scattering problem. Denoting the initial and final nuclear quantum numbers as m and n, respectively, we have that the number of transitions per second from the initial state of nucleus and electron $|m\mathbf{k}s)$ to the final state $|n\mathbf{k}'s')$, $W_{m\mathbf{k}s,n\mathbf{k}'s'}$, is

$$W_{m\mathbf{k}s,n\mathbf{k}'s'} = \frac{2\pi}{\hbar} |(m\mathbf{k}s|V|n\mathbf{k}'s')|^2 \, \delta(E_m + E_{\mathbf{k}s} - E_n - E_{\mathbf{k}'s'}) \tag{1}$$

where V is the interaction that provides the scattering, and where Eq. (1) assumes that there is an electron in $|\mathbf{k}s)$ and there is *none* in $|\mathbf{k}'s')$. The total probability per second of nuclear transitions is obtained by adding up the $W_{m\mathbf{k}s,n\mathbf{k}'s'}$'s for all initial and final electron states. We have

$$W_{mn} = \sum_{\substack{\mathbf{k}s \text{ occupied} \\ \mathbf{k}'s' \text{ unoccupied}}} W_{m\mathbf{k}s,n\mathbf{k}'s'} \tag{2}$$

The sum over "$\mathbf{k}s$ occupied" is, of course, equivalent to summing over electrons. We can remove the restrictions on $\mathbf{k}s$ and $\mathbf{k}'s'$ by introducing the quantity $p_{\mathbf{k}s}$,

† C. J. Gorter, *Paramagnetic Relaxation.* New York: Elsevier Publishing Co., Inc., 1947 (127 pp.).

which is defined to be unity if **ks** is occupied; zero, otherwise. This gives us

$$W_{mn} = \sum_{\substack{\mathbf{k}s \\ \mathbf{k}'s'}} W_{m\mathbf{k}s,n\mathbf{k}'s'} p_{\mathbf{k}s}[1 - p_{\mathbf{k}'s'}] \tag{3}$$

By averaging Eq. (3) over an ensemble of electron systems, we simply replace $p_{\mathbf{k}s}$ by the Fermi function $f(E_{\mathbf{k}s})$, which we abbreviate as $f(\mathbf{k}, s)$:

$$W_{mn} = \sum_{\substack{\mathbf{k}s \\ \mathbf{k}'s'}} W_{m\mathbf{k}s,n\mathbf{k}'s'} f(\mathbf{k}s)[1 - f(\mathbf{k}'s')] \tag{4}$$

We must now express $W_{m\mathbf{k}s,n\mathbf{k}'s'}$ explicitly. To do so, we must specify the interaction V. For metals with a substantial s-character to the wave function at the Fermi surface, the dominant contribution to V comes from the s-state coupling between the nuclear and electron spins:

$$V = \frac{8\pi}{3}\gamma_e\gamma_n\hbar^2 \mathbf{I}\cdot\mathbf{S}\,\delta(\mathbf{r}) \tag{5}$$

where we have chosen the nucleus **I** to be at the origin. For the electron wave function, we shall take a product of a spin function and a Bloch function, $u_{\mathbf{k}}(\mathbf{r})e^{i\mathbf{k}\cdot\mathbf{r}}$. Therefore the initial wave function is

$$|m\mathbf{k}s) = |m)|s)u_{\mathbf{k}}e^{+i\mathbf{k}\cdot\mathbf{r}} \tag{6}$$

It is a simple matter to compute the matrix element of Eq. (1):

$$(m\mathbf{k}s|V|n\mathbf{k}'s') = \frac{8\pi}{3}\gamma_e\gamma_n\hbar^2(m|\mathbf{I}|n)\cdot(s|\mathbf{S}|s')u_{\mathbf{k}}^*(0)u_{\mathbf{k}'}(0) \tag{7}$$

which gives us

$$W_{m\mathbf{k}s,n\mathbf{k}'s'} = \frac{2\pi}{\hbar}\frac{64\pi^2}{9}\gamma_e^2\gamma_n^2\hbar^4 \sum_{\substack{\alpha,\alpha' \\ =x,y,z}} (m|I_\alpha|n)(n|I_{\alpha'}|m) \times \tag{8}$$

$$(s|S_\alpha|s')(s'|S_{\alpha'}|s)|u_{\mathbf{k}}(0)|^2|u_{\mathbf{k}'}(0)|^2\,\delta(E_m + E_{\mathbf{k}s} - E_n - E_{\mathbf{k}'s'})$$

We can substitute this expression into Eq. (4) to compute W_{mn}. We are once again faced with a summation over **k** and **k′** of a slowly varying function. As before, we replace the summation by an integral, using the density of states $g(E_{\mathbf{k}}, A)$ introduced in Section 4.7. This gives us

$$W_{mn} = \frac{2\pi}{\hbar}\frac{64\pi^2}{9}\gamma_e^2\gamma_n^2\hbar^4 \sum_{\alpha\alpha'} (m|I_\alpha|n)(n|I_{\alpha'}|m)(s|S_\alpha|s')(s'|S_{\alpha'}|s) \tag{9}$$

$$\int |u_{\mathbf{k}}(0)|^2|u_{\mathbf{k}'}(0)|^2 f(\mathbf{k}, s)[1 - f(\mathbf{k}', s')]g(E_{\mathbf{k}}, A)$$

$$g(E_{\mathbf{k}'}, A')\,\delta(E_m - E_n + E_{\mathbf{k}s} - E_{\mathbf{k}'s'})\,dE_{\mathbf{k}}\,dA\,dE_{\mathbf{k}'}\,dA'$$

We integrate first over dA and dA', utilizing the relations of Eqs. (28) and (29) of Section 4.7, to perform the integrals, and introducing again the average of $|u_{\mathbf{k}}(0)|^2$ over the energy surface, $E_{\mathbf{k}}, \langle|u_{\mathbf{k}}(0)|^2\rangle_{E_{\mathbf{k}}}$. We also assume that the energy $E_{\mathbf{k}s}$ appearing in the Fermi functions remains constant on a surface of constant $E_{\mathbf{k}}$, an assumption that would be fulfilled unless the spin energy depended on the location on the surface $E_{\mathbf{k}}$. The integration over $dE_{\mathbf{k}'}$ is then easy because of the delta function. We have that

$$E_{\mathbf{k}s} + E_m = E_{\mathbf{k}'s'} + E_n \tag{10}$$

and, assuming $E_{\mathbf{k}s} = E_{\mathbf{k}} + E_s$, we get for W_{mn}:

$$W_{mn} = \frac{2\pi}{\hbar}\frac{64\pi^2}{9}\gamma_e^2\gamma_n^2\hbar^4 \sum_{\substack{\alpha,\alpha' \\ s,s'}} (m|I_\alpha|n)(n|I_{\alpha'}|m)(s|S_\alpha|s')(s'|S_{\alpha'}|s) \times$$

$$\int \langle|u_{\mathbf{k}}(0)|^2\rangle_{E_{\mathbf{k}}}\langle|u_{\mathbf{k}'}(0)|^2\rangle_{E_{\mathbf{k}'}} f(E_{\mathbf{k}s})[1 - f(E_{\mathbf{k}s} + E_m - E_n)] \times$$

$$\rho(E_{\mathbf{k}})\rho(E_{\mathbf{k}'})\, dE_{\mathbf{k}} \tag{11}$$

$$E_{\mathbf{k}'} = E_{\mathbf{k}} + E_s - E_{s'} + E_m - E_n \tag{12}$$

Since $E_m - E_n$, the nuclear energy change, is very small compared with kT, the Fermi function $f(E_{\mathbf{k}s} + E_m - E_n)$ may be replaced by $f(E_{\mathbf{k}s})$. Actually, doing so makes $W_{mn} = W_{nm}$. It is, in fact, at this point that the slight difference between W_{mn} and W_{nm} arises. It is this slight difference, we recall, that gives rise to the establishment of the thermal equilibrium nuclear population. We are allowed to neglect the difference here in computing W_{mn}, since we have already included the effect in Eq. (23) of Section 5.2.

Moreover, since both $\rho(E_{\mathbf{k}'})$ and $\langle|u_{\mathbf{k}'}(0)|^2\rangle_{E_{\mathbf{k}}}$ are slowly varying functions of $E_{\mathbf{k}'}$, we may set them equal to their values when $E_{\mathbf{k}} = E_{\mathbf{k}'}$. In fact we shall evaluate $\rho(E_{\mathbf{k}'})$, and so on at $E_{\mathbf{k}s}$. This gives us for the integral in Eq. (11):

$$\int_0^\infty \langle|u_{\mathbf{k}}(0)|^2\rangle_E^2\, \rho^2(E)f(E)[1 - f(E)]\, dE \tag{13}$$

where we have set the lower limits as zero, since the only contributions to the integral come from the region near the Fermi surface, $E = E_F$.

Since Eq. (13) is independent of the spin quantum numbers s and s', we may now evaluate the spin sum of Eq. (11):

$$\begin{aligned}\sum_{s,s'} (s|S_\alpha|s')(s'|S_{\alpha'}|s) &= \sum_s (s|S_\alpha S_{\alpha'}|s) \\ &= \mathrm{Tr} S_\alpha S_{\alpha'} = \delta_{\alpha\alpha'}\tfrac{1}{3}S(S+1)(2S+1) \\ &= \delta_{\alpha\alpha'}/2 \qquad \text{since } S = \tfrac{1}{2}\end{aligned} \tag{14}$$

This gives us

$$W_{mn} = \frac{64}{9}\pi^3\hbar^3\gamma_e^2\gamma_n^2 \sum_\alpha (m|I_\alpha|n)(n|I_\alpha|m) \times \tag{15}$$

$$\int \langle|u_{\mathbf{k}}(0)|^2\rangle_E^2\, \rho^2(E)f(E)[1 - f(E)]\, dE$$

Now

$$f(E)[1 - f(E)] = -kT\frac{\partial f}{\partial E} \tag{16}$$

which follows directly from the fact that

$$f(E) = \frac{1}{e^{(E-E_F)/kT} + 1}$$

and $f(E)[1 - f(E)]$ peaks up very strongly (Fig. 5.3) when $E \cong E_F$.

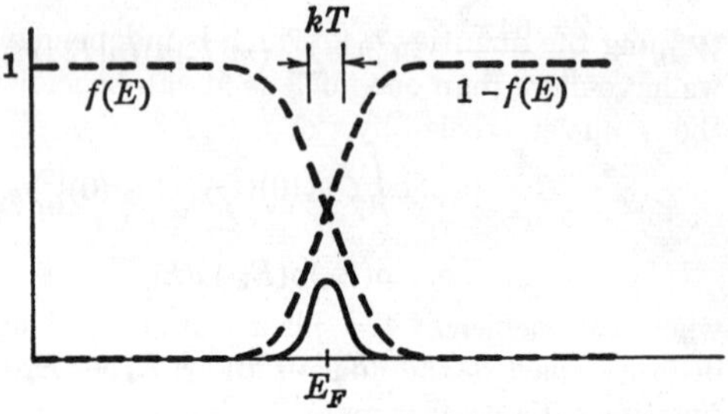

FIG. 5.3. Functions of $f(E)$, $1 - f(E)$, and $f(E)[1 - f(E)]$. The solid line shows $f(E) \times [1 - f(E)]$.

Since $f(0) = 1$ and $f(\infty) = 0$, and since $f(E)[1 - f(E)]$ peaks up only within a width kT, it is also closely related to a δ-function when in an integral of other functions that vary slowly over kT.

$$f(E)[1 - f(E)] = kT\,\delta(E - E_F)\dagger \tag{17}$$

By utilizing this fact, we have, finally,

$$W_{mn} = \frac{64}{9}\,\pi^3\hbar^3\gamma_e^2\gamma_n^2\langle|u_{\mathbf{k}}(0)|^2\rangle_{E_F}^2\,\rho^2(E_F)kT\sum_\alpha |(m|I_\alpha|n)|^2 \tag{18}$$

We note that W_{mn} is proportional to the temperature T. This fact has a simple physical interpretation. When the nuclei undergo a transition, they give an energy to the electrons that is very small compared with kT. Most of the electrons

† Equation (17) can be derived simply. Let $G(E)$ be a slowly varying function of energy. Then, utilizing the fact that $f(E)[1 - f(E)]$ is non-vanishing within only kT about E_F, we can expand $G(E)$ in a power series about E_F:

$$G(E) = G(E_F) + (E - E_F)\left.\frac{dG}{dE}\right|_{E_F} + \frac{(E - E_F)^2}{2!}\left.\frac{d^2G}{dE^2}\right|_{E_f} + \cdots$$

Thus

$$\int_0^\infty G(E)f(E)[1 - f(E)]\,dE$$
$$= G(E_F)\int_0^\infty f(E)[1 - f(E)]\,dE$$
$$+ \left.\frac{dG}{dE}\right|_{E_F}\int_0^\infty (E - E_F)f(1 - f)\,dE + \left.\frac{d^2G}{dE^2}\right|_{E_F}\int_0^\infty (E - E_F)^2 f(1 - f)\,dE + \cdots$$

The first term, using Eq. (16), gives $G(E_F)kT$. The second term vanishes, since the integrand is an odd function of $E - E_F$, and the third term gives a contribution proportional to $(kT)^3$, as seen by changing the integrand from E to $x \equiv E/kT$. If we neglect the third and higher terms, the answer is just what we should have if we replaced $f(1 - f)$ by $kT\,\delta(E - E_F)$. The corrections are generally of order $(kT/E_F)^2$ smaller, the exact form depending on the functional dependence of G on the energy E.

are unable to take part in the relaxation because they have no empty states nearby in energy into which they can make a transition. It is only those electrons in the tail of the distribution that are important. Their number is proportional to kT.

We can write Eq. (18) as

$$W_{mn} = a_{00} \sum_{\alpha} |(m|I_\alpha|n)|^2 \tag{19}$$

defining the quantity a_{00}, which is independent of the nuclear states n and m. If we have more than one nucleus, it can be shown† that W_{mn} is given by a sum over the N nuclei, labeled by i or j, $(i, j = 1 \text{ to } N)$:

$$W_{mn} = \sum_{i,j} a_{ij} \sum_{\alpha} (m|I_{i\alpha}|n)(n|I_{j\alpha}|m) \tag{20}$$

where the coefficient $i = j$ is a_{00}, and where a_{ij} for $i \neq j$ falls off rapidly with the distance apart of the nuclei i and j. These terms arise because the electron wave function extends over many nuclei, so that more than one nucleus may scatter the electron from a given initial to a given final state.

By returning to Eq. (19) and employing our formula for T_1, we have

$$\frac{1}{T_1} = a_{00}\,\frac{1}{2}\,\frac{\sum_{m,n,\alpha} (m|I_\alpha|n)(n|I_\alpha|m)(E_m - E_n)^2}{\sum_m E_m^2} \tag{21}$$

$$= -\frac{a_{00}}{2}\,\frac{\sum_{m,n,\alpha} (m|[\mathcal{H}, I_\alpha]|n)(n|[\mathcal{H}, I_\alpha]|m)}{\sum E_m^2}$$

$$= -\frac{a_{00}}{2}\,\frac{\sum_{\alpha=x,y,z} \mathrm{Tr}[\mathcal{H}, I_\alpha]^2}{\mathrm{Tr}\mathcal{H}^2}$$

A similar expression is found by using Eq. (20). The important point is that we do not need to solve for the explicit eigenstates and eigenvalues, but only evaluate the traces in a convenient representation.

For our problem of a single spin, the quantum numbers m and n would label the $2I + 1$ eigenstates of I_z. Then, using the fact that

$$\mathcal{H} = -\gamma_n \hbar H_0 I_z \tag{22}$$

and that

$$[I_z, I_x] = iI_y \qquad \text{etc.} \tag{23}$$

we find

$$\sum_{\alpha} \mathrm{Tr}[\mathcal{H}, I_\alpha]^2 = -\gamma_n^2 \hbar^2 H_0^2\, \mathrm{Tr}(I_x^2 + I_y^2) \tag{24}$$

$$\sum_{\alpha} \mathrm{Tr}\mathcal{H}^2 = \gamma_n^2 \hbar^2 H_0^2\, \mathrm{Tr} I_z^2$$

† See L. C. Hebel and C. P. Slichter, *Phys. Rev.*, **113**: 1504 (1959).

so that, since $\mathrm{Tr} I_x^2 = \mathrm{Tr} I_y^2 = \mathrm{Tr} I_z^2$,

$$\frac{\sum_\alpha \mathrm{Tr}[\mathcal{H}, I_\alpha]^2}{\mathrm{Tr}\mathcal{H}^2} = -2 \tag{25}$$

$$\frac{1}{T_1} = a_{00} = \frac{64}{9}\pi^3\hbar^3\gamma_e^2\gamma_n^2\langle|u_{\mathbf{k}}(0)|^2\rangle_{E_F}^2\,\rho^2(E_F)kT \tag{26}$$

The quantity $\langle|u_{\mathbf{k}}(0)|^2\rangle_{E_F}$ appearing in the expression also occurred in the expression for the Knight shift, $\Delta H/H$:

$$\frac{\Delta H}{H} = \frac{8\pi}{3}\langle|u_{\mathbf{k}}(0)|^2\rangle_{E_F}\chi_e^s \tag{27}$$

We can therefore use Eq. (27) to evaluate $\langle|u_{\mathbf{k}}(0)|^2\rangle_{E_F}$, giving

$$T_1\left(\frac{\Delta H}{H}\right)^2 = \left[\frac{\chi_e^s}{\rho(E_F)}\right]^2\frac{1}{\pi kT}\frac{1}{\gamma_n^2\gamma_e^2\hbar^3} \tag{28}$$

For a Fermi gas of non-interacting spins, one can show that χ_e^s is given by

$$\chi_0^s = \frac{\gamma_e^2\hbar^2}{2}\rho_0(E_F) \tag{29}$$

where we have put subscripts "0" on χ^s and $\rho(E_F)$ to label them as appropriate to non-interacting electrons. In this approximation one has

$$T_1\left(\frac{\Delta H}{H}\right)^2 = \frac{\hbar}{4\pi kT}\frac{\gamma_e^2}{\gamma_n^2} \tag{30}$$

Equation (30) is commonly called the "Korringa relation," after Dr. J. Korringa who first published it.† It provides a very convenient way to use measured Knight shifts to predict spin-lattice relaxation times. A more accurate expression is obtained from Eqs. (28) and (29):

$$T_1\left(\frac{\Delta H}{H}\right)^2 = \frac{\hbar}{4\pi kT}\frac{\gamma_e^2}{\gamma_n^2}\left[\frac{\chi_e^s}{\chi_0^s}\frac{\rho_0(E_F)}{\rho(E_F)}\right]^2 \tag{31}$$

The T_1 appearing in the Korringa relation represents only one contribution to the relaxation time—that due to the coupling of nuclei to the magnetic moment of s-state electrons. One expects that the experimental T_1 should, if anything, be shorter. It is therefore interesting to examine a table given by Pines.†† In it he lists experimental T_1's, those computed from Eq. (30), the Korringa relation, and those computed from Eq. (31), using Pines' theoretical values of χ_e^s/χ_0^s and $\rho_0(E_F)/\rho(E_F)$.

† J. Korringa, *Physica*, 16: 601 (1950).
†† D. Pines, *Solid State Physics*, Vol. 1, Seitz and Turnbull, eds. New York: Academic Press, Inc.

TABLE 5.1.

Experimental and Theoretical T_1's (all times in msec)

	T_1 (Experimental)	T_1 (Korringa)	T_1 (Pines)
Li	150 ± 5	88	232
Na	15.9 ± 0.3	10.3	18.1
Rb^{95}	2.75 ± 0.2	2.1	2.94
Cu	3.0 ± 0.6	2.3	4.0
Al	6.3 ± 0.1	5.1	6.5

We note that the Korringa T_1's are all *shorter* than the experimental ones. The discrepancy cannot be removed by appealing to other relaxation processes, since if we included them, the theoretical T_1 would be even shorter than those computed by the Korringa relation, and the discrepancy would be still greater. On the other hand, the Pines' values, based on inclusion of the electron-electron couplings, make the predicted values *longer* than the experimental. The discrepancy between the Pines' values and the experimental is perhaps a measure of the importance of relaxation processes we have not computed.

5·4 DENSITY MATRIX—GENERAL EQUATIONS

As we have remarked, the concept of a spin temperature is not always valid. We turn now to discussion of a method of attack that is very useful when the spin temperature concept breaks down—the technique of the density matrix.†

The method has the further advantage of giving one a discussion of both T_1 and T_2 processes in a natural way. It is ideally suited to treating problems in which the resonance is narrowed by the bodily motion of the nuclei. It is also applicable to broad line spectra, where it can in fact be used for an alternate derivation of our equation for T_1 of Section 5.3. As we shall see, the method is simply a variant of the usual time-dependent perturbation theory, but one that is in a particularly useful form.

We begin by considering a system described by a wave function Ψ, at some instant of time, and ask for the expectation value $\langle M_x \rangle$ of some operator such as the x-component of magnetization, M_x. We have, then,

$$\langle M_x \rangle = (\Psi, M_x \Psi) \tag{1}$$

Suppose we now expand Ψ in a complete set of orthonormal functions u_n, which are independent of time:

$$\Psi = \sum_n c_n u_n \tag{2}$$

† An exceptionally good discussion of the density matrix is that of R. C. Tolman, *The Principles of Statistical Mechanics*. New York: Oxford University Press.

If Ψ varies in time, so must the c_n's. In terms of the functions u_n, we have

$$\langle M_x \rangle = \sum_{n,m} c_m^* c_n (m|M_x|n) \tag{3}$$

If we change the wave function, $\langle M_x \rangle$ will differ because the coefficients $c_m^* c_n$ will differ, but the matrix elements $(m|M_x|n)$ will remain the same. Correspondingly, for a given Ψ, the effect of calculating expectation values of different operators is found in the different matrix elements, but the coefficients $c_m^* c_n$ remain the same. We can conveniently arrange the coefficients $c_n c_m^*$ to form a matrix. We note that, to compute any observable, we can specify either all the c_n's or all the products $c_n c_m^*$. However, since we always wish the c's in the form of products, to calculate observable properties of the system, we find knowledge of the products more useful than knowledge of the individual c's.

It is convenient to think of the matrix $c_n c_m^*$ as being the representation of an operator P, the operator being defined by its matrix elements:

$$(n|P|m) = c_n c_m^* \tag{4}$$

In terms of Eq. (4) we have, then,

$$\langle M_x \rangle = \sum_{n,m} (n|P|m)(m|M_x|n) \tag{5}$$

The result of the operator P acting on a function u_m may be written as

$$P u_m = \sum_n a_n u_n \tag{6}$$

since the u_n's form a complete set. As usual, we find the a_n's by multiplying both sides from the left by u_n^* and integrating:

$$a_n = \int u_n^* P u_m \, d\tau = (n|P|m) \tag{7}$$

so that

$$P u_m = \sum_n u_n (n|P|m) \tag{8}$$

Likewise we have

$$M_x u_n = \sum_m u_m (m|M_x|n) \tag{9}$$

Therefore

$$\begin{aligned} P M_x u_n &= \sum_m P u_m (m|M_x|n) \\ &= \sum_{m,n'} u_{n'} (n'|P|m)(m|M_x|n) \end{aligned} \tag{10}$$

so that

$$(n'|PM_x|n) = \sum_m (n'|P|m)(m|M_x|n) \tag{11}$$

By using Eq. (11), we have that

$$\begin{aligned}\langle M_x\rangle &= \sum_{m,n} (n|P|m)(m|M_x|n) \\ &= \sum_{n} (n|PM_x|n) \\ &= \mathrm{Tr}PM_x = \mathrm{Tr}M_xP\end{aligned} \tag{12}$$

Also we note that P is an Hermitian operator. This we prove by noting that the definition of an Hermitian operator, P, is

$$\begin{aligned}\int u_n^* P u_m \, d\tau &\equiv \int (Pu_n)^* u_m \, d\tau \\ &= \left[\int u_m^* P u_n \, d\tau\right]^*\end{aligned} \tag{13}$$

or

$$(n|P|m) = (m|P|n)^* \tag{14}$$

But

$$\begin{aligned}(n|P|m) &= c_n c_m^* \\ (m|P|n) &= c_m c_n^*\end{aligned} \tag{15}$$

so that Eq. (14) is satisfied.

Often we shall be concerned with problems in which we wish to compute the average expectation value of an ensemble of systems. The matrix elements $c_n c_m^*$ will then vary from system to system to the extent that they have differing wave functions, but the matrix elements $(m|M_x|n)$ will be the same. If we use a bar to denote an ensemble average, we have, then,

$$\overline{\langle M_x\rangle} = \sum_{n,m} \overline{c_n c_m^*}(m|M_x|n) \tag{16}$$

The quantities $\overline{c_n c_m^*}$ form a matrix, and it is this matrix that we call the "density matrix." We shall consider it to be the matrix of an operator ρ, defined by the equation

$$(n|\rho|m) = \overline{c_n c_m^*} = \overline{(n|P|m)} \tag{17}$$

Since P is an Hermitian operator, it is clear that ρ is as well. Eq. (5) becomes, then,

$$\begin{aligned}\overline{\langle M_x\rangle} &= \sum_{n,m} (n|\rho|m)(m|M_x|n) \\ &= \mathrm{Tr}\rho M_x \\ &= \mathrm{Tr}M_x\rho\end{aligned} \tag{18}$$

For the future, we shall omit the bar indicating an ensemble average to simplify the notation, but of course we realize that whenever the symbol ρ is used, an ensemble average is intended.

Of course the wave function Ψ, describing whatever system we are considering, will develop in time. Since the u_n's are independent of time, the coefficients c_n

must carry the time dependence. It is straightforward to find the differential equation they obey in terms of Hamiltonian $\mathcal{H}$ of the system, since

$$-\frac{\hbar}{i}\frac{\partial \Psi}{\partial t} = \mathcal{H}\Psi \tag{19}$$

which gives, using Eq. (2),

$$-\frac{\hbar}{i}\sum_n \frac{dc_n}{dt} u_n = \sum_n c_n \mathcal{H} u_n$$

We can pick out the equation for one particular coefficient, c_k, by multiplying both sides by u_k^* and integrating:

$$-\frac{\hbar}{i}\frac{dc_k}{dt} = \sum_n c_n (k|\mathcal{H}|n) \tag{20}$$

This equation is the well-known starting point for time-dependent perturbation theory. We can use Eq. (20) to find a differential equation for the matrix elements of the operator P, since

$$\begin{aligned} \frac{d}{dt}(k|P|m) &= \frac{d}{dt}(c_k c_m^*) \qquad (21) \\ &= c_k \frac{dc_m^*}{dt} + \frac{dc_k}{dt} c_m^* \\ &= \frac{i}{\hbar}\sum_n [c_k c_n^* (n|\mathcal{H}|m) - (k|\mathcal{H}|n) c_n c_m^*] \\ &= \frac{i}{\hbar}(k|P\mathcal{H} - \mathcal{H}P|m) \end{aligned}$$

where we have used Eq. (11) for the last step. We can write Eq. (21) in operator form as

$$\frac{dP}{dt} = \frac{i}{\hbar}[P, \mathcal{H}] \tag{22}$$

This equation looks very similar to that of Section 2.3, Eq. (5), for the time derivative of an observable, except for the sign change.

If we perform an ensemble average of the various steps of Eq. (21), assuming $\mathcal{H}$ to be identical for all members of the ensemble, we find a differential equation for the density matrix ρ. Since the averaging simply replaces P by ρ, the equation for ρ is

$$\frac{d\rho}{dt} = \frac{i}{\hbar}[\rho, \mathcal{H}] \tag{23}$$

The density matrix is the quantum mechanical equivalent of the classical density ρ of points in phase space, and Eq. (23) is the quantum mechanical form of Liouville's theorem describing the time rate of change of density at a fixed point in phase space.

In the event that $\mathcal{H}$ is independent of time, we may obtain a formal solution of Eq. (23):

$$\rho(t) = e^{-(i/\hbar)\mathcal{H}t}\rho(0)e^{(i/\hbar)\mathcal{H}t} \tag{24}$$

In terms of functions u_n, which are *eigenfunctions* of the Hamiltonian $\mathcal{H}$, we have, for example,

$$(k|\rho(t)|m) = \int u_k^* e^{-(i/\hbar)\mathcal{H}t}\rho(0)e^{(i/\hbar)\mathcal{H}t}u_m \, d\tau \tag{25}$$

$$= \int (e^{(i/\hbar)\mathcal{H}t}u_k)^*\rho(0)e^{(i/\hbar)\mathcal{H}t}u_m \, d\tau$$

By utilizing the fact that $\mathcal{H}u_m = E_m u_m$, and using the power series expansion of the exponential operator, we get

$$(k|\rho(t)|m) = e^{(i/\hbar)(E_m - E_k)t}(k|\rho(0)|m) \tag{26}$$

for the time-dependent matrix element in terms of the matrix element of ρ at $t = 0$.

So far we have talked about the density matrix without ever exhibiting explicitly an operator for ρ. For the sake of concreteness, we shall do so now. We shall take an example of a spin system in thermal equilibrium at a temperature T. We shall take as our basis states, u_n, the eigenstates of the Hamiltonian of the problem, $\mathcal{H}_0$. The populations of the eigenstates are then given by the Boltzmann factors, giving for the diagonal elements of ρ:

$$\overline{c_m c_m^*} = \frac{e^{-E_m/kT}}{Z} \tag{27}$$

where, as usual,

$$Z = \sum_n e^{-E_n/kT}$$

If we write

$$c_n = |c_n|e^{i\alpha_n}$$

we have that

$$\overline{c_m c_n^*} = \overline{|c_m|\,|c_n|e^{i(\alpha_m - \alpha_n)}} \tag{28}$$

It is customary in statistical mechanics to assume that the phases α_n are statistically independent of the amplitudes $|c_n|$ and that, moreover, α_m or α_n have all values with equal probability. This hypothesis, called the "hypothesis of random phases," causes all the off-diagonal elements of Eq. (28) to vanish. If, for example, we were to compute the average magnetization perpendicular to the static field for a group of non-interacting spins, as we did in Eq. (11) of Section 2.2, the vanishing of the off-diagonal elements of ρ would make the transverse components of magnetization vanish, as they must, of course, for a system to be in thermal equilibrium. More generally, we see from Eq. (26) that the off-diagonal elements of ρ oscillate harmonically in time. If they do not vanish, we expect that there will be some observable property of the system, which will oscillate in time according to Eq. (16). But we should then not have a true thermal equilibrium, since for thermal equilibrium we mean that all properties are independent of time. Therefore we must assume that all the off-diagonal elements vanish. Note, however, from Eq. (26) (which applies to the situation in which the basis functions are eigenfunctions of the Hamiltonian) that if the off-diagonal elements vanish at any one time, they vanish for all time.

We have, therefore,

$$(n|\rho|m) = (\delta_{nm}/Z)e^{-E_n/kT} \tag{29}$$

It is worth noting that the operator for ρ is on a different footing from most other operators such as that for momentum. In the absence of a magnetic field, the latter is always $\hbar\nabla/i$. For a given representation the density matrix may, however, be specified quite arbitrarily, subject only to the conditions that it be Hermitian, that its diagonal elements be greater than or equal to zero, and that they sum to unity. There is therefore no operator known a priori. However, in certain instances the matrix elements $(n|\rho|m)$ can be obtained very simply from a specific operator for ρ. When this is possible, we can use operator methods to calculate properties of the system. We now ask what operator will give the matrix elements of Eq. (29), bearing in mind that the u_n's, and so on, are eigenfunctions of $\mathcal{H}_0$.

Using the fact that

$$e^{-\mathcal{H}_0/kT}u_m = e^{-E_m/kT}u_m \tag{30}$$

(which can be proved from the expansion of the exponentials), we can see readily that the explicit form of ρ is

$$\rho = \frac{1}{Z}\,e^{-\mathcal{H}_0/kT} \tag{31}$$

We can use this expression now to compute the average value of any physical property. Thus suppose we have an ensemble of single spins with spin I, acted on by a static external field. Then $\mathcal{H}_0$ is that of a single spin:

$$\mathcal{H}_0 = -\gamma_n\hbar H_0 I_z \tag{32}$$

We shall illustrate the use of the density matrix to compute the average value of the z-magnetization, $\overline{\langle M_z\rangle}$. It is

$$\begin{aligned}\overline{\langle M_z\rangle} &= \mathrm{Tr} M_z\rho \\ &= \frac{1}{Z}\,\mathrm{Tr} M_z e^{-\mathcal{H}_0/kT}\end{aligned} \tag{33}$$

In the high-temperature approximation we can expand the exponential, keeping only the first terms. By utilizing the fact that $\mathrm{Tr} M_z = 0$, we have

$$\begin{aligned}\overline{\langle M_z\rangle} &= \frac{1}{Z}\,\mathrm{Tr} M_z\left(1 - \frac{\mathcal{H}_0}{kT} + \cdots\right) \\ &\cong \frac{1}{Z}\,\mathrm{Tr}\left(\frac{\gamma_n^2\hbar^2 H_0 I_z^2}{kT}\right)\end{aligned} \tag{34}$$

Now, in the high-temperature limit, $Z = 2I + 1$. Since $\mathrm{Tr} I_z^2 = \frac{1}{3}I(I+1)(2I+1)$, we get

$$\overline{\langle M_z\rangle} = \frac{\gamma_n^2\hbar^2 I(I+1)}{3kT}\,H_0 \tag{35}$$

which we recognize as Curie's law for the magnetization. The density matrix gives, therefore, a convenient and compact way of computing thermal equilibrium properties of a system.

One situation commonly encountered is that of a Hamiltonian consisting of a large time-independent interaction, $\mathcal{H}_0$, and a much smaller but time-dependent term, $\mathcal{H}_1(t)$. The equation of motion of the density matrix is then

$$\frac{d\rho}{dt} = \frac{i}{\hbar}[\rho, \mathcal{H}_0 + \mathcal{H}_1] \tag{36}$$

If $\mathcal{H}_1$ were zero, the solution of Eq. (36) would be

$$\rho(t) = e^{-(i/\hbar)\mathcal{H}_0 t}\rho(0)e^{(i/\hbar)\mathcal{H}_0 t} \tag{37}$$

Let us then define a quantity ρ^* (the star does not mean complex conjugate) by the equation

$$\rho(t) = e^{-(i/\hbar)\mathcal{H}_0 t}\rho^*(t)e^{(i/\hbar)\mathcal{H}_0 t} \tag{38}$$

If, in fact, $\mathcal{H}_1$ were zero, comparison of Eqs. (37) and (38) would show that ρ^* would be a constant. (Note, moreover, that at $t = 0$, ρ^* and ρ are identical.) For small $\mathcal{H}_1$, then, we should expect ρ^* to change slowly in time. Substituting Eq. (38) into the left side of Eq. (36) gives us the differential equation obeyed by ρ^*:

$$-\frac{i}{\hbar}[\mathcal{H}_0, \rho] + e^{-(i/\hbar)\mathcal{H}_0 t}\frac{d\rho^*}{dt}e^{(i/\hbar)\mathcal{H}_0 t} = \frac{i}{\hbar}[\rho, \mathcal{H}_0 + \mathcal{H}_1] \tag{39}$$

We note that the commutator of ρ with $\mathcal{H}_0$ can now be removed from both sides. Then, multiplying from the left by $\exp(i\mathcal{H}_0 t/\hbar)$ and from the right by $\exp(-i\mathcal{H}_0 t/\hbar)$, and defining

$$\mathcal{H}_1^* = e^{i\mathcal{H}_0 t/\hbar}\mathcal{H}_1 e^{-(i/\hbar)\mathcal{H}_0 t} \tag{40}$$

we get, from Eq. (39),

$$\frac{d\rho^*}{dt} = \frac{i}{\hbar}[\rho^*, \mathcal{H}_1^*(t)] \tag{41}$$

Eq. (41) shows us, as we have already remarked, that the operator ρ^* would be constant in time if the perturbation $\mathcal{H}_1$ were set equal to zero.

The transformation of the operator $\mathcal{H}_1$ given by Eq. (40) is a canonical transformation, and the new representation is termed the *interaction representation.* The relationship of ρ and ρ^* is illustrated by considering the expansion of the wave function Ψ in a form:

$$\Psi = \sum_n a_n e^{-(i/\hbar)E_n t}u_n \tag{42}$$

instead of

$$\Psi = \sum_n c_n u_n \tag{43}$$

where the u_n's and E_n's are the eigenfunctions and eigenvalues of the Hamiltonian $\mathcal{H}_0$. In the absence of $\mathcal{H}_1$, the a_n's would then be constant in time. We shall show that the matrix $\overline{a_n a_m^*}$ is simply $(n|\rho^*|m)$. We note first that replacing $\rho(0)$ by ρ^* in Eqs. (24) to (26) gives that

$$(n|\rho^*|m) = e^{(i/\hbar)(E_n - E_m)t}(n|\rho|m) \tag{44}$$

Since Eqs. (42) and (43) give the same Ψ, we must have

$$c_n = a_n e^{-(i/\hbar)E_n t} \tag{45}$$

So that

$$a_n a_m^* = c_n c_m^* e^{(i/\hbar)(E_n - E_m)t} \tag{46}$$

Comparison with Eq. (44) shows that

$$\overline{a_n a_m^*} = (n|\rho^*|m) \qquad \text{Q.E.D.} \tag{47}$$

There is likewise a simple relationship between $(n|\mathcal{H}_1^*|m)$ and $(n|\mathcal{H}_1|m)$. By an argument quite identical to that of Eqs. (24) to (26) we have

$$\begin{aligned}(n|\mathcal{H}_1^*|m) &= \int u_n^* e^{(i/\hbar)\mathcal{H}_0 t} \mathcal{H}_1 e^{-(i/\hbar)\mathcal{H}_0 t} u_m \, d\tau \\ &= e^{(i/\hbar)(E_n - E_m)t} (n|\mathcal{H}_1|m)\end{aligned} \tag{48}$$

Now we proceed to solve the equation of motion for ρ^*, Eq. (41). By integrating from $t = 0$, we have

$$\rho^*(t) = \rho^*(0) + \frac{i}{\hbar} \int_0^t [\rho^*(t'), \mathcal{H}_1^*(t')] \, dt' \tag{49}$$

This has not as yet produced a solution, since $\rho^*(t')$ in the integral is unknown. We can make an approximate solution by replacing $\rho^*(t')$ by $\rho^*(0)$, its value at $t = 0$. This gives us

$$\rho^*(t) = \rho^*(0) + \frac{i}{\hbar} \int_0^t [\rho^*(0), \mathcal{H}_1^*(t')] \, dt' \tag{50}$$

We can make a closer approximation by an iteration procedure, using Eq. (50) to get a better value of $\rho^*(t')$, to put into the integrand of Eq. (49). Thus we find

$$\begin{aligned}\rho^*(t) &= \rho^*(0) + \frac{i}{\hbar} \int_0^t \left[\left(\rho^*(0) + \frac{i}{\hbar} \int_0^{t'} [\rho^*(0), \mathcal{H}_1^*(t'')] \, dt''\right), \mathcal{H}_1^*(t')\right] dt' \\ &= \rho^*(0) + \frac{i}{\hbar} \int_0^t [\rho^*(0), \mathcal{H}_1^*(t')] \, dt' \\ &\qquad + \left(\frac{i}{\hbar}\right)^2 \int_0^t \int_0^{t'} [[\rho^*(0), \mathcal{H}_1^*(t'')], \mathcal{H}_1^*(t')] \, dt' \, dt''\end{aligned} \tag{51}$$

We could continue this iteration procedure. Since each iteration adds a term one power higher in the perturbation $\mathcal{H}_1^*$, the successive iterations are seen to consist of higher and higher perturbation expansions in the interaction $\mathcal{H}_1$. For our purposes, we shall not go higher than the second. Actually, we shall find it most convenient to calculate the derivative of ρ^*. Taking the derivative of Eq. (51) gives

$$\frac{d\rho^*(t)}{dt} = \frac{i}{\hbar} [\rho^*(0), \mathcal{H}_1^*(t)] + \left(\frac{i}{\hbar}\right)^2 \int_0^t [[\rho^*(0), \mathcal{H}_1^*(t')], \mathcal{H}_1^*(t)] \, dt' \tag{52}$$

It is important to note that Eq. (52) is entirely equivalent to ordinary time-dependent perturbation theory carried to second order. However, instead of solving for the behaviors of a_n and a_m, we are solving for the behavior of the products $a_n a_m^*$, which are more directly useful for calculating expectation values.

5·5 DENSITY MATRIX—AN INTRODUCTORY EXAMPLE

Since the formal equations of the density matrix get rather involved, it is a good idea at this point to consider an example that will make the notation more concrete. We shall calculate the probability per second of transitions from a state k to a state m. We consider that only state k is occupied at $t = 0$. This assumption is not necessary, but it has the advantage that, with it $(d/dt)(m|\rho|m)$ is directly the probability per second of a transition.

Thus initially all c_n's are zero except c_k. As a result, at $t = 0$, the only non-vanishing element of the density matrix is $(k|\rho|k)$, which is equal to 1. By using Eq. (44) of the preceding section, we see that

$$\begin{aligned}(n|\rho^*(0)|m) &= (n|\rho(0)|m) \\ &= 0 \quad \text{unless } n = m = k \\ (k|\rho^*(0)|k) &= (k|\rho(0)|k) = 1\end{aligned} \tag{1}$$

Then, taking the mm matrix element of Eq. (52) of the preceding section, and using Eq. (44) also, we have

$$\begin{aligned}\frac{d}{dt}(m|\rho^*(t)|m) &= \frac{d}{dt}(m|\rho|m) \\ &= \frac{i}{\hbar}\sum_n [\underbrace{(m|\rho^*(0)|n)(n|\mathcal{H}_1^*|m)}_{A} \\ &\quad - \underbrace{(m|\mathcal{H}_1^*|n)(n|\rho^*(0)|m)]}_{B} \\ &\quad + \left(\frac{i}{\hbar}\right)^2 \int_0^t \underbrace{(m|[\rho^*(0)\mathcal{H}_1^*(t')\mathcal{H}_1^*(t)}_{C} \\ &\quad - \underbrace{\mathcal{H}_1^*(t')\rho^*(0)\mathcal{H}_1^*(t)}_{D} \\ &\quad - \underbrace{\mathcal{H}_1^*(t)\rho^*(0)\mathcal{H}_1^*(t')}_{E} \\ &\quad + \underbrace{\mathcal{H}_1^*(t)\mathcal{H}_1^*(t')\rho^*(0)]|m)}_{F}\, dt'\end{aligned} \tag{2}$$

We consider first the terms A and B. Since $m \neq k$ (the transition is between two distinct states), A and B both vanish according to Eq. (1). To treat terms such as C, we write

$$(m|\rho^*(0)\mathcal{H}_1^*(t')\mathcal{H}_1^*(t)|m) = \sum_{m'} (m|\rho^*(0)|m')(m'|\mathcal{H}_1^*(t')\mathcal{H}_1^*(t)|m)$$

Since

$$(m|\rho^*(0)|m') = 0 \ (m \neq k)$$

the terms C and F vanish, leaving

$$\frac{d}{dt}(m|\rho|m) = \frac{1}{\hbar^2}\int_0^t [(m|\mathcal{H}_1^*(t')|k)(k|\mathcal{H}_1^*(t)|m) + (m|\mathcal{H}_1^*(t)|k)(k|\mathcal{H}_1^*(t')|m)]\,dt' \tag{3}$$

We convert the matrix elements in the integrand by Eq. (48) of the preceding section:

$$(m|\mathcal{H}_1^*(t)|n) = e^{(i/\hbar)(E_m-E_n)t}(m|\mathcal{H}_1(t)|n) \tag{4}$$

We shall also adopt a convenient abbreviation. We shall define the quantum numbers m, n, and so on in terms of the corresponding energies, measured in radians per second:

$$\frac{E_m}{\hbar} \equiv m \qquad \frac{E_k}{\hbar} \equiv k \qquad \text{etc.} \tag{5}$$

Then we have, using Eqs. (4) and (5),

$$\frac{d}{dt}(m|\rho|m) = \frac{1}{\hbar^2}\int_0^t [(m|\mathcal{H}_1(t')|k)(k|\mathcal{H}_1(t)|m)e^{i(m-k)(t'-t)} + (m|\mathcal{H}_1(t)|k)(k|\mathcal{H}_1(t')|m)e^{i(m-k)(t-t')}]\,dt' \tag{6}$$

So far, our equations have been quite general as to the nature of the perturbation $\mathcal{H}_1(t)$. For example, it could vary sinusoidally in time. We shall assume for our example, however, that $\mathcal{H}_1(t)$ varies randomly in time. By this we mean that we shall consider a number of ensembles of systems of identical $\mathcal{H}_0$ and identical $\rho(0)$. However, we shall consider that $\mathcal{H}_1(t)$ varies from ensemble to ensemble, with properties described below. We shall therefore perform an average of the ensembles. We denote this average by a bar. Then

$$\frac{d}{dt}\overline{(m|\rho|m)} = \frac{1}{\hbar^2}\int_0^t [\overline{(m|\mathcal{H}_1(t')|k)(k|\mathcal{H}_1(t)|m)}e^{i(m-k)(t'-t)} + \overline{(m|\mathcal{H}_1(t)|k)(k|\mathcal{H}_1(t')|m)}e^{i(m-k)(t-t')}]\,dt' \tag{7}$$

As an example, suppose $\mathcal{H}_1(t)$ were the dipolar coupling between nuclear moments in a liquid. It might vary in time, owing to the thermal motion of nuclei in the liquid. These motions would in general be different among various parts of the fluid, all at the same temperature. We shall assume, moreover, that the ensemble average, such as

$$\overline{(m|\mathcal{H}_1(t')|k)(k|\mathcal{H}_1(t)|m)} \tag{8}$$

depends on t and t' *only* through their difference τ, defined by

$$t - t' = \tau \tag{9}$$

That is, we assume

$$\overline{(m|\mathcal{H}_1(t-\tau)|k)(k|\mathcal{H}_1(t)|m)} \tag{10}$$

is independent of t but is a function both of τ and of the pair of levels, m and k, with which we are concerned. The fact that Eq. (1) is independent of t is expressed by the statement that the perturbation is stationary. (A more complex case could be handled, but it would make everything much more complicated.) The dependence on τ, m, and k leads us to define a quantity $G_{mk}(\tau)$ by the equation

$$G_{mk}(\tau) = \overline{(m|\mathcal{H}_1(t - \tau)|k)(k|\mathcal{H}_1(t)|m)} \tag{11}$$

Since $\mathcal{H}_1(t)$ is a stationary perturbation, we have that

$$\begin{aligned} G_{mk}(\tau) &= \overline{(m|\mathcal{H}_1(t)|k)(k|\mathcal{H}_1(t + \tau)|m)} \\ &= \overline{(k|\mathcal{H}_1(t + \tau)|m)(m|\mathcal{H}_1(t)|k)} \\ &= G_{km}(-\tau) \end{aligned} \tag{12}$$

The function $G_{mk}(\tau)$ is called the "correlation function" of $\mathcal{H}_1(t)$, since it tells how $\mathcal{H}_1$ at one time is correlated to its value at a later time. For a typical perturbation we have

$$\overline{(k|\mathcal{H}_1(t)|m)} = 0 \tag{13}$$

Thus, if $\mathcal{H}_1(t)$ and $\mathcal{H}_1(t + \tau)$ were unrelated, we could average the two terms in the product separately, getting

$$G_{mk}(\tau) = \overline{(k|\mathcal{H}_1(t)|m)}\ \overline{(m|\mathcal{H}_1(t + \tau)|k)} = 0 \tag{14}$$

However, we have, for $\tau = 0$,

$$G_{mk}(0) = |\overline{(k|\mathcal{H}_1(t)|m)}|^2 \geq 0 \tag{15}$$

For typical physical systems, the perturbation $\mathcal{H}_1(t)$ varies in time, owing to some physical movement. For times less than some critical time, τ_c, called the "correlation time," the motion may be considered negligible, so that $\mathcal{H}_1(t) \cong \mathcal{H}_1(t + \tau)$. For $\tau > \tau_c$, the values of $\mathcal{H}_1(t+\tau)$ become progressively less correlated to $\mathcal{H}_1(t)$ as

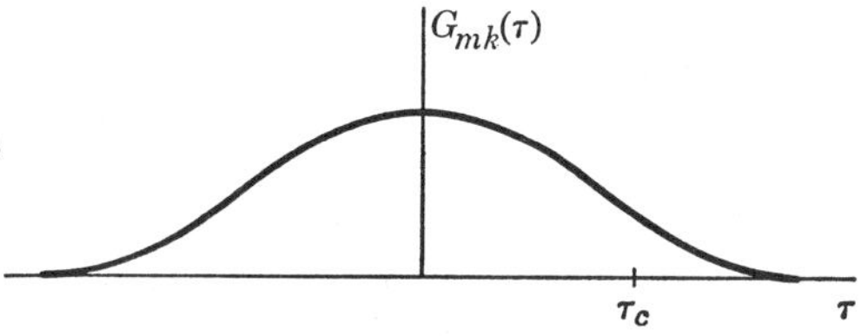

FIG. 5.4. Function $G_{mk}(\tau)$ for a typical physical system.

τ is lengthened, so that G_{km} goes to zero. Thus $G_{mk}(\tau)$ has a maximum at $\tau = 0$, and falls off for $|\tau| > \tau_c$, as in Fig. 5.4. A function $\mathcal{H}_1(t)$ with the above properties will be called a "stationary random function of time."

Bearing in mind these properties, we now rewrite Eq. (7) in terms of $G_{mk}(\tau)$:

$$\begin{aligned} \frac{d}{dt}(m|\rho|m) &= \frac{1}{\hbar^2}\int_0^t [G_{mk}(\tau)e^{-i(m-k)\tau} + G_{mk}(-\tau)e^{i(m-k)\tau}]\, d\tau \\ &= \frac{1}{\hbar^2}\int_{-t}^{t} G_{mk}(\tau)e^{-i(m-k)\tau}\, d\tau \end{aligned} \tag{16}$$

This equation tells us the rate of change of $(m|\rho|m)$ at a variable time t. We now note that if $t \gg \tau_c$, the limits of integration may be taken as $\pm\infty$, so that

$(d/dt)(m|\rho|m)$ becomes independent of time. There is a range of $0 < t < \tau_c$ for which the transition rate is not constant. And, of course, if $(m|\rho|m)$ becomes comparable to unity, we do not expect our perturbation approximation to hold, since the initial population $(k|\rho|k)$ would necessarily be strongly depleted.

We shall now confine our attention to times longer than τ_c, assuming that for them $(m|\rho|m)$ has not grown unduly. Then we have

$$\frac{d}{dt}(m|\rho|m) = \frac{1}{\hbar^2}\int_{-\infty}^{+\infty} G_{mk}(\tau)e^{-i(m-k)\tau}\,d\tau \qquad (17)$$
$$\equiv W_{km}$$

where W_{km} is the probability per second of a transition from state k to m.

Equation (17) is closely related to the well-known result from time-dependent perturbation theory:

$$W_{km} = \frac{2\pi}{\hbar}|(k|V|m)|^2\rho(E_f)$$

where $(k|V|m)$ is the matrix element of the interaction between states k and m, and $\rho(E_f)$ is the density of final states in energy. In fact, by utilizing Eq. (11) we see that W_{km} of Eq. (16) involves a product of two matrix elements of the perturbation. In the present case the energy levels are sharp, but the perturbation is spread in frequency, whereas the usual time-dependent perturbation is monochromatic, but the energy levels are smeared. In view of the similarity to the usual time-dependent theory, we are not surprised that the terms A and B of Eq. (2), which involve only one matrix element of the perturbation, vanish.

The integral of Eq. (17) is reminiscent of a Fourier transform. Let us then define a quantity $J_{mk}(\omega)$ by the equation

$$J_{mk}(\omega) = \int_{-\infty}^{+\infty} G_{mk}(\tau)e^{-i\omega\tau}\,d\tau \qquad (18)$$

with the inverse relation

$$G_{mk}(\tau) = \frac{1}{2\pi}\int_{-\infty}^{+\infty} J_{mk}(\omega)e^{i\omega\tau}\,d\omega \qquad (19)$$

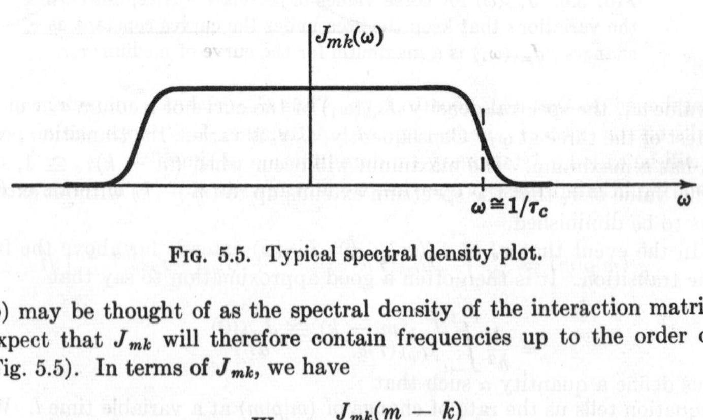

FIG. 5.5. Typical spectral density plot.

$J_{mk}(\omega)$ may be thought of as the spectral density of the interaction matrix G_{mk}. We expect that J_{mk} will therefore contain frequencies up to the order of $1/\tau_c$ (see Fig. 5.5). In terms of J_{mk}, we have

$$W_{km} = \frac{J_{mk}(m-k)}{\hbar^2} \qquad (17a)$$

Now, in a typical case, the interaction matrix element $(m|\mathcal{H}_1(t)|k)$ runs over a set of values as time goes on. As one varies something such as the temperature, the *rate* at which $(m|\mathcal{H}_1(t)|k)$ changes may speed up or slow down (τ_c changes), but the set of values covered remains unchanged. As a physical example, the dipole-dipole coupling of a pair of nuclei depends on their relative positions. If the nuclei diffuse relative to each other, the coupling takes on different values. The possible values are independent of the rate of diffusion, since they depend only on the radius vector from one nucleus to the other and on the spatial orientation of the moments. However, the duration of any magnitude of interaction will depend on the rate of diffusion. Then we have that

$$\overline{|(m|\mathcal{H}_1(t)|k)|^2} = G_{mk}(0) \tag{20}$$

is independent of τ_c. But, from Eq. (19),

$$G_{mk}(0) = \frac{1}{2\pi}\int_{-\infty}^{+\infty} J_{mk}(\omega)\,d\omega \tag{20a}$$

which tells us that the area of the spectral density curve remains *fixed* as τ_c varies. A set of curves of $J_{mk}(\omega)$ for three different τ_c's is shown in Fig. 5.6. A simple consequence of the fact that the area remains fixed as τ_c varies is found by considering Fig. 5.6. We note that if the frequency difference $m - k$ were equal to

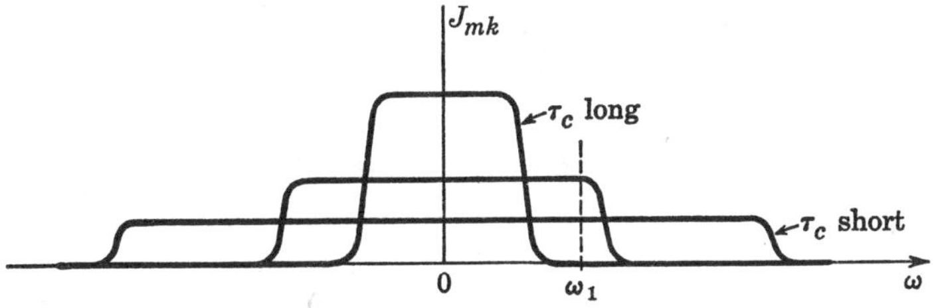

FIG. 5.6. $J_{mk}(\omega)$ for three values of correlation time, illustrating the variations that keep the area under the curves constant as τ_c changes. $J_{mk}(\omega_1)$ is a maximum for the curve of medium τ_c.

the value ω_1, the spectral density $J_{mk}(\omega_1)$ of the curve of medium τ_c would be the greatest of the three at ω_1. Consequently, as τ_c is varied, the transition probability W_{km} has a maximum. The maximum will occur when $(m - k)\tau_c \cong 1$, since it is for this value of τ_c that the spectrum extends up to $(m - k)$ without extending so far as to be diminished.

In the event that $\tau_c \ll 1/(m - k)$, $J_{mk}(\omega)$ extends far above the frequency of the transition. It is then often a good approximation to say that

$$J_{mk}(m - k) \cong J_{mk}(0) \tag{21}$$

Let us define a quantity α such that

$$2\left(\frac{\alpha}{\tau_c}\right) J_{mk}(0) = \int_{-\infty}^{+\infty} J_{mk}(\omega)\,d\omega \tag{22}$$

where $2(\alpha/\tau_c)$ is the width of a rectangular $J_{mk}(\omega)$ whose height is $J_{mk}(0)$ and whose area is the same as that of the real $J_{mk}(\omega)$. From our remarks, $\alpha \cong 1$. Then we have, combining Eqs. (20), (20a), and (22),

$$J_{mk}(0) = \frac{\tau_c}{2\alpha} 2\pi \overline{|(m|\mathcal{H}_1(t)|k)|^2} \tag{23}$$

By utilizing Eqs. (17a) and (21), then, we have

$$W_{km} = \frac{\overline{|(m|\mathcal{H}_1(t)|k)|^2}}{\hbar^2} \frac{\pi}{\alpha} \tau_c \tag{24}$$

which holds for $\tau_c \ll 1/(m - k)$.

Since one can often estimate the mean squared interaction as well as the correlation time, Eq. (24) provides a very simple method of computing the transition probability in the limit of short correlation time (rapid motion). As a side remark, we note that for a flat spectrum $J_{mk}(\omega)$, Eq. (24) will hold approximately for all $\tau_c \leq 1/(m - k)$. We can use it to estimate roughly the *maximum* rate of transition that $\mathcal{H}_1(t)$ is capable of producing under the most favorable circumstances, by noting that this occurs when $\tau_c \cong 1/(m - k)$. We get the approximate relation, then,

$$W_{km})_{\max} \cong \frac{\overline{|(m|\mathcal{H}_1(t)|k)|^2}}{\hbar^2} \frac{\pi}{\alpha(m - k)} \tag{25}$$

Our remarks so far apply to many forms of interaction $\mathcal{H}_1(t)$. In order to be more concrete, we now specialize, to consider a particular form for the interaction $\mathcal{H}_1(t)$. We shall assume that it consists of a fluctuating magnetic field with x-, y-, and z-components that couple to the components of the nuclear moment:

$$\begin{aligned} \mathcal{H}_1(t) &= -\gamma_n\hbar[H_x(t)I_x + H_y(t)I_y + H_z(t)I_z] \\ &= -\gamma_n\hbar \sum_{q=x,y,z} H_q(t)I_q \end{aligned} \tag{26}$$

Then

$$\begin{aligned} G_{mk}(\tau) &= \overline{(m|\mathcal{H}_1(t)|k)(k|\mathcal{H}_1(t+\tau)|m)} \\ &= \gamma_n^2\hbar^2 \sum_{q,q'} (m|I_q|k)(k|I_{q'}|m)\overline{H_q(t)H_{q'}(t+\tau)} \end{aligned} \tag{27}$$

where we have recognized that it is $H_q(t)$ that varies from one member of the ensemble to another. For simplicity we shall suppose that the x-, y-, and z-components of field fluctuate independently. This means in effect that knowledge of H_x at some time is not sufficient to predict H_y at that time. With this assumption, we get in Eq. (27) only terms for which $q = q'$. Let us define

$$j^q_{mk}(\omega) = \gamma_n^2\hbar^2|(m|I_q|k)|^2 \int_{-\infty}^{+\infty} \overline{H_q(t)H_q(t+\tau)}e^{-i\omega\tau}\,d\tau \tag{28}$$

Then we have

$$W_{km} = \frac{1}{\hbar^2} \sum_q j^q_{mk}(m - k) \tag{29}$$

Evaluation of $j^q_{mk}(\omega)$ requires information on the physical basis of the field fluctuation. Moreover, even when one possesses that information, the mathematical problem of finding the correlation function may still be too difficult to solve. One can then often assume a function that, on general physical grounds, has about the correct behavior. For certain simple cases one can actually compute the correlation function. One such case arises when the field $H_q(\tau)$ takes on either of two values and makes transitions from one value to the other at a rate that is independent of the time since the preceding transition. Assuming the field takes on values of $\pm h_q$, we show in Appendix C that

$$\overline{H_q(t)H_q(t+\tau)} = h_q^2 e^{-|\tau|/\tau_0} \tag{30}$$

where τ_0 is time defined by Eq. (31) in terms of the probability per second, W, that $H_q(\tau)$ will jump from $+h_q$ to $-h_q$:

$$\frac{1}{\tau_0} = 2W \tag{31}$$

We assume for our example that this time is the same for all three components of field. Clearly τ_0 may be taken as the correlation time.† Substituting this form into Eq. (28), we find

$$j_{mk}^q(\omega) = \gamma_n^2\hbar^2|(k|I_q|m)|^2 h_q^2 \frac{2\tau_0}{1+\omega^2\tau_0^2} \tag{32}$$

The transition probability W_{km} is then

$$W_{km} = \left[\sum_q \gamma_n^2 h_q^2 |(m|I_q|k)|^2\right] \frac{2\tau_0}{1+(m-k)^2\tau_0^2} \tag{33}$$

It is interesting to apply this formula to compute the T_1 for the case of spin $\frac{1}{2}$. For this case, as we saw in Chapter 1,

$$\frac{1}{T_1} = 2W_{1/2,-1/2} \tag{34}$$

Assuming a strong static field in the z-direction, the matrix elements between the levels are

$$\begin{aligned} |(\tfrac{1}{2}|I_x|-\tfrac{1}{2})|^2 &= \tfrac{1}{4} \\ |(\tfrac{1}{2}|I_y|-\tfrac{1}{2})|^2 &= \tfrac{1}{4} \\ |(\tfrac{1}{2}|I_z|-\tfrac{1}{2})|^2 &= 0 \end{aligned} \tag{35}$$

We shall assume $h_x = h_y = h_z$, so that

$$h_x^2 = \tfrac{1}{3}h_0^2 \tag{36}$$

where $h_0^2 = h_x^2 + h_y^2 + h_z^2$. Then, since $m - k = \omega_0$, the Larmor frequency

$$\frac{1}{T_1} = 2\gamma_n^2 \frac{h_0^2}{3} \frac{\tau_0}{1+\omega_0^2\tau_0^2} \tag{37}$$

† Note that although we have not given a precise definition of the correlation time, once the correlation function is specified, there is always a precisely defined parameter (in this case τ_0) that enters the problem and characterizes the time scale.

This function is plotted in Fig. 5.7. We see that it indeed has the sort of variation we had predicted earlier from our general arguments based on the "constant area" under the curve of $J_{mk}(\omega)$. We note that the minimum comes when $\omega_0\tau_0 = 1$.

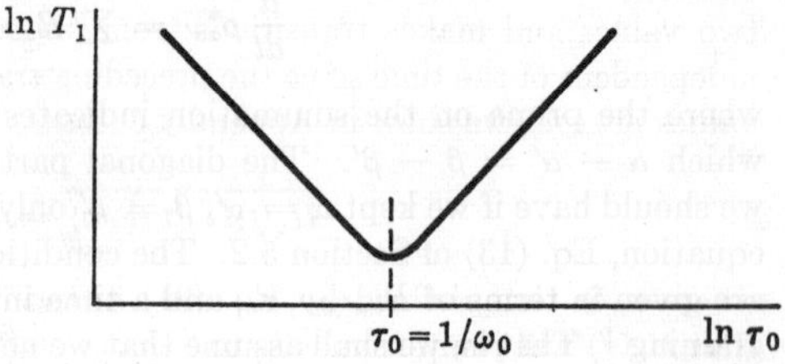

FIG. 5.7. Variation of T_1 with the correlation time τ_0.

By utilizing this fact, we can calculate the minimum value of T_1 from Eq. (37) and obtain, in agreement with Eq. (25),

$$\left.\frac{1}{T_1}\right)_{\min} = \frac{1}{3}\frac{\gamma_n^2 h_0^2}{\omega_0} \tag{38}$$

Now, when τ_0 gets very long, the field H_z simply gives rise to a static line broadening (in this case, since only two discrete values can occur, the static line consists of a pair of lines at $\pm h_z$) and h_0^2 is simply related to this static width. Of course ω_0 is known for a typical experiment. Equation (38) therefore tells us the remarkable fact that knowledge of the rigid lattice line breadth, plus the resonant frequency, enables us to compute the most effective relaxation possible from allowing the line broadening interaction to fluctuate. In general the correlation time is changed by changing the temperature of the sample. Although Eq. (38) enables us to predict the minimum value of T_1, it cannot tell us at what temperature the minimum will occur unless, of course, we *know* the dependence of τ_0 on temperature. We note in addition that the measurement of T_1 as a function of temperature can provide information about the temperature variation of whatever physical process produces the fluctuations.

5·6 BLOCH-WANGSNESS-REDFIELD THEORY

We turn now to a more general treatment of the density matrix, following the ideas of Redfield,† which are closely related to a treatment of relaxation due to Wangsness and Bloch.†† All of the basic ideas are anticipated physically in the basic work of Bloembergen, Purcell, and Pound.§ The development of the basic equation of Redfield's theory is a generalization of the treatment given in the previous section for computing transition probabilities. Redfield shows that the elements of the density matrix obey a set of linear differential equations of the following form§§:

$$\frac{d}{dt}\rho^*_{\alpha\alpha'} = \sum_{\beta,\beta'} R_{\alpha\alpha',\beta\beta'} e^{i(\alpha-\alpha'-\beta+\beta')t}\rho^*_{\beta\beta'} \tag{1}$$

† A. G. Redfield, *IBM J. Research Develop.*, **1**: 19(1957).

†† R. K. Wangsness and F. Bloch, *Phys. Rev.*, **89**: 728(1953) and F. Bloch, *Phys. Rev.*, **102**: 104(1956).

§ N. Bloembergen, E. M. Purcell, and R. V. Pound, *Phys. Rev.*, **73**: 679(1948).

§§ For compactness in writing, we use the notation $\rho_{\alpha\alpha'}$ for the matrix element $(\alpha|\rho|\alpha')$.

where $R_{\alpha\alpha',\beta\beta'}$ is constant in time. In this equation the time-dependent exponential has the property of making any terms unimportant unless $\alpha - \alpha' = \beta - \beta'$. Therefore we could write Eq. (1) as

$$\frac{d}{dt}\rho^*_{\alpha\alpha'} = \sum{}' R_{\alpha\alpha',\beta\beta'}\rho^*_{\beta\beta'} \tag{2}$$

where the prime on the summation indicates that we keep only those terms for which $\alpha - \alpha' = \beta - \beta'$. The diagonal part of this equation (that is, the part we should have if we kept $\alpha = \alpha'$, $\beta = \beta'$ only) has the same form as the "master" equation, Eq. (13) of Section 5.2. The conditions under which Eqs. (1) or (2) hold are given in terms of $R_{\alpha\alpha',\beta\beta'}$, τ_c, and a time interval Δt. Δt defines a sort of "coarse graining." That is, we shall assume that we never try to follow the details of ρ^* for time intervals *less* than Δt. We must be able to choose such a time, subject to the simultaneous conditions that

$$\Delta t \gg \tau_c \tag{3}$$

and

$$\frac{1}{R_{\alpha\alpha',\beta\beta'}} \gg \Delta t \tag{4}$$

Eq. (3) will permit us to set the limits of certain integrals as $\pm\infty$, as we did in Eq. (17) of the preceding section. Equation (4) will guarantee that, during Δt, the density matrix does not change too drastically, so that our perturbation expansion has validity. Since the $R_{\alpha\alpha',\beta\beta'}$'s are comparable to the inverse of the relaxation times, these conditions are equivalent to saying that T_1 and T_2 are much longer than τ_c. These are also the conditions of motional narrowing. The reader will perhaps note that these are the very conditions stated in Section 2.10, which must hold if simple time-independent transition probabilities are to hold. What we are doing here is to generalize the usual time-dependent perturbation theory so that it includes the coherence effects associated with phase factors in the wave function.

The beauty of Eq. (2) is that it provides us with a simple set of linear differential equations among the elements of the density matrix, which in principle we can always solve. They will lead to a set of "normal modes." We note that there is a great deal of similarity to the rate equation describing population changes. Moreover, expressions for the $R_{\alpha\alpha'\beta\beta'}$'s are given by Redfield's theory, so that we have the relaxation times given in terms of the atomic properties.

Before outlining the derivation of Eqs. (1) and (2), we remark that there are two ways of utilizing Eqs. (1) or (2). In the first method one solves for the behavior of each separate element of the density matrix and then computes the time dependence of the physical variables of interest (such as the x-components of magnetization M_x) by the fundamental equation:

$$\overline{\langle M_x \rangle} = \sum_{\alpha,\alpha'} \rho_{\alpha\alpha'}(\alpha'|M_x|\alpha) \tag{5}$$

The second method involves seeking a differential equation for $\overline{\langle M_x \rangle}$. One does this by writing

$$\frac{d}{dt}\overline{\langle M_x \rangle} = \frac{d}{dt}\sum_{\alpha,\alpha'} \rho_{\alpha\alpha'}(\alpha'|M_x|\alpha) \tag{6}$$

$$= \sum_{\alpha,\alpha'} \left(\frac{d\rho_{\alpha\alpha'}}{dt}\right)(\alpha'|M_x|\alpha)$$

We then use Eq. (1) to express the time derivative $(d/dt)\rho_{\alpha\alpha'}$. In fact, since

$$\rho^*_{\alpha\alpha'} = e^{i(\alpha-\alpha')t}\rho_{\alpha\alpha'} \tag{7}$$

we have

$$\frac{d\rho^*_{\alpha\alpha'}}{dt} = i(\alpha - \alpha')\rho^*_{\alpha\alpha'} + e^{i(\alpha-\alpha')t}\frac{d\rho_{\alpha\alpha'}}{dt} \tag{8}$$

This relation enables us to transform Eq. (1). By substituting into Eq. (1) and utilizing Eq. (7), we find

$$\begin{aligned}\frac{d\rho_{\alpha\alpha'}}{dt} &= i(\alpha' - \alpha)\rho_{\alpha\alpha'} + \sum_{\beta,\beta'} R_{\alpha\alpha',\beta\beta'}\rho_{\beta\beta'} \\ &= \frac{i}{\hbar}[\rho, \mathcal{H}_0]_{\alpha\alpha'} + \sum_{\beta,\beta'} R_{\alpha\alpha',\beta\beta'}\rho_{\beta\beta'}\end{aligned} \tag{9}$$

We then substitute this expression into Eq. (6), obtaining

$$\frac{d\overline{\langle M_x\rangle}}{dt} = \sum_{\substack{\alpha,\alpha'\\ \beta,\beta'}} \left\{\frac{i}{\hbar}[\rho, \mathcal{H}_0]_{\alpha\alpha'} + R_{\alpha\alpha',\beta\beta'}\rho_{\beta\beta'}\right\}(\alpha'|M_x|\alpha) \tag{10}$$

Although it is not obvious from Eq. (10), under some circumstances the right-hand side is proportional to a linear combination of $\overline{\langle M_x(t)\rangle}$, $\overline{\langle M_y(t)\rangle}$, and $\overline{\langle M_z(t)\rangle}$, giving us a set of differential equations similar to those of Bloch. If these equations are fewer in number than are the equations of the elements of the density matrix, their solution may be considerably simpler than the original set. This trick will work when the relaxation mechanism and operators are such that the expectation values of the operators pick out only a small number of the possible normal modes. We shall illustrate this use of Eq. (10) shortly. First, however, we turn to a description of the derivation of Redfield's fundamental equation.

Our starting point is the basic equation for the time derivative of ρ^*, Eq. (52) of Section 5.4:

$$\frac{d\rho^*}{dt} = \frac{i}{\hbar}[\rho^*(0), \mathcal{H}_1^*(t)] + \left(\frac{i}{\hbar}\right)^2 \int_0^t [[\rho^*(0), \mathcal{H}_1^*(t')], \mathcal{H}_1^*(t)]\, dt' \tag{11}$$

We compute the $\alpha\alpha'$ matrix element. There will be contributions from both terms on the right. We consider first the contribution of $[\rho^*(0), \mathcal{H}_1^*(t)]$:

$$\begin{aligned}(\alpha|[\rho^*(0), \mathcal{H}_1^*(t)]|\alpha') = \sum_\beta &(\alpha|\rho^*(0)|\beta)(\beta|\mathcal{H}_1^*(t)|\alpha') \\ &- (\alpha|\mathcal{H}_1^*(t)|\beta)(\beta|\rho^*(0)|\alpha')\end{aligned} \tag{12}$$

We shall now introduce the idea of an ensemble of ensembles whose density matrix coincides at $t = 0$ but whose perturbations $\mathcal{H}_1(t)$ are different. (We are therefore *not* allowing an applied alternating field to be present. That is, we are describing relaxation in the absence of an alternating field. One could add the effect of the alternating field readily. We discuss it in the next section.) We shall assume that the ensemble average of $\mathcal{H}_1(t)$ vanishes. This amounts to our assuming that $\mathcal{H}_1(t)$ does not produce an average frequency shift.†

---

† If there *is* a shift, we can *include* the average shift in $\mathcal{H}_0$, redefining $\mathcal{H}_1(t)$ to give a zero shift.

Let us discuss this point. In general we expect

$$\mathcal{H}_1(t) = \sum_q H_q(t) K^q \tag{13}$$

where K^q is a function of the spin coordinates, and $H_q(t)$ is independent of spin. For example, we saw that $\mathcal{H}_1(t)$ had this form if it consisted of the coupling of a fluctuating magnetic field with the x-, y-, or z-components of spin. In that case q took on three values corresponding to the three components x, y, and z. If $\mathcal{H}_1(t)$ represented the dipole-dipole interaction of two spins, there would be six values of q corresponding to the terms $A, B, \cdots, F$ into which we broke the dipolar coupling in Chapter 3.

Since we are dealing with stationary perturbations, the ensemble average of $\mathcal{H}_1^*(t)$ is equivalent to a time average. In general we assume that the time average of $H_q(t)$ vanishes, causing $\mathcal{H}_1^*(t)$ to have a vanishing ensemble average. As a consequence we shall set

$$\overline{(\alpha|\mathcal{H}_1^*(t)|\beta)} = 0 \tag{14}$$

where the bar indicates an ensemble average. This means, as we have remarked, that we cannot let $\mathcal{H}_1(t)$ be a time-dependent driving field such as that applied to observe a resonance.

On the basis of Eq. (14) the first term on the right of Eq. (11) vanishes when averaged over an ensemble.

We proceed in a similar way to compute the $\alpha\alpha'$ matrix element of the second term on the right of Eq. (11). By utilizing the fact that

$$(\beta|\mathcal{H}_1^*(t)|\beta') = e^{i(\beta-\beta')t}(\beta|\mathcal{H}_1(t)|\beta') \tag{15}$$

and defining

$$\tau = t - t' \tag{16}$$

we find

$$\begin{aligned}\frac{d\rho^*_{\alpha\alpha'}}{dt} = \frac{1}{\hbar^2}\sum_{\beta,\beta'}\int_0^t [&(\alpha|\mathcal{H}_1(t-\tau)|\beta)(\beta'|\mathcal{H}_1(t)|\alpha')e^{-i(\alpha-\beta)\tau}e^{i(\alpha-\beta+\beta'-\alpha')t}\rho^*_{\beta\beta'} \\ &+ (\alpha|\mathcal{H}_1(t)|\beta)(\beta'|\mathcal{H}_1(t-\tau)|\alpha')e^{i(\alpha'-\beta')\tau}e^{i(\alpha-\beta+\beta'-\alpha')t}\rho^*_{\beta\beta'} \\ &- \rho^*_{\alpha\beta}(\beta|\mathcal{H}_1(t-\tau)|\beta')(\beta'|\mathcal{H}_1(t)|\alpha')e^{i(\beta'-\beta)\tau}e^{i(\beta-\alpha')t} \\ &- (\alpha|\mathcal{H}_1(t)|\beta)(\beta|\mathcal{H}_1(t-\tau)|\beta')e^{i(\beta'-\beta)\tau}e^{i(\alpha-\beta')t}\rho^*_{\beta'\alpha'}]\,d\tau\end{aligned} \tag{17}$$

We now perform an average over ensembles of differing $\mathcal{H}_1(t)$, obtaining such terms as

$$\frac{1}{\hbar^2}\int_0^t \overline{(\alpha|\mathcal{H}_1(t-\tau)|\beta)(\beta'|\mathcal{H}_1(t)|\alpha')}e^{-i(\alpha-\beta)\tau}e^{i(\alpha-\beta+\beta'-\alpha')t}\,d\tau \tag{18}$$

We assume that the average,

$$\overline{(\alpha|\mathcal{H}_1(t-\tau)|\beta)(\beta'|\mathcal{H}_1(t)|\alpha')} \tag{19}$$

is independent of t and goes to zero when τ exceeds some critical value τ_c. In this case we can consider times t greater than τ_c, permitting us to extend the upper limits of integration to $\tau = +\infty$.

We now define the correlation function $G_{\alpha\beta\alpha'\beta'}(\tau)$ as

$$G_{\alpha\beta\alpha'\beta'}(\tau) \equiv \overline{(\alpha|\mathcal{H}_1(t)|\beta)(\beta'|\mathcal{H}_1(t+\tau)|\alpha')} \tag{20}$$

By utilizing Eq. (13), we have that

$$G_{\alpha\beta\alpha'\beta'}(\tau) = \sum_{q,q'} (\alpha|K^q|\beta)(\beta'|K^{q'}|\alpha')\overline{H_q(t)H_{q'}(t+\tau)} \tag{21}$$

We then define the spectral density $L_{qq'}(\omega)$ of the interaction as

$$L_{qq'}(\omega) \equiv \int_0^{\infty} \overline{H_q(t)H_{q'}(t+\tau)}e^{-i\omega\tau}\, d\tau \tag{22}$$

By utilizing the fact that $\overline{H_q(t)H_{q'}(t+\tau)}$ is real† and is an even function of τ, it is convenient to define the real and imaginary parts $L_{qq'}(\omega)$:

$$\begin{aligned} \mathrm{Re}L_{qq'}(\omega) &= \tfrac{1}{2}\int_{-\infty}^{+\infty} \overline{H_q(t)H_{q'}(t+\tau)} \cos\omega\tau\, d\tau \equiv k_{qq'} \\ \mathrm{Im}L_{qq'}(\omega) &= -\int_0^{\infty} \overline{H_q(t)H_{q'}(t+\tau)} \sin\omega\tau\, d\tau \end{aligned} \tag{23}$$

Since the only important contributions to Eq. (17) come from terms that satisfy the condition $\alpha - \alpha' = \beta - \beta'$, we can combine the first two terms on the right of Eq. (17) as

$$\frac{1}{\hbar^2}\left[\sum_{\beta,\beta'}\sum_{q,q'} \{(\alpha|K^q|\beta)(\beta'|K^{q'}|\alpha')[k_{qq'}(\alpha-\beta) + k_{qq'}(\alpha'-\beta')]e^{i(\alpha-\beta+\beta'-\alpha')t}\rho^*_{\beta\beta'}\}\right. \tag{24}$$

The last two terms of Eq. (17) are

$$\begin{aligned} \frac{1}{\hbar^2}\sum_{\substack{\beta,\beta'\\ q,q'}} \{&\rho^*_{\alpha\beta}[(\beta|K^q|\beta')(\beta'|K^{q'}|\alpha')L_{qq'}(\beta-\beta')]e^{i(\beta-\alpha')t} \\ &+ \rho^*_{\beta'\alpha'}[(\beta|K^q|\beta')(\alpha|K^{q'}|\beta)L_{qq'}(\beta-\beta')]e^{i(\alpha-\beta')t}\} \end{aligned} \tag{25}$$

The imaginary part of $L_{qq'}$ can be shown to give rise to a frequency shift corresponding to the second-order frequency shift of a static interaction.

We shall neglect this effect, keeping only terms proportional to $\mathrm{Re}L_{qq'}$ because they give the relaxation. Therefore we replace the $L_{qq'}$'s by the $k_{qq'}$'s.

In analogy to our earlier discussion we now define the spectral densities $J_{\alpha\alpha'\beta\beta'}(\omega)$ as

$$J_{\alpha\alpha'\beta\beta'}(\omega) = \int_{-\infty}^{+\infty} \overline{(\alpha|\mathcal{H}_1(t)|\alpha')(\beta'|\mathcal{H}_1(t+\tau)|\beta)}e^{-i\omega\tau}\, d\tau \tag{26}$$

† As long as the K_q's are taken as Hermitian operators, the H_q's are real. If one chooses the K_q's as non-Hermitian, the H_q's become complex, but the only $L_{qq'}$'s that are non-zero then involve q and q''s which make $\overline{H_q(t)H_{q'}(t+\tau)}$ real.

Then, combining Eqs. (24), (25), and (26), we have

$$\frac{d\rho^*_{\alpha\alpha'}}{dt} = \sum_{\beta,\beta'} R_{\alpha\alpha',\beta\beta'} e^{i(\alpha-\alpha'-\beta+\beta')t} \rho^*_{\beta\beta'}(0) \tag{27}$$

where $R_{\alpha\alpha',\beta\beta'}$ is given as

$$R_{\alpha\alpha',\beta\beta'} = \frac{1}{2\hbar^2} [J_{\alpha\beta\alpha'\beta'}(\alpha' - \beta') + J_{\alpha\beta\alpha'\beta'}(\alpha - \beta) - \delta_{\alpha'\beta'} \sum_{\gamma} J_{\gamma\beta\gamma\alpha}(\gamma - \beta) - \delta_{\alpha\beta} \sum_{\gamma} J_{\gamma\alpha'\gamma\beta'}(\gamma - \beta')] \tag{28}$$

Equation (27) relates $d\rho^*/dt$ at time $t > \tau_c$ to ρ^* at $t = 0$. It is the first term in a power-series expansion. In order for the convergence to be good, it must imply that $\rho^*_{\beta\beta'}$ at time t not be vastly different from its value at $t = 0$. This implies that we can find a range of times t such that $t \gg \tau_c$, but still $\rho^*_{\beta\beta'}(t) \cong \rho^*_{\beta\beta'}(0)$. This latter condition implies that

$$\frac{1}{R_{\alpha\alpha',\beta\beta'}} \gg t \tag{29}$$

The important trick now is to note that if Eq. (29) holds true, we can replace $\rho^*_{\beta\beta}(0)$ by $\rho^*_{\beta\beta}(t)$ on the right side of Eq. (27). By this step, we convert Eq. (27) into a differential equation for ρ^*, which will enable us to find ρ^* by "integration" at times so much later than $t = 0$ that $\rho^*_{\beta\beta'}(t)$ will no longer be nearly its value at $t = 0$. The resulting equation is Eq. (1).

The physical significance of our conditions is now seen to be that we never ask for information over time intervals comparable to τ_c, and that in this time interval the density matrix must not change too much. In practice, this implies that

$$T_1, \quad T_2 \gg \tau_c \tag{30}$$

As we shall see in greater detail, the condition $\tau_c \ll T_2$ is just that for which the resonance lines are "narrowed" by the "motion" that produces the fluctuations in $\mathcal{H}_1(t)$.

Because

$$R_{\alpha\alpha,\beta\beta} = R_{\beta\beta,\alpha\alpha} \tag{31}$$

(that is, the transition probability from α to β is equal to that from β to α), the solution of the Redfield equation is an *equal* distribution among all states. This situation corresponds to an infinite temperature. Clearly the equations do not describe the approach to an equilibrium at a finite temperature. The reason is immediately apparent—our equation involves the spin variables only, making no mention of a thermal bath. The bath coordinates are needed to enable the spins to "know" the temperature.

A rigorous method of correcting for the bath is to consider that the density matrix of Eq. (11) is for the total system of bath and spins. Since in the absence of $\mathcal{H}_1$ the spins and lattice are decoupled, we may take the density matrix to consist of a product of that for the spins, σ, and that for the lattice, ρ^L. We take for our basic Hamiltonian $\mathcal{H}_0$ the *sum* of the lattice and the spin Hamiltonians (which, of course, commute). $\mathcal{H}_1$ commutes with neither and induces simultaneous transitions in the lattice and the spin system. Then we have

$$\rho^* = \sigma^* \rho^{L*} \tag{32}$$

Introducing spin quantum numbers s and s', and lattice quantum numbers f and f', we replace α by sf, and so on. Then we assume that the lattice remains in thermal equilibrium despite the spin relaxation:

$$\rho^L_{ff'} = \delta_{ff'} \frac{e^{-\hbar f/kT}}{\sum_{f''} e^{-\hbar f''/kT}} \tag{33}$$

We then find the differential equation for

$$\frac{d}{dt}(\rho^{L*}_{ff'}\sigma^*_{ss'}) = \delta_{ff'}\rho^{L*}_{ff'}\frac{d}{dt}\sigma^*_{ss'} \tag{34}$$

and sum over f. The result, in the high temperature limit, is simply to give a modified version of Redfield's equation, with the density matrix for spin σ replaced by the difference between σ and its value for thermal equilibrium at the lattice temperature $\sigma(T)$.

We therefore simply assert that for an interaction in which the lattice couples to the spins via an interaction $\mathcal{H}_1$ (which, to the spins, is time dependent),† the role of the lattice is to modify the Redfield equation to be

$$\frac{d\sigma^*_{\alpha\alpha'}}{dt} = \sum_{\beta,\beta'} R_{\alpha\alpha',\beta\beta'}e^{+i(\alpha-\alpha'-\beta+\beta')t}(\sigma^*_{\beta\beta'} - \sigma^*_{\beta\beta'}(T)] \tag{35}$$

where α, α', β, β' stand for spin quantum numbers, and where $\sigma_{\beta\beta'}(T)$ is the thermal equilibrium value of $\sigma_{\beta\beta'}$:

$$\sigma_{\beta\beta'}(T) = \delta_{\beta\beta'}\frac{e^{-\hbar\beta/kT}}{\sum_{\beta''} e^{-\hbar\beta''/kT}} \tag{36}$$

That Eq. (35) should hold true is not surprising in view of our remarks in Chapter 1 concerning the approach to thermal equilibrium. We note here, however, that our remarks apply not only to the level populations (the diagonal elements of σ) but also to the off-diagonal elements.

5·7 EXAMPLE OF REDFIELD THEORY

We turn now to an example to illustrate both the method of Redfield and some simple physical consequences. The example we choose is that of an ensemble of spins which do not couple to one another but which couple to an external fluctuating field, different at each spin. The external field possesses x-, y-, and z-components. This example possesses many of the features of a system of spins with dipolar coupling. However, it is substantially simpler to treat; moreover, it can be solved exactly in the limit of very short correlation time. For the case of dipolar coupling,

† $\mathcal{H}_1$ involves both spin and lattice coordinates. If we treat the lattice quantum mechanically, the lattice variables are operators, and $\mathcal{H}_1$ does not involve the time explicitly. If we treat the lattice classically, $\mathcal{H}_1$ involves the time explicitly. That this must be so is evident, since the coupling must be time dependent to induce spin transitions between spin states of different energy. However, it is time independent when the lattice makes a simultaneous transition that just absorbs the spin energy.

the fluctuations of the dipole field arise from bodily motion of the nuclei, as when self-diffusion occurs. The correlation time corresponds to the mean time a given pair of nuclei are near each other before diffusing away. Our simple model gives the main qualitative features of the dipolar coupling if we simply consider the correlation time to correspond to that for diffusion. In particular, then, our model will exhibit the important phenomenon of motional narrowing, which has been so beautifully explained in the original work of Bloembergen, Purcell, and Pound.

Before plunging into the analysis, we can remark on certain simple features that will emerge. At the end of this section we develop these simple arguments further, showing how to use them for more quantitative results.

We may distinguish between the effects of the x-, y-, and z-components of the fluctuating field. A component H_z causes the precession rate to be faster or slower. It, so to speak, causes a spread in precessions. It will evidently *not* contribute to the spin-lattice relaxation because that requires changes in the component of magnetization parallel to H_0, but it will contribute to the decay of the transverse magnetization even if the fluctuations are so slow as to be effectively static. In fact, as we shall see, it is H_z that contributes to the rigid-lattice line breadth. The phenomenon of motional narrowing corresponds to a sort of averaging out of the H_z effect when the fluctuations become sufficiently rapid.

The x- and y-components of fluctuating field are most simply viewed from the reference frame rotating with the precession. Components fluctuating at the precession frequency in the laboratory frame can produce quasi-static components in the rotating frame perpendicular to the static field. They can cause changes in components of magnetization, either parallel or perpendicular to the static field. The former is a T_1 process; the latter, a T_2 process. Clearly the two processes are intimately related, since the magnetization vector of an individual spin is of fixed length. The transverse components of fluctuating magnetic fields will be most effective when their Fourier spectrum is rich at the Larmor frequency. For either very slow or very rapid motion, the spectral density at the Larmor frequency is low, but for motions whose correlations time τ is of order $1/\omega_0$, the density is at a maximum. The contribution of H_x and H_y to the longitudinal and transverse relaxation rates therefore has a maximum as τ is changed.

Let us consider, then, an interaction $\mathcal{H}_1(t)$ given by

$$\mathcal{H}_1(t) = -\gamma_n \hbar \sum_q H_q(t) I_q \tag{1}$$

where $q = x, y, z$, and

$$\mathcal{H}_0 = -\gamma_n \hbar H_0 I_z = -\hbar\omega_0 I_z \tag{2}$$

where ω_0 is the Larmor frequency. We characterize the eigenstates by α, the eigenvalues of Eq. (2). These are ω_0 times the usual m-values of the operator I_z. (Here $m = I, I - 1, \cdots - I$.) We shall continue to use the notation $\alpha, \alpha', \beta, \beta'$, however, rather than m, in order to keep the equations similar to those we have just developed. The matrix elements $(\alpha|\mathcal{H}_1(t)|\alpha')$ are

$$(\alpha|\mathcal{H}_1(t)|\alpha') = -\gamma_n \hbar \sum_q H_q(t)(\alpha|I_q|\alpha') \tag{3}$$

Then the spectral density functions $J_{\alpha\beta\alpha'\beta'}(\omega)$ are

$$\frac{1}{2\hbar^2} J_{\alpha\beta\alpha'\beta'}(\omega) = \frac{1}{2\hbar^2} \int_{-\infty}^{+\infty} \overline{(\alpha|\mathcal{H}_1(t)|\beta)(\beta'|\mathcal{H}_1(t+\tau)|\alpha')}e^{-i\omega\tau}\, d\tau$$

$$= \frac{\gamma_n^2}{2} \sum_{q,q'} (\alpha|I_q|\beta)(\beta'|I_{q'}|\alpha') \cdot \int_{-\infty}^{+\infty} \overline{H_q(t)H_{q'}(t+\tau)}e^{-i\omega\tau}\, d\tau \tag{4}$$

We now use the symbol $k_{qq'}(\omega)$ introduced in the preceding section as

$$k_{qq'}(\omega) = \tfrac{1}{2}\int_{-\infty}^{+\infty} \overline{H_q(t)H_{q'}(t+\tau)}e^{-i\omega\tau}\, d\tau \tag{5}$$

Clearly the fluctuation effects, correlation time, and so on are all associated with the $k_{qq'}$'s. For simplicity let us assume that the fluctuations of the three components of field are independent. That is, we shall assume

$$\overline{H_q(t)H_{q'}(t+\tau)} = 0 \qquad \text{if } q \neq q' \tag{6}$$

For example, Eq. (6) will hold true if, for any value of the component H_q, the values of $H_{q'}$ occur with equal probability as $|H_{q'}|$ or $-|H_{q'}|$. We note that $k_{qq}(\omega)$ gives the spectral density at frequency ω of the q-component of the fluctuating field. With the assumption of Eq. (6) we have, then,

$$\frac{1}{2\hbar^2} J_{\alpha\beta\alpha'\beta'} = \gamma_n^2 \sum_q (\alpha|I_q|\beta)(\beta'|I_q|\alpha')k_{qq}(\omega) \tag{7}$$

We now seek to find the effect of relaxation on the x-, y-, and z-components of the spins. To do this, we utilize the second technique described in the preceding section, that of finding a differential equation for the expectation value of the spin components. Let us therefore ask for $(d/dt)\langle I_r\rangle$, $r = x, y,$ or z. By using Eq. (10) of the preceding section, we find

$$\frac{d\langle I_r\rangle}{dt} = \sum_{\alpha,\alpha'} \frac{i}{\hbar} [\rho, \mathcal{H}_0]_{\alpha\alpha'}(\alpha'|I_r|\alpha) \tag{8}$$

$$+ \sum_{\substack{\alpha,\alpha'\\ \beta,\beta'}} R_{\alpha\alpha',\beta\beta'}\rho_{\beta\beta'}(\alpha'|I_r|\alpha)$$

The first term on the right, involving $\mathcal{H}_0$, can be handled readily:

$$\sum_{\alpha,\alpha'} \frac{i}{\hbar} [\rho, \mathcal{H}_0]_{\alpha\alpha'}(\alpha'|I_r|\alpha) = \frac{i}{\hbar} \operatorname{Tr}(\rho\mathcal{H}_0 - \mathcal{H}_0\rho)I_r \tag{9}$$

$$= \frac{i}{\hbar} \operatorname{Tr}[\rho\mathcal{H}_0 I_r - \rho I_r \mathcal{H}_0]$$

$$= \frac{i}{\hbar} \operatorname{Tr}\rho[\mathcal{H}_0, I_r]$$

$$= -i\gamma_n H_0 \operatorname{Tr}\rho[I_z, I_r]$$

If $r = z$, this term vanishes. If $r = x$, we have

$$-i\gamma_n H_0 \operatorname{Tr}\rho[I_z, I_x] = -i\gamma_n H_0 \operatorname{Tr}(iI_y\rho) \qquad (10)$$
$$= +\gamma_n H_0\langle I_y\rangle$$

If $r = y$, we get $-\gamma_n H_0\langle I_x\rangle$. Thus we have

$$\sum_{\alpha,\alpha'} \frac{i}{\hbar} [\rho, \mathcal{H}_0]_{\alpha\alpha'}(\alpha'|I_r|\alpha) = \gamma_n\{\langle \mathbf{I}\rangle \times \mathbf{H}_0\}_r \qquad (11)$$

which is the driving term of the Bloch equations describing the torque due to the external field. The second term on the right of Eq. (8) involves the relaxation terms:

$$\sum_{\substack{\alpha,\alpha'\\ \beta,\beta'}} R_{\alpha\alpha',\beta\beta'}\rho_{\beta\beta'}(\alpha'|I_r|\alpha) \qquad (12)$$

As we have seen, $R_{\alpha\alpha',\beta\beta'}$ is itself the sum of four terms (Eq. (28) of the preceding section). We shall discuss the first term, $J_{\alpha\beta\alpha'\beta'}(\alpha' - \beta')$. By using Eq. (7), we find

$$\frac{1}{2\hbar^2} \sum_{\substack{\alpha,\alpha'\\ \beta,\beta'}} J_{\alpha\beta\alpha'\beta'}(\alpha' - \beta')\rho_{\beta\beta'}(\alpha'|I_r|\alpha)$$
$$= \gamma_n^2 \sum_{\substack{\alpha,\alpha'\\ \beta,\beta'\\ q}} (\alpha|I_q|\beta)(\beta'|I_q|\alpha')(\beta|\rho|\beta')(\alpha'|I_r|\alpha)k_{qq}(\alpha' - \beta') \qquad (13)$$
$$= \gamma_n^2 \sum_{\substack{\alpha',\beta'\\ q}} (\beta'|I_q|\alpha')(\alpha'|I_rI_q\rho|\beta')k_{qq}(\alpha' - \beta')$$

where the last step follows from the basic properties of orthogonality and completeness of the wave functions $|\alpha)$, and so on. We were able to "collapse" the indices α and β, but we cannot do the same trick for α' and β' because they occur not only in the matrix elements but also in the k_{qq}'s.

In a similar way one can obtain expressions for the other three terms in $R_{\alpha\alpha',\beta\beta'}$, getting finally

$$\sum_{\substack{\alpha,\alpha'\\ \beta,\beta'}} R_{\alpha\alpha',\beta\beta'}\rho_{\beta\beta'}(\alpha'|I_r|\alpha) = \gamma_n^2 \sum_{\substack{\alpha,\beta\\ q}} (\beta|I_q|\alpha)(\alpha|(I_rI_q - I_qI_r)\rho|\beta)k_{qq}(\alpha - \beta)$$
$$+ \gamma_n^2 \sum_{\substack{\alpha,\beta\\ q}} (\beta|I_q|\alpha)(\alpha|\rho(I_qI_r - I_rI_q)|\beta)k_{qq}(\beta - \alpha)$$
$$= \gamma_n^2 \sum_{\substack{\alpha,\beta\\ q}} (\beta|I_q|\alpha)(\alpha|[[I_r, I_q], \rho]|\beta)k_{qq}(\beta - \alpha) \qquad (14)$$

where, in the last step, we have utilized the fact that $k_{qq}(\omega)$ is an even function of ω.

To proceed further, we must now specify whether r is x, y, or z. First let us consider $r = z$. Then, since I_r will commute with I_z, we get nothing from $q = z$ in the last line of Eq. (14). Since matrix elements of I_x vanish except for $\Delta m = \pm 1$, the only states (α and β) that are joined by I_q for $q = x$ have $|\beta - \alpha| = \omega_0$, the Larmor frequency. Since $[I_z, I_x] = iI_y$ and $[I_x, I_y] = iI_z$, we have, then,

$$\begin{aligned}
\gamma_n^2 \sum_{\alpha,\beta} (\beta|I_x|\alpha)(\alpha|[[I_z, I_x]\rho]|\beta)k_{xx}(\alpha - \beta) \\
&= \gamma_n^2 \left\{ \sum_{\alpha,\beta} (\beta|I_x|\alpha)(\alpha|iI_y\rho - i\rho I_y|\beta) \right\} k_{xx}(\omega_0) \\
&= i\gamma_n^2 k_{xx}(\omega_0)\, \mathrm{Tr}(I_x I_y \rho - I_x \rho I_y) \\
&= i\gamma_n^2 k_{xx}(\omega_0)\, \mathrm{Tr}(I_x I_y - I_y I_x)\rho \\
&= -\gamma_n^2 k_{xx}(\omega_0)\, \mathrm{Tr} I_z \rho \\
&= -\gamma_n^2 k_{xx}(\omega_0)\langle I_z \rangle \qquad \text{(14a)}
\end{aligned}$$

The term $q = y$ gives, in a similar manner,

$$-\gamma_n^2 k_{yy}(\omega_0)\langle I_z \rangle \tag{15}$$

All told, then,

$$\sum_{\substack{\alpha,\alpha' \\ \beta,\beta'}} R_{\alpha\alpha',\beta\beta'}\rho_{\beta\beta'}(\alpha'|I_z|\alpha) = -\gamma_n^2[k_{xx}(\omega_0) + k_{yy}(\omega_0)]\langle I_z \rangle \tag{16}$$

By combining Eqs. (8), (11), and (16), we have

$$\frac{d\langle I_z \rangle}{dt} = \gamma[\langle \mathbf{I} \rangle \times \mathbf{H}_0]_z - \gamma_n^2[k_{xx}(\omega_0) + k_{yy}(\omega_0)]\langle I_z \rangle \tag{17}$$

This equation relaxes toward $\langle I_z \rangle = 0$ rather than the thermal equilibrium value I_0. To remedy the situation, we should replace ρ by $\rho - \rho(T)$, as discussed in the preceding section. This result simply makes $\langle I_z \rangle$ relax toward the thermal equilibrium value I_0:

$$\frac{d\langle I_z \rangle}{dt} = \gamma[\langle \mathbf{I} \rangle \times \mathbf{H}_0]_z - \gamma_n^2[k_{xx}(\omega_0) + k_{yy}(\omega_0)][\langle I_z \rangle - I_0] \tag{18}$$

This is clearly one of the Bloch equations, with T_1 given by the expression

$$\frac{1}{T_1} = \gamma_n^2[k_{xx}(\omega_0) + k_{yy}(\omega_0)] \tag{19}$$

We can proceed in a similar way to find the relaxation of the x-component. For it, the value $q = x$ contributes nothing, but $q = y$ or z does. The situation for $q = y$ is similar to the one we have just discussed, connecting states α and β which differ by ω_0. On the other hand, when $q = z$, the states α and β are the *same* (I_z is diagonal), so that $\alpha - \beta = 0$. The spectral density of H_z at zero frequency enters. Therefore we find

$$\sum_{\substack{\alpha,\alpha' \\ \beta,\beta'}} R_{\alpha\alpha',\beta\beta'}\rho_{\beta\beta'}(\alpha'|I_x|\alpha) = -\gamma_n^2[k_{yy}(\omega_0) + k_{zz}(0)]\langle I_x \rangle \tag{20}$$

which gives for the derivative of $\langle I_x \rangle$:

$$\frac{d\langle I_x\rangle}{dt} = \gamma_n[\langle \mathbf{I}\rangle \times \mathbf{H}_0]_x - \gamma_n^2[k_{yy}(\omega_0) + k_{zz}(0)]\langle I_x\rangle \tag{21}$$

For this equation there is no effect from replacing ρ by $\rho - \rho(T)$, since in thermal equilibrium $\langle I_x\rangle = 0$. Eq. (21), and a similar one for $\langle I_y\rangle$, is also clearly the transverse Bloch equation describing T_2 processes, with T_2 given by

$$\frac{1}{T_2} = \gamma_n^2[k_{yy}(\omega_0) + k_{zz}(0)] \tag{22}$$

Our relaxation mechanism therefore leads to the Bloch equations. Of course one cannot expect that in general the Bloch equations follow from an arbitrary $\mathcal{H}_1(t)$, and one would have to study each case to see whether or not the Bloch equations resulted.

To proceed further, we need to know something about the spectral densities of the x-, y-, and z-components of the fluctuating field. We shall once again assume a simple exponential correlation function, with the same correlation time τ_0, for $q = x, y$, and z:

$$\overline{H_q(t)H_q(t+\tau)} = \overline{H_q^2}e^{-|\tau|/\tau_0} \tag{23}$$

which gives

$$k_{qq}(\omega) = \overline{H_q^2}\,\frac{\tau_0}{1+\omega^2\tau_0^2} \tag{24}$$

In terms of Eq. (24) we have, then,

$$\frac{1}{T_1} = \gamma_n^2[\overline{H_x^2} + \overline{H_y^2}]\,\frac{\tau_0}{1+\omega_0^2\tau_0^2} \tag{25}$$

$$\frac{1}{T_2} = \gamma_n^2\left[\overline{H_z^2}\tau_0 + \overline{H_y^2}\,\frac{\tau_0}{1+\omega_0^2\tau_0^2}\right]$$

We note first of all that T_1 goes through a minimum as a function of τ_0 when $\omega_0\tau_0 = 1$. The fluctuating fields that determine T_1 are the x- and y-components at the Larmor frequency. If we view the problem from the rotating frame (that is, one rotating at the Larmor frequency), these results are reasonable, since the T_1 corresponds to a change in the z-magnetization. Such a change is brought about by "static" fields in either the x- or y-directions in the rotating frame, since in the rotating frame the effective field is zero (H_1, of course, is zero). But "static" x- or y-fields in the rotating frame oscillate at ω_0 in the laboratory frame.

On the other hand, the decay of the x-magnetization must arise from the "static" y- or z-fields in the rotating frame. Since the z-axis of the laboratory and rotating frames coincide, for the z-field it is the static laboratory component that counts, but for the y-field, it is the laboratory component at the Larmor frequency that is important. We note that in the limit of very rapid motion ($\omega_0\tau_0 \ll 1$), and assuming an isotropic fluctuating field

$$\overline{H_x^2} = \overline{H_y^2} = \overline{H_z^2} \tag{26}$$

T_1 and T_2 are equal. Physically, for our model, this result signifies that for a very short correlation time, the spectral density of the fluctuating field is "white" to frequencies far above the Larmor frequency, so that the x-, y-, and z-directions in the *rotating* reference frame see equivalent fluctuating fields.

The two terms in the expression for T_2 have simple physical meanings. One term depends on H_z. It represents the dephasing of the spins due to the spread in precession rates arising from the fact that H_z can aid or oppose H_0. This term can be readily derived by a simple argument, which we give below. The second term, as we shall explain, results from broadening of the energy levels due to the finite lifetime a spin is in a given energy state.

Let us now turn to a simple derivation of the first term of the equation for T_2. We assume the field has a value $|H_z|$ for a time τ; then it jumps randomly to $\pm|H_z|$. Such a change in field in practice arises because a nucleus moves relative to its neighbors by diffusion. In the time τ, a spin will precess an *extra* phase angle, $\delta\phi$, over its normal precession:

$$\delta\phi = \pm\gamma_n|H_z|\tau \tag{27}$$

After n such intervals, the mean square dephasing, $\overline{\Delta\phi^2}$, will be

$$\begin{aligned}\overline{\Delta\phi^2} &= n\,\delta\phi^2 \\ &= n\gamma_n^2 H_z^2 \tau^2\end{aligned} \tag{28}$$

The number of intervals n in a time t is simply

$$n = \frac{t}{\tau} \tag{29}$$

If we take as T_2 the time for a group of spins in phase at $t = 0$ to get about 1 radian out of step, we find

$$1 = \frac{T_2}{\tau}\,\gamma_n^2 H_z^2 \tau^2 \tag{30}$$

or

$$\frac{1}{T_2} = \gamma_n^2 H_z^2 \tau \tag{31}$$

We note that the *shorter* τ (that is, the more *rapid* the motion†), the narrower the resonance. This phenomenon is therefore called *motional narrowing*. We see that the motion narrows the resonance because it allows a given spin to sample many fields H_z, some of which cause it to advance in phase; others, to be retarded. The dephasing takes place, then, by a random walk of small steps, each one much less than a radian.

In contrast, when there is no motion, a given spin experiences a constant local field. It precesses either faster or slower than the average, and the dephasing of a group of spins arises from the inexorable accumulation of positive or negative phase.

The contrast with "collision broadening" of spectral lines is great. In that case the *phase* of the oscillation is changed by each collision. Since the frequency is unperturbed between collisions, there is no loss in phase memory except during a

† Of course the word "motion" here refers to translation of the position of the nucleus, not to the change in spin orientation.

collision. Since each collision gives a loss in phase memory, a more rapid collision rate produces a shorter phase memory and a broader line. With motional narrowing, there is no phase change when H_z is changing from one value to another because the change is very rapid, but there is a phase change during the time a given value of H_z persists. More rapid motion diminishes the loss in phase memory in each interval.

We have considered just one term of our expression for T_2. The other term, which involves $\overline{H_y^2}$, clearly has the same dependence on τ_0 as does the spin-lattice relaxation. We interpret it as the broadening of the line due to the finite life of a spin in any eigenstate as a result of the spin-lattice relaxation. The lifetime is finite because a field in the y-direction can change the z-magnetization. We should estimate the order of magnitude of the lifetime broadening to be

$$\Delta E = \frac{\hbar}{T_1} \tag{32}$$

or

$$\Delta\omega = \frac{\Delta E}{\hbar} = \frac{1}{T_1}$$

Assuming isotropic fluctuating fields, we see that our example actually gives

$$\frac{1}{T_2} = \frac{1}{T_{2'}} + \frac{1}{2T_1} \tag{33}$$

where $T_{2'}$ is the broadening due to the spread in the z-field. The quantity $1/T_{2'}$ is often called the *secular broadening;* the term $1/2T_1$ is called the *non-secular* or *lifetime broadening.* More generally, we replaced $1/2T_1$ by $1/T_{1'}$, where $T_{1'}$ (which gives the non-secular broadening) is related to T_1.

As we have remarked, if we consider the secular broadening, we note that as τ_0 decreases, T_2 increases, or the line narrows. Of course, we have seen that as one increases τ_0 (slows the motion), the validity of the Redfield equations ceases when $T_2 \cong \tau_0$. For longer τ_0's, we cannot apply the Redfield equation. The longest τ_0 for which the Redfield theory can apply, then, is $\tau_0 = T_2$, or

$$\frac{1}{\tau_0} = \frac{1}{T_2} = \gamma_n^2\overline{H_z^2}\tau_0 \tag{34}$$

or

$$\gamma_n|H_z|\tau_0 = 1 \tag{35}$$

As we can see from our simple model, this is just the value of τ_0 at which a typical spin gets one radian out of phase *before* there is a jump. For *longer* τ_0's, the spins

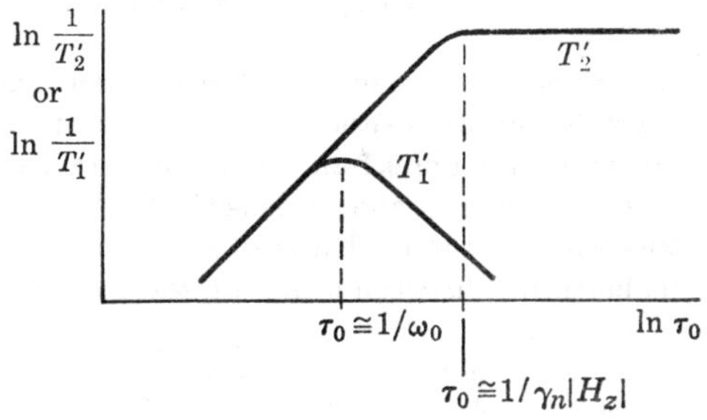

FIG. 5.8. Secular ($T_{2'}$) and non-secular ($T_{1'}$) broadening versus τ_0. For the example in the text, $T_{1'} = 2T_1$.

are dephased before there is a chance for a jump. That is, they do not dephase by a random walk. The line breadth is then independent of the jump rate, giving one the temperature-independent, rigid-lattice line breadth.

The two contributions to the line breadth (secular and non-secular) are plotted in Fig. 5.8.

If one analyzes the relaxation via other mechanisms, the same general features are found. The fact that more than one transition may be induced will make important the spectral densities at frequencies other than 0 and ω_0. Often, $2\omega_0$ comes in. For example, when the relaxation arises from the coupling of one nucleus with another by means of their magnetic dipole moments, the E and F terms of Chapter 3, which involve the product of two raising or two lowering operators, connect states differing in energy by $2\hbar\omega_0$.

Our formulas show us that the measurement of T_1 and T_2 will enable us to determine τ_0. When the fluctuations in the interaction $\mathcal{H}_1(t)$ arise from bodily motion that varies with temperature, we can use resonance to study the temperature variation of τ_0. Often one has a "barrier" to motion and an activation energy E such that

$$\tau_0 = \tau_\infty e^{E/kT} \tag{36}$$

where τ_∞ is the value of τ_0 for infinite temperature. The temperature variation of T_1 or T_2 gives one a convenient measure of E and τ_∞. The narrowing studies of Andrew and Eades, performed on molecular crystals, provide one such example. Another one is the work of Holcomb and Norberg on self-diffusion in the alkali metals, and subsequently, Seymour and Spokas, on aluminum. Here one has the interesting fact that, using resonance, these workers could measure the self-diffusion rate of both Li and Al (for which there is no radioactive isotope for use in the conventional tracer technique).

5·8 EFFECT OF APPLIED ALTERNATING FIELDS

So far we have excluded applied alternating fields from the time-dependent coupling $\mathcal{H}_1(t)$. Let us now assume that such fields are present, giving an extra term, $\mathcal{H}_2(t)$, in the Hamiltonian. We can include its effect in a straightforward way, as has been shown by Bloch. Introduction of $\mathcal{H}_2(t)$ simply replaces $\mathcal{H}_1^*(t)$ by $\mathcal{H}_1^*(t) + \mathcal{H}_2^*(t)$ in Eq. (11) of Section 5.6:

$$\frac{d\rho^*}{dt} = \frac{i}{\hbar}[\rho^*(0), \mathcal{H}_1^*(t) + \mathcal{H}_2^*(t)] + \left(\frac{i}{\hbar}\right)^2 \int_0^t [[\rho^*(0), (\mathcal{H}_1^*(t') + \mathcal{H}_2^*(t'))], (\mathcal{H}_1^*(t) + \mathcal{H}_2^*(t))]\, dt' \tag{1}$$

The effect of $\mathcal{H}_1^*$ in the first term on the right vanished when averaged over an ensemble. For that reason we were forced to consider the second term. In general the contribution of $\mathcal{H}_2^*(t)$ to the first term does *not* vanish, since $\mathcal{H}_2^*(t)$ is identical for all members of the ensemble. If $\mathcal{H}_2^*(t)$ is not too strong, we expect that the first-order term is all that is necessary, and therefore we neglect the role of $\mathcal{H}_2^*$ in the integral. Physically, this approximation amounts to our saying that

$$\frac{d\rho^*}{dt} = \left.\frac{d\rho^*}{dt}\right)_{\mathcal{H}_2} + \left.\frac{d\rho^*}{dt}\right)_{\text{relax}} \tag{2}$$

where $d\rho^*/dt)_{\mathcal{H}_2}$ is the rate of change of ρ^* due solely to $\mathcal{H}_2$, and $d\rho^*/dt)_{\text{relax}}$ is the rate of change of ρ^* we should have if $\mathcal{H}_2$ were zero. What we are neglecting are, therefore, non-linear effects in the interactions.

Under what circumstances do we expect this approximation to work? The answer is that neither perturbation must change ρ^* too much during the time t (which is the upper limit of the integral), for the $\mathcal{H}_2^*$ terms in the integral represent the fact that $\mathcal{H}_1^*$ is acting on a ρ^*, which is not in fact $\rho^*(0)$ but must be corrected for the driving by $\mathcal{H}_2^*$. Since we wish to choose t as about τ_c, this requirement means that

$$\frac{|(\alpha|\mathcal{H}_2|\alpha')|\tau_c}{\hbar} \ll 1 \tag{3}$$

If $\mathcal{H}_2$ is too large to satisfy Eq. (3), we should then attempt to solve first for the combined effect of $\mathcal{H}_0$ and $\mathcal{H}_2$, using perturbation theory for $\mathcal{H}_1$. For example, we may use a rotating coordinate transformation rather than a transformation to the interaction representation, thereby converting $\mathcal{H}_2(t)$ to a static interaction, which could then be removed by a second transformation to the interaction representation of the effective field.

It is interesting to note that there is in fact a very close similarity between the interaction representation and the usual rotating coordinate transformation that renders H_1 a static field. Both are transformations to rotating coordinate systems. The interaction representation is a transformation to a system rotating at the Larmor frequency, whereas the usual transformation goes to a coordinate system rotating with H_1.

For simplicity we shall assume that Eq. (3) is satisfied. Note that since T_1 and T_2 are much longer than τ_c for all our equations to be valid, Eq. (3) can still be easily satisfied even under conditions of saturation.

There is one further consequence of the addition of a term $\mathcal{H}_2(t)$. We have remarked that when we treat the lattice classically, the density matrix relaxes to its value at infinite temperature rather than to the thermal equilibrium value $\rho(T)$:

$$\rho(T) = \frac{1}{Z(T)}\, e^{-\mathcal{H}_0/kT} \tag{4}$$

where $Z(T)$ is the sum of states. When the change of $\mathcal{H}_2$ is small during the time τ_c, which characterizes the "lattice" motion, we expect that $\mathcal{H}_2$ looks like a "static" coupling to the lattice and that we should assume that the system relaxes at each instant toward the instantaneous density matrix:

$$\rho(T, t) = \frac{e^{-[\mathcal{H}_0+\mathcal{H}_2(t)]/kT}}{Z(T, t)} \tag{5}$$

This equation can be verified by treating the lattice quantum mechanically. When τ_c is long compared with the period of $\mathcal{H}_2$, Eq. (4) applies.

Under circumstances where the Bloch equations hold, the short τ_c leads often to $T_1 = T_2$, and the Bloch equations become

$$\frac{d\mathbf{M}}{dt} = \gamma\mathbf{M} \times \mathbf{H}(t) + \frac{\mathbf{M}_0 - \mathbf{M}}{T_1} \tag{6}$$

where

$$\mathbf{M}_0 = \chi_0\mathbf{H}(t) \tag{7}$$

and $\mathbf{H}(t)$ is the instantaneous applied field. Explicit solution shows that the solution of Eq. (6) differs significantly from the normal Bloch equations (assuming $T_1 = T_2$, but $\mathbf{M}_0 = \chi_0\mathbf{H}_0$) only when the line width is comparable to the resonance frequency.

We can combine Eq. (2) with Eq. (9) of Section 5.6 to obtain the complete differential equation for the density matrix, including an applied alternating field:

$$\frac{d\rho_{\alpha\alpha'}}{dt} = \frac{i}{\hbar}(E_{\alpha'} - E_\alpha)\rho_{\alpha\alpha'} + \frac{i}{\hbar}\sum_{\alpha''}[\rho_{\alpha\alpha''}(\alpha''|\mathcal{H}_2(t)|\alpha') - (\alpha|\mathcal{H}_2(t)|\alpha'')\rho_{\alpha''\alpha'}] \quad (8)$$
$$+ \sum_{\beta,\beta'} R_{\alpha\alpha',\beta\beta'}[\rho_{\beta\beta'} - \rho_{\beta\beta'}(T)]$$

where, for $\rho_{\beta\beta'}(T)$, we use either Eq. (4) or (5), depending on the circumstances.

In order to make Eq. (8) more concrete, let us suppose we have a two-level system. Thus we may have a spin $\frac{1}{2}$ particle quantized by a static field in the z-direction. We label the states 1 and 2 and find that the density matrix has four elements $\rho_{11}, \rho_{22}, \rho_{12}, \rho_{21}$.

In the relaxation terms, $R_{\alpha\alpha',\beta\beta'}$, the only terms of importance (as we have seen) involve $\alpha - \alpha' = \beta - \beta'$. The only terms that count are therefore:

$$R_{11,22} = R_{22,11} \equiv \frac{1}{\tau_1}$$
$$R_{12,12} = R_{21,21} \equiv -\frac{1}{\tau_2} \quad (9)$$

By assuming $\mathcal{H}_2$ joins states 1 and 2 only, and denoting $(1|\mathcal{H}_2(t)|2)$ by $\mathcal{H}_{12}(t)$, we find

$$\frac{d\rho_{11}}{dt} = -\frac{d\rho_{22}}{dt} \quad (10)$$
$$= \frac{\rho_{22} - \rho_{11} - [\rho_{22}(T) - \rho_{11}(T)]}{\tau_1}$$
$$+ \frac{i}{\hbar}[\rho_{12}\mathcal{H}_{21}(t) - \mathcal{H}_{12}(t)\rho_{21}]$$

and

$$\frac{d\rho_{12}}{dt} = -\frac{\rho_{12}}{\tau_2} + \frac{i}{\hbar}(E_2 - E_1)\rho_{12} + \frac{i}{\hbar}(\rho_{11} - \rho_{22})\mathcal{H}_{12}(t) \quad (11)$$

If E_2 is larger than E_1 and $\mathcal{H}_{12}$ oscillates at frequency ω, we can solve Eqs. (10) and (11) in steady state by assuming that

$$\rho_{12} = r_{12}e^{i\omega t}$$
$$\rho_{21} = r_{21}e^{-i\omega t}$$
$$\rho_{11} = r_{11} \quad (12)$$
$$\rho_{22} = r_{22}$$

where the $r_{\alpha\alpha'}$'s are complex constants. The details of the solution are left as a problem, but the form of the answer is identical to that of the Bloch equations. If we write

$$\mathcal{H}_2(t) = V\cos\omega t \quad (13)$$

where V is an operator, and define ω_0 by the relation $E_2 - E_1 \equiv \hbar\omega_0$, we have in the limit of small V (that is, no saturation):

$$r_{11} = \rho_{11}(T) = \frac{e^{-E_1/kT}}{e^{-E_1/kT} + e^{-E_2/kT}} \cong \frac{1}{2} e^{-E_1/kT} \tag{14}$$

$$r_{12} = \frac{i}{2\hbar} \frac{V_{12}\tau_2}{1 + i(\omega - \omega_0)\tau_2} [\rho_{11}(T) - \rho_{22}(T)]$$

$$\cong \frac{i\tau_2}{1 + i(\omega - \omega_0)\tau_2} \frac{V_{12}\omega_0}{4kT}$$

We note that r_{12} differs from zero only near to resonance and that τ_2 characterizes the width of frequency over which r_{12} is non-zero. If the states 1 and 2 are the two Zeeman states of a spin ½ nucleus in a static magnetic field parallel to the z-direction, then the transverse magnetization M_x has matrix elements only between states 1 and 2, the diagonal elements being zero. Therefore

$$\langle M_x(t)\rangle = r_{12}e^{i\omega t}(2|M_x|1) + r_{21}e^{-i\omega t}(1|M_x|2) \tag{15}$$

$$= 2\mathrm{Re}[r_{12}e^{i\omega t}(2|M_x|1)]$$

Taking

$$V = M_x H_{x0} \tag{16}$$

and recalling that χ is defined as

$$\langle M_x(t)\rangle = \mathrm{Re}[\chi H_{x0} e^{i\omega t}] \tag{17}$$

we see that

$$\chi(\omega) = \frac{i\tau_2}{1 + i(\omega - \omega_0)\tau_2} \frac{\omega_0|(1|M_x|2)|^2}{2kT} \tag{18}$$

Now, using the fact that $I = ½$, we have

$$\chi(\omega) = \frac{i\tau_2}{1 + i(\omega - \omega_0)\tau_2} \frac{\omega_0}{2} \frac{\gamma^2\hbar^2 I(I+1)}{3kT} \tag{19}$$

which agrees with the expression for the Bloch equation derived in Chapter 2.

We note that we could determine both τ_1 and τ_2 from first principles by computing $R_{11,22}$ and $R_{12,12}$. Alternatively we could simply treat τ_1 and τ_2 as phenomenological constants to be given by experiment.

If there are more than two levels to a system, the solution may be carried out analogously by simply setting all off-diagonal elements of $\rho_{\alpha\alpha'}$ equal to zero, except those near resonance with the alternating frequency ($E_\alpha - E_{\alpha'} \cong \hbar\omega$).

CHAPTER 6

ELECTRIC QUADRUPOLE EFFECTS

6·1 INTRODUCTION

So far we have considered only the magnetic interactions of the nucleus with its surroundings. To be sure, by implication we have considered the effect of the nuclear charge, since it determines the electron orbits and where the nucleus sits in a molecule. However, we have not considered any electrical effects on the energy required to reorient the nucleus. That such effects do exist can be seen by considering a non-spherical nucleus. Suppose it is somewhat elongated and is acted on by the charges shown in Fig. 6.1. We see that Fig. 6.1b will correspond

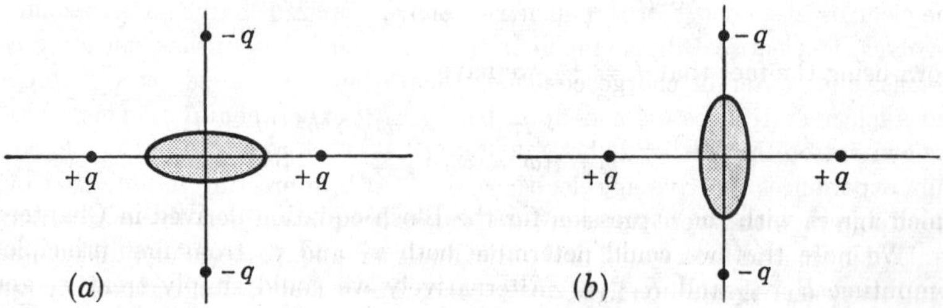

FIG. 6.1. (a) A cigar-shaped nucleus in the field of four charges, $+q$ on the x-axis; $-q$ on the y-axis. The configuration of (b) is energetically more favorable because it puts the positive charge of the ends of the cigar closer to the negative charges $-q$.

to a lower energy, since it has put the tips of the positive nuclear charge closer to the negative external charges. There is, therefore, an electrostatic energy that varies with the nuclear orientation. Of course,† turning the nucleus end for end does not affect the electrostatic energy. Consequently, for spin ½ nuclei the electrostatic energy does not split the m_I degeneracy.

† See references to "Quadrupole Effects" in the Bibliography and the articles by Cohen and Reif and by Das and Hahn under "Books, Monographs, or Review Articles" in the Bibliography.

6·2 QUADRUPOLE HAMILTONIAN — PART 1

To develop a more quantitative theory, we begin by a description in terms of the classical charge density of the nucleus, ρ. We shall obtain a quantum mechanical answer by replacing the classical ρ by its quantum mechanical operator. Classically, the interaction energy E of a charge distribution of density ρ with a potential V due to external sources is

$$E = \int \rho(\mathbf{r})\, V(\mathbf{r})\, d\tau \tag{1}$$

We expand $V(\mathbf{r})$ in a Taylor's series about the origin:

$$V(\mathbf{r}) = V(0) + \sum_{\alpha} x_\alpha \left.\frac{\partial V}{\partial x_\alpha}\right)_{\mathbf{r}=0} + \frac{1}{2!}\sum_{\alpha,\beta} x_\alpha x_\beta \left.\frac{\partial^2 V}{\partial x_\alpha \partial x_\beta}\right)_{\mathbf{r}=0} + \cdots \tag{2}$$

where x_α ($\alpha = 1, 2, 3$) stands for x, y, or z, respectively. Defining

$$V_\alpha \equiv \left.\frac{\partial V}{\partial x_\alpha}\right)_{\mathbf{r}=0} \tag{3}$$

$$V_{\alpha\beta} \equiv \left.\frac{\partial^2 V}{\partial x_\alpha \partial x_\beta}\right)_{\mathbf{r}=0}$$

we have

$$E = V(0)\int \rho\, d\tau + \sum_{\alpha} V_\alpha \int x_\alpha \rho\, d\tau + \frac{1}{2!}\sum_{\alpha,\beta} V_{\alpha\beta}\int x_\alpha x_\beta \rho\, d\tau \cdots \tag{4}$$

Choosing the origin at the mass center of the nucleus, we have for the first term the electrostatic energy of the nucleus taken as a point charge. The second term involves the electrical dipole moment of the nucleus. It vanishes, since the center of mass and center of charge coincide. That they do coincide can be proved if the nuclear states possess a definite parity. All experimental evidence supports the contention that nuclei do have definite parity. Moreover, a nucleus in equilibrium experiences *zero* average electric field V_α. It is interesting to note that even if the dipole moment were not zero, the tendency of a nucleus to be at a point of vanishing electric field would make the dipole term hard to see. In fact it was for just this reason that Purcell, Ramsey, and Smith looked for signs of a possible nuclear electrical dipole moment in neutrons rather than in charged nuclei.

The third term is the so-called electrical quadrupole term. We note at this point that one can always find principal axes of the potential V such that

$$V_{\alpha\beta} = 0 \qquad \text{if } \alpha \neq \beta \tag{5}$$

Moreover, V must satisfy LaPlace's equation:

$$\nabla^2 V = 0 \tag{6}$$

This equation, evaluated at the origin, gives us

$$\sum_{\alpha} V_{\alpha\alpha} = 0 \tag{7}$$

(We note that sometimes Poisson's equation applies instead. Some care must then be exercised because we are, of course, interested only in the orientation dependent part of the potential, and must therefore subtract off the spherically symmetric parts.) If one has a nucleus at a site of cubic symmetry,

$$V_{xx} = V_{yy} = V_{zz} \quad \text{(cubic symmetry)} \tag{8}$$

which, combined with Eq. (7), makes all three derivatives zero. The quadrupole coupling then vanishes. This situation arises, for example, with Na^{23} in Na metal. The face-centered cubic crystal structure puts each nucleus at a site of cubic symmetry.

It is convenient to consider the quantities $Q_{\alpha\beta}$ defined by the equation

$$Q_{\alpha\beta} = \int [3x_\alpha x_\beta - \delta_{\alpha\beta} r^2]\rho \, d\tau \tag{9}$$

In terms of the $Q_{\alpha\beta}$'s, we have

$$\int x_\alpha x_\beta \rho \, d\tau = \tfrac{1}{3}[Q_{\alpha\beta} + \int \delta_{\alpha\beta} r^2 \rho \, d\tau] \tag{10}$$

As we shall see, the introduction of the $Q_{\alpha\beta}$'s amounts to our subtracting from the left side of Eq. (10) a term that does not depend on the orientation of the nucleus. We have, then, for the quadrupole energy $E^{(2)}$,

$$E^{(2)} = \tfrac{1}{2}\sum_{\alpha,\beta} V_{\alpha\beta} \int x_\alpha x_\beta \, d\tau \tag{11}$$

$$= \tfrac{1}{6}\sum_{\alpha,\beta}\left[V_{\alpha\beta}Q_{\alpha\beta} + V_{\alpha\beta}\,\delta_{\alpha\beta}\int r^2 \rho \, d\tau\right]$$

Since V satisfies LaPlace's equation, the second term on the right of Eq. (11) vanishes, giving us

$$E^{(2)} = \tfrac{1}{6}\sum_{\alpha,\beta} V_{\alpha\beta} Q_{\alpha\beta} \tag{12}$$

Even if this term were not zero, we note that it would be independent of nuclear orientation.†

To obtain a quantum mechanical expression for the quadrupole coupling, we simply replace the classical ρ by its quantum mechanical operator, $\rho^{(op)}$, given by

$$\rho^{(op)}(\mathbf{r}) = \sum_k q_k \, \delta(\mathbf{r} - \mathbf{r}_k) \tag{13}$$

---

† If there is an electronic charge at the nucleus, we must use Poisson's equation. Then

$$\sum_\alpha V_{\alpha\alpha} = -4\pi e|\Psi(0)|^2$$

where $|\Psi(0)|^2$ is the electronic probability density at the nucleus. The orientation independent term, ΔE, of Eq. (11) becomes

$$\Delta E = \frac{1}{6}\sum_\alpha V_{\alpha\alpha}\int r^2\rho \, d\tau = -\frac{4\pi e}{6}|\Psi(0)|^2 \int r^2 \rho \, d\tau$$

This ΔE will be different for two nuclei of the same charge but different charge distributions (isotopes), or for two nuclei of the same mass and charge but different nuclear states (isomers). In an electronic transition between an s and a p-state, ΔE will make a contribution that will in general be different for different isotopes or isomers. Effects also show up in nuclear transitions. See L. R. Walker, G. K. Wertheim, and V. Jaccarino, *Phys. Rev. Letters*, **6**: 98 (1961).

where the sum runs over the nuclear particles $1, 2, \cdots k \cdots N$, of charge q_k. Since the neutrons have zero charge, and the protons a charge e, we can simply sum over the protons:

$$\rho^{(\mathrm{op})}(\mathbf{r}) = e \sum_{\text{protons}} \delta(\mathbf{r} - \mathbf{r}_k) \tag{14}$$

By substituting Eq. (14) into the classical expression for $Q_{\alpha\beta}$, we obtain the quadrupole operator $Q_{\alpha\beta}^{(\mathrm{op})}$:

$$\begin{aligned} Q_{\alpha\beta}^{(\mathrm{op})} &= \int (3x_\alpha x_\beta - \delta_{\alpha\beta} r^2) \rho^{(\mathrm{op})}(\mathbf{r})\, d\tau \\ &= e \sum_{\text{protons}} \int (3x_\alpha x_\beta - \delta_{\alpha\beta} r^2)\, \delta(\mathbf{r}_k - \mathbf{r})\, d\tau \\ &= e \sum_{\text{protons}} (3x_{\alpha k} x_{\beta k} - \delta_{\alpha\beta} r_k^2) \end{aligned} \tag{15}$$

We have, then, a quadrupole term for the Hamiltonian $\mathcal{H}_Q$, given by

$$\mathcal{H}_Q = \frac{1}{6} \sum_{\alpha,\beta} V_{\alpha\beta} Q_{\alpha\beta}^{(\mathrm{op})} \tag{16}$$

The expressions of Eqs. (15) and (16) look exceedingly messy to handle because they involve all the nuclear particles. They appear to require us to treat the nucleus as a many-particle system, a complication we have avoided in discussing the magnetic couplings. Actually a similar problem is involved in both magnetic dipole and electric quadrupole cases, but we have simply avoided discussion in the magnetic case.

The quadrupole interaction represented by Eq. (15) enables us to treat problems of much greater complexity than those we encounter in a discussion of resonance phenomena. When performing resonances, we are in general concerned only with the ground state of a nucleus, or perhaps with an excited state when the excited state is sufficiently long-lived. The eigenstates of the nucleus are characterized by the total angular momentum, I, of each state, $2I + 1$ values of a component of angular momentum, and a set of other quantum numbers, η, which we shall not bother to specify. Since we shall be concerned only with the spatial reorientation of the nucleus for a given nuclear energy state, we shall be concerned only with matrix elements diagonal in both I and η. Thus we shall need only matrix elements of the quadrupole operator, such as

$$(Im\eta|Q_{\alpha\beta}^{(\mathrm{op})}|Im'\eta)$$

These can be shown to obey the equation

$$(Im\eta|Q_{\alpha\beta}^{(\mathrm{op})}|Im'\eta) = C(Im|\tfrac{3}{2}(I_\alpha I_\beta + I_\beta I_\alpha) - \delta_{\alpha\beta} I^2|Im') \tag{17}$$

where C is a constant, different for each set of the quantum numbers I and η. In order to justify Eq. (17), we need to digress to discuss the Clebsch-Gordan coefficients, the so-called irreducible tensor operators T_{LM}, and the Wigner-Eckart theorem.

6·3 CLEBSCH-GORDAN COEFFICIENTS, IRREDUCIBLE TENSOR OPERATORS, AND THE WIGNER-ECKART THEOREM

The Wigner-Eckart theorem is one of the most useful theorems in quantum mechanics. In order to state it, we must introduce the Clebsch-Gordan coefficients $C(LJ'J; MM_{J'} M_J)$, and the irreducible tensor operators, T_{LM}. We shall first state the Wigner-Eckart theorem and then define the Clebsch-Gordan coefficients. Next we shall discuss irreducible tensor operators, and lastly we shall indicate the derivation of the Wigner-Eckart theorem.

We consider a set of wave functions characterized by quantum numbers J or J' for the total angular momentum, M_J or $M_{J'}$ for the z-component of angular momentum, and as many other quantum numbers η or η' as are needed to specify the state. We are then concerned with calculating the matrix elements of the operators T_{LM}, using these functions as the basis functions. The Wigner-Eckart theorem states that all such matrix elements are related to the appropriate Clebsch-Gordan coefficients through a set of quantities $(J\eta \| T_L \| J'\eta')$ that depend on J, J', η, η' and L but which are independent of M_J, $M_{J'}$, and M. Stated mathematically, the Wigner-Eckart theorem is

$$(JM_J\eta|T_{LM}|J'M_{J'}\eta') = C(J'LJ; M_{J'}MM_J)(J\eta\|T_L\|J'\eta') \tag{1}$$

Let us now define the Clebsch-Gordan coefficients. They are encountered when one discusses the addition of two angular momenta to form a resultant. We therefore consider a system made up of two parts. Let us describe one part of the system by the quantum numbers L and M, to describe the total angular momentum of that part and its z-component. Let us use the quantum numbers J' and $M_{J'}$ correspondingly for the second part of the system. For the system as a whole we introduce quantum numbers J and M_J. We have, then, wave functions ψ_{LM} and $\phi_{J'M_{J'}}$, to describe the two parts, and Ψ_{JM_J} for the whole system. The function Ψ_{JM_J} can be expressed as a linear combination of product functions of the two parts, since such products form a complete set:

$$\Psi_{JM_J} = \sum_{\substack{J'M_{J'}\\ LM}} C(J'LJ; M_{J'}MM_J)\phi_{J'M_{J'}}\psi_{LM} \tag{2}$$

The coefficients $C(J'LJ; M_{J'}MM_J)$ are called the *Clebsch-Gordan coefficients*. Certain of their properties are very well known. For example, $C(J'LJ; M_{J'}MM_J)$ vanishes unless $M_J = M + M_{J'}$. A second property, often called the *triangle rule*, is that $C(J'LJ; M_{J'}MM_J)$ vanishes unless J equals one of the values $J' + L$, $J' + L - 1, \cdots |J' - L|$, a fact widely used in atomic physics.

Let us now define the irreducible tensor operators T_{LM}. Suppose we have a system whose angular momentum operators have components J_x, J_y, and J_z. We define the raising and lowering operators J^+ and J^- as usual by the relations

$$J^+ \equiv J_x + iJ_y \tag{3}$$

$$J^- \equiv J_x - iJ_y$$

One can construct functions, G, of the operators of the system and examine the commutators such as $[J^+, G]$, $[J^-, G]$, and $[J_z, G]$. It is often possible to define a family of $2L + 1$ operators (L is an integer) labeled by an integer $M(M = L, L - 1, \cdots - L)$ which we shall term *irreducible tensor operators* T_{LM}, which obey the commutation rules

$$[J^{\pm}, T_{LM}] = \sqrt{L(L+1) - M(M+1)}\, T_{LM\pm1} \tag{4}$$
$$[J_z, T_{LM}] = MT_{LM}$$

An example of such a set for $L = 1$ is

$$T_{11} = \frac{-1}{\sqrt{2}} J^+ \tag{5}$$
$$T_{10} = J_z$$
$$T_{1-1} = \frac{1}{\sqrt{2}} J^-$$

Another example of a T_{1M} can be constructed for an atom with spin and orbital angular momentum operators $\mathbf{s}$ and $\mathbf{l}$, respectively, and total angular momentum $\mathbf{J}$. Then we define the operators

$$l^+ = l_x + il_y \tag{6}$$
$$l^- = l_x - il_y$$

One can then verify that the operators T_{1M}, defined by

$$T_{11} = -\frac{l^+}{\sqrt{2}} \tag{7}$$
$$T_{10} = l_z$$
$$T_{1-1} = \frac{1}{\sqrt{2}} l^-$$

obey Eq. (4). (Actually the operators of Eq. (7) form components of an irreducible tensor T_{1M} with respect to the operators l^+, l^-, and l_z as well as J^+, J^-, and J_z.) We may write the T_{1M}'s of Eq. (20) as $T_{1M}(\mathbf{J})$, to signify that they are functions of the components J_x, J_y, and J_z of $\mathbf{J}$. The T_{1M}'s of Eq. (7) are in a similar manner signified as $T_{1M}(\mathbf{l})$.

It is helpful to have a more physical feeling for the definition of the operators T_{LM} by the commutation rules of Eq. (4). We realize that angular momentum operators can be used to generate rotations, as discussed in Chapter 2. It is not surprising, therefore, that Eq. (4) can be shown to guarantee that a T_{LM} transforms under rotations of the coordinate axes into linear combinations $T_{LM'}$, in exactly the same way that the spherical harmonics Y_{LM} transform into linear combinations of $Y_{LM'}$'s. This theorem is shown in Chapter 5 of Rose's excellent book.†

We shall wish to compute matrix elements of the T_{LM}'s. We are familiar with the fact that it is possible to derive expressions for the matrix elements of angular momentum from the commutation rules among the components. It is

† M. E. Rose, *Elementary Theory of Angular Momentum.* New York: John Wiley & Sons, Inc., 1957.

possible to compute the matrix elements of the T_{LM}'s by means of Eq. (4) in a similar manner. Let us illustrate.

We have in mind a set of commuting operators J^2, J_z, plus others, with eigenvalues J, $M_{J'}$, and η. We use η to stand for all other quantum numbers needed. We wish to compute matrix elements such as

$$(JM_J\eta|T_{LM}|J'M_{J'}\eta') \tag{8}$$

By means of the commutation rule

$$[J_z, T_{LM}] = MT_{LM} \tag{9}$$

we have

$$(JM_J\eta|[J_z, T_{LM}]|J'M_{J'}\eta') = M(JM_J\eta|T_{LM}|J'M_{J'}\eta') \tag{10}$$

But

$$(JM_J\eta|[J_z, T_{LM}]|J'M_{J'}\eta') = \underbrace{(JM_J\eta|J_zT_{LM}|J'M_{J'}\eta')}_{1} - \underbrace{(JM_J\eta|T_{LM}J_z|J'M_{J'}\eta')}_{2}$$

$$= (M_J - M_{J'})(JM_J\eta|T_{LM}|J'M_{J'}\eta')$$

where the last step follows from allowing the Hermitian operator J_z to operate on the function to its left in term 1 and to its right in term 2.

Therefore

$$(M_J - M_{J'})(JM_J\eta|T_{LM}|J'M_{J'}\eta) = M(JM_J\eta|T_{LM}|J'M_{J'}\eta) \tag{10b}$$

Equation (10b) shows that

$$(JM_J\eta|T_{LM}|J'M_{J'}\eta') = 0 \qquad \text{unless} \qquad M_J - M_{J'} = M \tag{11}$$

In a similar way we may find conditions on the matrix elements of the other terms of Eq. (4). Thus

$$(JM_J\eta|[J^\pm, T_{LM}]|J'M_{J'}\eta') = \sqrt{L(L+1) - M(M \pm 1)}\,(JM_J\eta|T_{LM\pm1}|J'M_{J'}\eta') \tag{12}$$

But

$$\begin{aligned}(JM_J\eta|J^\pm\, T_{LM}|J'M_{J'}\eta')\\ &= (JM_J\eta|J^\pm|JM_J \mp 1\eta)(JM_J \mp 1\eta|T_{LM}|J'M_{J'}\eta')\\ &= \sqrt{J(J+1) - (M_J \mp 1)M_J}\,(JM_J \mp 1\eta|T_{LM}|J'M_{J'}\eta')\end{aligned} \tag{13}$$

By combining Eqs. (12) and (13), we obtain the other recursion relations:

$$\begin{aligned}&\sqrt{J(J+1) - (M_J \mp 1)M_J}\,(JM_J \mp 1\eta|T_{LM}|J'M_{J'}\eta')\\ &\quad -(JM_J\eta|T_{LM}|J'M_{J'} \pm 1\eta')\sqrt{J'(J'+1) - M_{J'}(M_{J'} \pm 1)}\\ &\quad = \sqrt{L(L+1) - M(M+1)}\,(JM_J\eta|T_{LM\pm1}|J'M_{J'}\eta')\end{aligned} \tag{14}$$

We note that the only non-vanishing terms must satisfy Eq. (10b). However, if any one term in Eq. (14) satisfies this relation, all do. Equations (10b) and (14) constitute a set of recursion relations relating matrix elements for T_{LM} to one another and to those of $T_{LM'}$. These equations turn out to be sufficient to enable one to solve for all T_{LM} matrix elements for given J, J', η, η' in terms of any one matrix element.

A further insight into the significance of the recursion relations is shown by returning to the Clebsch-Gordan coefficients. In so doing, we shall sketch the proof of the Wigner-Eckart theorem.

As is shown by Rose, the C's obey recursion relations identical to those of the T_{LM}'s. We shall derive one, the selection rule on M, M_J, and M'_J. Consider the operator

$$J_z \equiv L_z + J'_z \tag{15}$$

where

$$\begin{aligned} J_z\Psi_{JM_J} &= M_J\Psi_{JM_J} \\ L_z\psi_{LM} &= M\psi_{LM} \\ J'_z\phi_{J'M_{J'}} &= M_{J'}\phi_{J'M_{J'}} \end{aligned} \tag{16}$$

Then consider the following matrix element of the operator J_z:

$$\begin{aligned} (\psi_{LM}\phi_{J'M_{J'}}, J_z\Psi_{JM_J}) &= M_J(\psi_{LM}\phi_{J'M_{J'}}, \Psi_{JM_J}) \\ &= M_JC(J'LJ; M_{J'}MM_J) \end{aligned} \tag{17}$$

where we have let J_z operate to the right. But, writing J_z as $L_z + J'_z$ and operating on the functions to the left, we get

$$(\psi_{LM}\phi_{J'M_{J'}}, J_z\Psi_{JM_J}) = (M + M_{J'})C(J'LJ; M_{J'}MM_J) \tag{18}$$

By equating Eqs. (33) and (34), we find

$$(M + M_{J'} - M_J)C(J'LJ; M_{J'}MM_J) = 0 \tag{19}$$

This equation is quite analogous to Eq. (10b), provided we replace

$$(JM_J\eta|T_{LM}|J'M_{J'}\eta')$$

by

$$C(J'LJ; M_{J'}MM_J)$$

One can proceed in a similar manner to compute matrix elements of the raising and lowering operators, to get equations similar to Eq. (14). In fact the $C(J'LJ; M_{J'}MM_J)$'s obey the recursion relations identical to those of the $(JM_J\eta|T_{LM}|J'M_{J'}\eta')$'s. As a result, one can say that the C's and the matrix elements of the T_{LM}'s are related. The relationship is called the *Wigner-Eckart theorem:*

$$(JM_J\eta|T_{LM}|J'M_{J'}\eta') = C(J'LJ; M_{J'}MM_J)(J\eta\|T_L\|J'\eta') \tag{20}$$

where the notation $(J\eta\|T_L\|J'\eta')$ stands for a quantity that is a constant for a given J, L, J', η, η' independent of M_J, $M_{J'}$, and M.

As we can see specifically from Eqs. (5) and (7), for a given L and M there may be a variety of functions, all of which are T_{LM}'s. The Clebsch-Gordan coefficient is the same for all functions T_{LM} that have the same L and M, but the constant $(J\eta\|T_L\|J'\eta')$ will depend on what variable is used to construct the T_{LM}'s.

To illustrate this point further, let us consider a particle with spin $\mathbf{s}$ and orbital angular momentum $\mathbf{l}$ and position $\mathbf{r}$. The total angular momentum $\mathbf{J}$ is given by

$$\mathbf{J} = \mathbf{s} + \mathbf{l} \tag{21}$$

where

$$l_x = \frac{1}{i}\left[y\frac{\partial}{\partial z} - z\frac{\partial}{\partial y}\right] \tag{22}$$

$$l_y = \frac{1}{i}\left[z\frac{\partial}{\partial x} - x\frac{\partial}{\partial z}\right]$$

$$l_z = \frac{1}{i}\left[x\frac{\partial}{\partial y} - y\frac{\partial}{\partial x}\right]$$

We shall now list two T_{2M}'s, one a function of the angular momentum $\mathbf{J}$; the other, of the coordinate $\mathbf{r}$. One can verify that the functions of Table 6.1, which we shall call $T_{2M}(\mathbf{J})$ and $T_{2M}(\mathbf{r})$, indeed obey the commutation rules of Eq. (4) with respect to J^+, J^-, and J_z.

TABLE 6.1.

	$T_{2M}(\mathbf{J})$	$T_{2M}(\mathbf{r})$
T_{22}	J^{+2}	$(x + iy)^2$
T_{21}	$-(J_zJ^+ + J^+J_z)$	$-2z(x + iy)$
T_{20}	$\sqrt{\frac{2}{3}}\,(3J_z^2 - J^2)$	$\sqrt{\frac{2}{3}}\,(3z^2 - r^2)$
T_{2-1}	$J_zJ^- + J^-J_z$	$2z(x - iy)$
T_{2-2}	J^{-2}	$(x - iy)^2$

We have used the notation $T_{2M}(\mathbf{r})$ as shorthand for a T_{2M} constructed from the components x, y, and z of $\mathbf{r}$. There is an obvious similarity between $T_{2M}(\mathbf{J})$ and $T_{2M}(\mathbf{r})$: Replacement of J^+ by $(x + iy)$, J^- by $(x - iy)$, J_z by z will convert $T_{2M}(\mathbf{J})$ into $T_{2M}(\mathbf{r})$. This similarity is a direct consequence of the similarity of the commutation relations of components of $\mathbf{J}$ and $\mathbf{r}$ with J_x, J_y, and J_z:

$$[J_x, y] = iz \tag{23a}$$

$$[J_x, J_y] = iJ_z \qquad \text{etc.} \tag{23b}$$

where Eq. (23a) can be verified by means of Eqs. (21) and (22). It is clear that any function $G(x, y, z)$ of x, y, z, constructed from a function $G(J_x, J_y, J_z)$ of J_x, J_y, J_z by direct substitution of x for J_x, and so on, will obey the same commutation rules with respect to J_x, J_y, and J_z. Thus, if a function of J_x, J_y, J_z is known to be a T_{LM}, the same will be true of the function formed by replacing J_x, J_y, J_z by x, y, z, respectively. The only caution we note in procedures such as this is that we must remember that the components of some operators do not commute among themselves; so that for example in $T_{21}(\mathbf{J})$ we have the symmetrized product $J^+J_z + J_zJ^+$, not $2J^+J_z$. The method of direct replacement will work for other variables as long as they obey commutation relations such as those of Eq. (23).†

Returning now to Eq. (20), let us consider two T_{LM}'s, one a function of variables q and the other a function of variables p. Then Eq. (20) tells us that

$$(JM_J\eta|T_{LM}(q)|J'M_{J'}\eta') = (JM_J\eta|T_{LM}(p)|J'M_{J'}\eta')\,\frac{(J\eta\|T_L(q)\|J'\eta')}{(J\eta\|T_L(p)\|J'\eta')} \tag{24}$$

Since the factor $(J\eta\|T_L(q)\|J'\eta')/(J\eta\|T_L(p)\|J'\eta')$ is a constant (that is, independent of M, M_J, and $M_{J'}$), we see that we can compute all the matrix elements of $T_{LM}(q)$ of fixed J, J', η, and η' from knowledge of the constant and of the matrix elements $(JM_J\eta|T_{LM}(p)|J'M_{J'}\eta')$.

One word of caution is necessary. It may be that Eq. (24) is not meaningful, since for some operators p, the matrix element $(JM_J\eta|T_{LM}(p)|J'M_{J'}\eta')$ vanishes even though the matrix element $(JM_J\eta|T_{LM}(q)|J'M_{J'}\eta')$ does not. An example of such a case is when $T_{LM}(p)$ is made up of components of $\mathbf{J}$. Then all matrix elements in which $J' \neq J$ vanish. Of course $(J'\|T_2(\mathbf{J})\|J)$ vanishes too, so that Eq. (24) becomes indeterminant.

6·4 QUADRUPOLE HAMILTONIAN — PART 2

We now apply the Wigner-Eckart theorem to evaluate the matrix elements of $Q_{\alpha\beta}{}^{(\mathrm{op})}$. Now

$$Q_{\alpha\beta}^{(\mathrm{op})} = e\sum_{k}^{\text{protons}} [3x_{\alpha k}x_{\beta k} - \delta_{\alpha\beta}r_k^2] \tag{1}$$

By recalling that I_x, I_y, and I_z are the operators of the total angular momentum of the nucleus

$$I_x = \sum_k l_{xk} + s_{xk} \qquad \text{etc., for } I_y \text{ and } I_z \tag{2}$$

where l_{xk} and s_{xk} are the x-components of the orbital and spin angular momentum of the kth nucleon; and by recalling that

$$[l_{xk}, y_k] = iz_k \qquad [s_{xk}, y_k] = 0 \qquad \text{etc.} \tag{3}$$

we see that

$$[I_x, y_k] = iz_k \qquad \text{etc.} \tag{4}$$

The terms $3x_{\alpha k}x_{\beta k} - \delta_{\alpha\beta}r_k^2$ are linear combinations of $T_{2M}(\mathbf{r}_k)$'s such as found in the right-hand column of Table 6.1.

Equation (24) of the preceding section applies in a somewhat more general form not only to T_{LM}'s but also to functions that are linear combinations of T_{LM}'s, all of the *same L*. Thus consider such a function $F(p)$, which is a function of the operators p:

$$F(p) = \sum_M a_M T_{LM}(p) \tag{5}$$

---

† For an excellent review article including tables of T_{LM}'s of various L and M, see E. Ambler, J. C. Eisenstein, and J. F. Schooley, *Journal of Mathematical Physics*, **3**, 118(1962) and **3**, 760(1962).

Let us define a function $G(q)$ of the operators q, using the same coefficients a_M:

$$G(q) \equiv \sum_M a_M T_{LM}(q) \tag{6}$$

Then one can easily verify, using Eqs. (24), (5) and (6), that

$$(JM_J\eta|G(q)|J'M_{J'}\eta') = (JM_J\eta|F(p)|J'M_{J'}\eta')\frac{(J\eta\|T_L(q)\|J'\eta')}{(J\eta\|T_L(p)\|J'\eta')} \tag{7}$$

We may apply this theorem to show that

$$\left(Im\eta\left|e\sum_k^{\text{protons}}[3x_{\alpha k}x_{\beta k} - \delta_{\alpha\beta}r_k^2]\right|Im'\eta\right) = \left(Im\eta\left|3\frac{(I_\alpha I_\beta + I_\beta I_\alpha)}{2} - \delta_{\alpha\beta}I^2\right|Im'\eta\right)C \tag{8}$$

where C† is a constant, the same for all m, m', α, and β. We can express C in terms of the matrix element for which $m = m' = I$, $\alpha = \beta = z$ as follows:

$$\begin{aligned}\left(II\eta\left|e\sum_k^{\text{protons}}[3z_k^2 - r_k^2]\right|II\eta\right) &= C(II\eta|3I_z^2 - I^2|II\eta) \\ &= CI(2I-1)\end{aligned} \tag{9}$$

Since the quantum number η is assumed to be associated with a variable that commutes with I^2 and I_z, we can omit it in evaluating the right-hand equality of Eq. (9). We shall also define a symbol eQ:

$$eQ = \left(II\eta\left|e\sum_k^{\text{protons}}(3z_k^2 - r_k^2)\right|II\eta\right) \tag{10}$$

Q is called the *quadrupole moment* of the nucleus. We have, by combining Eqs. (9) and (10),

$$C = \frac{eQ}{I(2I-1)} \tag{11}$$

The fact that we are concerned with matrix elements internal to one set of quantum numbers I, η enables us to use Eqs. (8) and (11) to replace $Q_{\alpha\beta}^{(\text{op})}$ in the Hamiltonian. All matrix elements diagonal in I and η are just what we should calculate by adding an effective quadrupolar contribution $\mathcal{H}_Q$ to the Hamiltonian:

$$\mathcal{H}_Q = \frac{eQ}{6I(2I-1)}\sum_{\alpha,\beta} V_{\alpha\beta}[\tfrac{3}{2}(I_\alpha I_\beta + I_\beta I_\alpha) - \delta_{\alpha\beta}I^2] \tag{12}$$

It is interesting to note that of the nine components of $Q_{\alpha\beta}^{(\text{op})}$, only one nuclear constant, eQ, is needed. The reason is as follows: The fact that the nucleus is in a state of definite angular momentum is equivalent to the classical statement that the charge has cylindrical symmetry. Taking z as the symmetry axis, the energy change on reorientation depends, then, only on the *difference* between the charge distribution parallel and transverse to z.

$$\int z^2\rho\,d\tau \quad\text{and}\quad \int x^2\rho\,d\tau$$

† Do not confuse C with the symbol for the Clebsch-Gordan coefficients.

This gives us the critical quantity

$$\int (z^2 - x^2)\rho\, d\tau = \tfrac{1}{2}\int (2z^2 - x^2 - y^2)\rho\, d\tau \tag{13}$$

$$= \tfrac{1}{2}\int (3z^2 - r^2)\rho\, d\tau$$

The last integral, we see, is the classical equivalent of our eQ.

The effective quadrupole interaction of Eq. (12) applies for an arbitrary orientation of the rectangular coordinates $\alpha = x, y, z$. The tensor coupling to the symmetric (in x, y, z) tensor $V_{\alpha\beta}$ can be simplified by choice of a set of principal axes relative to which $V_{\alpha\beta} = 0$ for $\alpha \neq \beta$. In terms of these axes, we have

$$\mathcal{H}_Q = \frac{eQ}{6I(2I-1)}\left[V_{xx}(3I_x^2 - I^2) + V_{yy}(3I_y^2 - I^2) + V_{zz}(3I_z^2 - I^2)\right] \tag{14}$$

This expression can be rewritten, using LaPlace's equation $\sum_\alpha V_{\alpha\alpha} = 0$, to give

$$\mathcal{H}_Q = \frac{eQ}{4I(2I-1)}\left[V_{zz}(3I_z^2 - I^2) + (V_{xx} - V_{yy})(I_x^2 - I_y^2)\right] \tag{15}$$

Equation (15) shows that only two parameters are needed to characterize the derivatives of the potential: V_{zz} and $V_{xx} - V_{yy}$. It is customary to define two symbols, η and q, called the *asymmetry parameter* and the *field gradient*, by the equations

$$eq = V_{zz} \tag{16}$$

$$\eta = \frac{V_{xx} - V_{yy}}{V_{zz}}$$

The case of axial symmetry, often a good approximation, is handled by taking the axis to be the z-direction, giving $\eta = 0$.

Since we have seen that the raising and lowering operators often provide particularly convenient selection rules, it is useful to write Eq. (12) in terms of I^+, I^-, and I_z for an arbitrary (that is, non-principal) set of axes. By defining

$$V_0 = V_{zz} \tag{17}$$

$$V_{\pm 1} = V_{zx} \pm iV_{zy}$$

$$V_{\pm 2} = \tfrac{1}{2}(V_{xx} - V_{yy}) \pm iV_{xy}$$

we find by straightforward algebraic manipulation that

$$\mathcal{H}_Q = \frac{eQ}{4I(2I-1)}\{V_0(3I_z^2 - I^2) + V_{+1}(I^-I_z + I_zI^-) \tag{18}$$

$$+ V_{-1}(I^+I_z + I_zI^+) + V_{+2}(I^-)^2 + V_{-2}(I^+)^2\}$$

Equation (18) gives a form of the quadrupole coupling that is particularly useful when considering relaxation for which the principal axes are not fixed in space but rather are functions of time. An attempt to use principal axes would then be exceedingly cumbersome. We shall not attempt to describe nuclear relaxation by the quadrupolar coupling, although it is a very important mechanism in insulating crystals, often dominant at room temperature.

6·5 EXAMPLES AT STRONG AND WEAK MAGNETIC FIELDS

In order to illustrate the use of the effective quadrupolar interaction, we shall make the simplifying assumption of a field with axial symmetry (or any other symmetry such that $V_{xx} = V_{yy}$ for a set of principal axes). Let us then consider a magnetic field applied along the z' axis where in general the z and z' axes differ. Then we have, for our Hamiltonian,

$$\mathcal{H} = -\gamma_n \hbar H_0 I_{z'} + \frac{e^2 qQ}{4I(2I-1)}(3I_z^2 - I^2) \tag{1}$$

First we shall consider what happens when the quadrupole coupling is weak compared to the magnetic interaction. In this case we can consider the spin quantized along the z' axis. We proceed to treat the quadrupolar coupling by perturbation theory. Defining the x' axis to lie in the plane containing z' and z, we have (see Fig. 6.2)

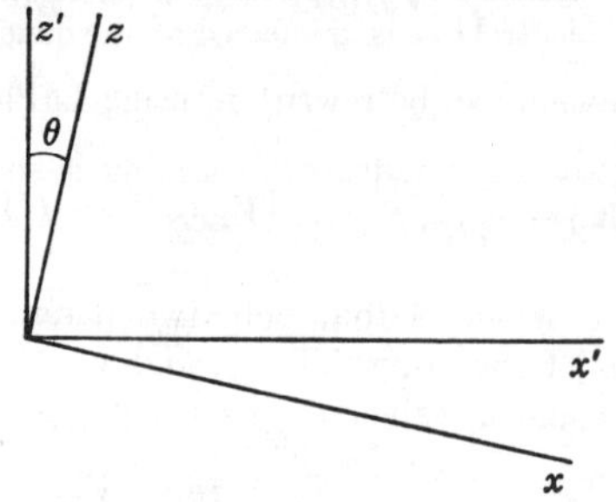

FIG. 6.2. Axes x', z', and z.

$$I_z = I_{z'} \cos\theta + I_{x'} \sin\theta \tag{2}$$

By substituting in Eq. (1), we have

$$\mathcal{H} = -\gamma_n \hbar H_0 I_{z'} + \frac{e^2 qQ}{4I(2I-1)}[3I_{z'}^2 \cos^2\theta + 3I_{x'}^2 \sin^2\theta + 3(I_{z'}I_{x'} + I_{x'}I_{z'}) \sin\theta\cos\theta - I^2] \tag{3}$$

In this equation, since $I_{z'}$ is diagonal in first order, and $I_{x'}$ has vanishing diagonal elements, we have no contribution from terms such as $I_{z'}I_{x'}$ in first order. On the other hand, $I_{x'}^2$ has diagonal elements, since it involves the *product* of off-diagonal elements. By expressing $I_{x'} = \frac{1}{2}(I'^+ + I'^-)$ and $I_{y'} = (1/2i)(I'^+ - I'^-)$, it is straightforward to show that the diagonal elements of $I_{x'}^2$ and $I_{y'}^2$ are identical. We can therefore compute the diagonal matrix element

$$(m|I_{x'}^2|m) = (m|I_{y'}^2|m) = \tfrac{1}{2}(m|I^2 - I_{z'}^2|m) = \tfrac{1}{2}[I(I+1) - m^2] \tag{4}$$

By collecting terms, we find

$$E_m = -\gamma_n \hbar H_0 m + \frac{e^2 qQ}{4I(2I-1)}\left(\frac{3\cos^2\theta - 1}{2}\right)[3m^2 - I(I+1)]$$

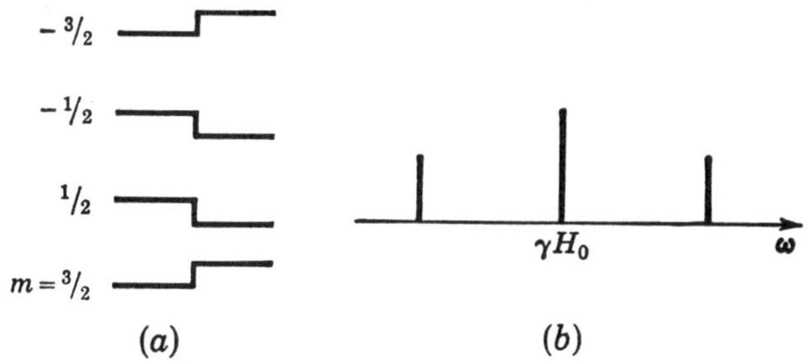

FIG. 6.3. (a) Effect of a quadrupole coupling in first order. The shifts of all levels for $I = 3/2$ have the same magnitude. (b) Spectral absorption corresponding to the energy levels of (a). The central line is unaffected by the quadrupole coupling in first order.

The effect of the quadrupole coupling is shown in Fig. 6.3 for the case of a spin $I = \frac{3}{2}$. It is helpful to note, since

$$\sum_m [3m^2 - I(I+1)] = \mathrm{Tr}(3I_z^2 - I^2) \qquad (5)$$
$$= 0$$

that the quadrupole coupling does not shift the center of gravity of the resonance in first order. Moreover, the shift of $+m$ and $-m$ is identical. With these points in mind we realize that the energy levels must look as shown.

One interesting result is that for a half-integral spin, the $m = \pm\frac{1}{2}$ levels are shifted the same amount and the transition frequency between them is unaffected in first order by the quadrupole coupling. The $\frac{1}{2}$ to $-\frac{1}{2}$ transitions are quite insensitive to effects such as crystalline strains, which may tend to shift the frequency of the other transitions. When a nucleus has a particularly large quadrupole coupling, the chance is great that even for well-annealed crystals one sees only the $+\frac{1}{2}$ to $-\frac{1}{2}$ transition.

If we carry the perturbation to the next higher order, even the $\frac{1}{2}$ to $-\frac{1}{2}$ transition is shifted, the shift being of order $(e^2qQ)^2/\gamma_n\hbar H_0$.

A contrasting experimental situation arises when the quadrupole coupling is larger than that to the magnetic field H_0. Then it is appropriate to consider the quadrupole coupling as a first approximation. We have for the Hamiltonian, in the absence of an external field (still assuming axial symmetry),

$$\mathcal{H} = \frac{e^2qQ}{4I(2I-1)}(3I_z^2 - I^2) \qquad (6)$$

Clearly I^2 and I_z commute with $\mathcal{H}$, giving the quantum numbers I and m, respectively. The energies are

$$E = \frac{e^2qQ}{4I(2I-1)}[3m^2 - I(I+1)] \qquad (7)$$

A set of levels is shown for $I = \frac{5}{2}$ in Fig. 6.4.

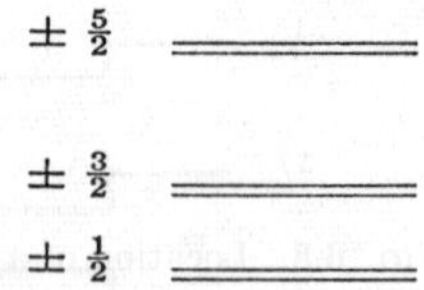

FIG. 6.4. Energy levels of a quadrupole coupling when the Zeeman coupling is negligible.

We note that there is a degeneracy of $\pm m$, corresponding to the fact that turning the nucleus end for end does not affect the electrostatic energy. If an alternating magnetic field is applied with a non-vanishing component perpendicular to the z-axis, it produces non-vanishing matrix elements of $|\Delta m| = 1$. It can therefore produce resonant transitions between the quadrupole levels. It is customary to speak then of "pure quadrupole resonance," although the transition is still induced by magnetic dipole coupling to the alternating field.

An important observation related to Eq. (7) is that when I is $\frac{1}{2}$, $\frac{3}{2}$, and so on (in general when $I = n + \frac{1}{2}$, where n is an integer), the energy levels are all doubly degenerate in the absence of a magnetic field but that for integral spin, the degeneracy may be completely removed, with the $m = 0$ state. This result is an example of an important theorem, due to Kramers, and applies to both electron and nuclear magnetic resonance. Kramers' theorem states:

For a system of angular momentum $I = n + \frac{1}{2}$, where n is 0, 1, 2, and so on, the degeneracy of any state can never be completely lifted by electric fields.

A corollary is that when a system is composed of an odd number of spin $\frac{1}{2}$ particles, electric fields can never completely lift the degeneracy.

The degeneracy is commonly called the *Kramers' degeneracy*. Proof of its existence actually depends on the properties of the system under time reversal.

6·6 COMPUTATION OF FIELD GRADIENTS

We have seen that the quadrupole coupling depends on the second derivatives $V_{\alpha\beta}$ of the potential, which reduce for the case of axes x, y, z, which are principal axes to V_{zz} and $V_{xx} - V_{yy}$. The potential V arises from external charges of either other nuclei or electrons. It is a straightforward matter of taking derivatives of the potential to show that a charge e at a point x, y, z produces a V_{zz} at the origin of

$$V_{zz} = e\,\frac{(3z^2 - r^2)}{r^5} \tag{1}$$

$$r^2 = x^2 + y^2 + z^2$$

In terms of spherical coordinates we have (see Fig. 6.5)

$$V_{zz} = e\,\frac{(3\cos^2\theta - 1)}{r^3} \tag{2}$$

Equations (1) and (2) emphasize, through the $1/r^3$ dependence, that charges close to the nucleus have the most important effect. We may suppose that the electrons belonging to the atom containing the nucleus would make major contributions to V_{zz}. Such is indeed the case. However, if we have a closed shell, the electronic

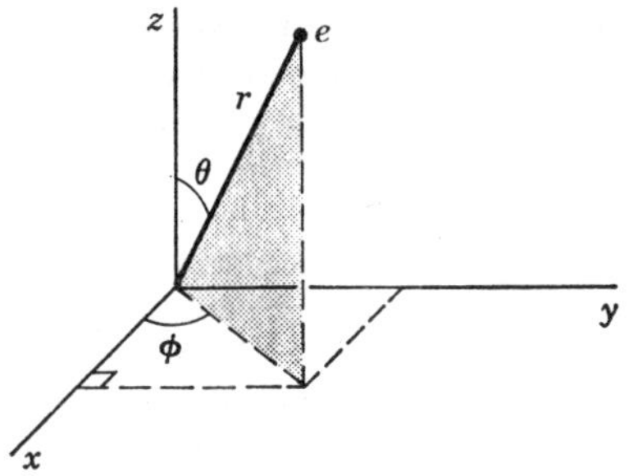

FIG. 6.5. Location of a charge e in terms of the spherical coordinates r, θ, ϕ.

charge is spherically symmetric, and there is no quadrupole coupling (see, however, some further remarks on closed shells below). The case of an incomplete shell is readily illustrated by an example of a single p-electron in an orbit $zf(r)$.

We wish, then, to compute the quadrupole operator for this example. Since the electronic motion is rapid, we shall average the expression of Eq. (2) over the electronic orbit. This procedure is equivalent to saying that, of the total Hamiltonian describing both the electron orbit and the nuclear spin, we shall compute only matrix elements that are diagonal in the electron orbital quantum numbers, and that we shall neglect the perturbation of the electron orbit by the nucleus. We have, then,

$$V_{zz} = -e\int \psi_e^* \frac{(3\cos^2\theta - 1)}{r^3}\psi_e\, d\tau_e \tag{3}$$

$$= -e\int \cos^2\theta \frac{(3\cos^2\theta - 1)}{r^3}\frac{r^2 f^2(r)}{4\pi}\sin\theta\, r^2\, dr\, d\phi\, d\theta$$

$$= -e\frac{4}{15}\overline{\left(\frac{1}{r^3}\right)}$$

where we have designated the electronic charge as $-e$ and where, as usual, $\overline{(1/r^3)}$ is the average of $1/r^3$ for the p-orbit. We note that large Z-atoms, for which $\overline{(1/r^3)}$ is very large, will have large field gradients. This trend is shown by Table 6.2, which lists typical values of e^2qQ of halogen nuclei in covalently bonded crystals.

TABLE 6.2.

Typical Values of e^2qQ for Halogen Nuclei in Covalently Bonded Crystals

Nucleus	e^2qQ (Mc)	$Q(10^{-24}\ \text{cm}^2)$
Cl^{35}	80	-7.97×10^{-2}
Br^{79}	500	0.30
I^{127}	2000.	-0.59

It is interesting to note that the values of e^2qQ of Table 6.2 put the frequency of pure quadrupole transitions for covalently bonded halogens at much higher frequencies than that of their Zeeman transitions $\gamma_n H_0$ for typical laboratory magnetic fields.

When the electronic wave function contains a mixture of *s*- and *p*-states (a "hybridized bond") the *s*-part contributes nothing to the quadrupole coupling. A similar situation arises when a halogen atom is in a state corresponding to a mixture of a pure covalent bond (that is, a *p*-state) and an ionic bond (closed shell). The quadrupole coupling of the ionic bonding vanishes. One can therefore utilize quadrupole couplings to study bond hybridization, degree of covalency, double bonding, and so on.

The fact that the closed shell electrons are very close to the nucleus makes it important to consider their distortion from spherical symmetry. For example, a charge e will produce fields that will disturb the closed shell electrons. This effect has been studied extensively by various workers. It leads to a correction to the gradient, V_{zz}^0, due to e alone. The actual field gradient V_{zz} is in fact given by

$$V_{zz} = V_{zz}^0[1 - \gamma(r)] \tag{4}$$

The quantity $\gamma(r)$ is called the *Sternheimer*† *antishielding factor*, after one of the workers who has made some of the most important contributions to understanding of the phenomenon. The fact that it is a function of the distance r from the charge e to the nucleus is emphasized by writing $\gamma(r)$. In general $\gamma(r) \ll 1$ as long as e is well inside the closed shell charge distribution. Once r is well outside, γ becomes independent of r. We shall denote this value by γ_∞. Some theoretical values for $1 - \gamma_\infty$ are shown in Table 6.3.

TABLE 6.3.
Theoretical Values of $1 - \gamma_\infty$

Ion	$1 - \gamma_\infty$
Cl^-	48
Cu^+	10
Rb^+	51
Cs^+	99

As we can see, the correction is enormous, amplifying the direct effect V_{zz}^0 by one or two orders of magnitude.

The existence of the Sternheimer effect greatly complicates the determination of nuclear quadrupole moments. It is difficult to know how accurate the theoretical γ's are. However, examination of Eq. (2) reminds us of the magnetic dipole coupling between a nucleus and an electron spin. The radial and angular terms are the same as the A and B terms of the dipolar coupling. Since the nuclear and electronic magnetic moments are known, it is therefore possible to use measured hyperfine couplings to get the average of $(3\cos^2\theta - 1)/r^3$. Since we are not using closed shells (the hyperfine coupling of a closed shell vanishes, since the electron spin is zero), the Sternheimer factor is only a small correction. This technique has been applied to the atomic beam experiments of halogens and is the basis of the most reliable experimental measurements of nuclear quadrupole moments.

† R. M. Sternheimer, *Phys. Rev.*, **84**: 244 (1951); **86**: 316 (1952); **95**: 736 (1954).

CHAPTER 7

ELECTRON SPIN RESONANCE

7·1 INTRODUCTION

So far we have confined our attention to nuclear magnetic resonance, although many of the basic principles apply to electron spin resonance. We have also considered questions concerning the electrons, such as the quenching of orbital angular momentum and the magnetic coupling of the nuclear spin to that of the electron. In this chapter we shall add a few more concepts that are important to the study of electron spin resonance† but which are not encountered in the study of nuclear resonance.

Probably the major difference between electron and nuclear magnetic resonance is the fact that the nuclear properties such as spin, magnetic moment, and quadrupole moment are to a very high degree of approximation unaffected by the surroundings, whereas for electronic systems, the relatively much greater physical size and the much smaller energy to excited states make the system strongly dependent on the surroundings. An atom, when placed in a crystal, may have angular momentum, magnetic moment, and quadrupole moment values entirely different from those of its free atom. It is as though in nuclear resonance we had to compute γ_n, I, and Q for each material in which the nucleus was to be studied.

The fact that the state of an atom in a solid or liquid is very different from that when it is free means that we can not predict the properties or even the existence of a resonance from the free atom electronic angular momentum and magnetic moment.

For example, a sodium atom has zero orbital magnetic moment and angular momentum, but it has a spin of $\frac{1}{2}$ and a corresponding spin magnetic moment. The magnetic properties can be studied by the method of atomic beams. In sodium metal, the valence electrons form a conduction band, with substantial pairing of spins. However, there is a weak electronic spin magnetization whose spin resonance has been studied. In sodium chloride, the sodium gives up its outermost electron to complete the unfilled p-shell of the chlorines. The result is a zero spin magnetization and no electron spin resonance. Even if one has atoms whose

† See references to "Electron Spin Resonance" listed in the Bibliography.

bonding is covalent, as in molecular hydrogen, there is usually no net spin magnetization because the electron spins pair off into a spin singlet. There are exceptions, of course, such as the oxygen molecule. As we remarked in connection with chemical shifts, the orbital angular momentum is usually quenched, so that there is no first-order orbital contribution to a resonance.

We see that most insulators will not exhibit a resonance, unless one takes special pains to unpair the spins. Some atoms, such as those in the iron group or rare earths, have incomplete inner shells. Even when ionized, they still possess a net moment. Thus neutral copper has a configuration $(3d)^{10}4s$. Cu^{++} has $(3d)^9$, which is paramagnetic. In an ionic substance such as $CuSO_4 \cdot 4H_2O$ (copper sulfate), the copper atoms are paramagnetic, and a resonance results.

We may list several classes of substances or circumstances in which one may expect to find resonances, although in individual cases the general rules may break down:

1. Materials containing atoms of the transition elements with incomplete inner shells; as, for example, the iron group or rare earths.
2. Ordinary metals, the conduction electrons.
3. Ferro- and ferrimagnets.
4. Imperfections in insulators, which may trap electrons or holes. For example, the F-center (electron trapped at the site of a missing halogen ion in an alkali halide) or donor and acceptor sites of semiconductors.

Treatment of all these situations on a unified basis is so hopelessly general that none of the interesting features emerges. The approximations important in one problem may not be at all justified in another. For example, if one is dealing with the resonance due to Cu^{++}, one knows already a great deal about the electronic wave function, since it will be closely related to that of a free Cu^{++} ion. One can therefore start by considering states of a free copper ion. On the other hand, there is no equivalent to the "free ion" if one is dealing with an F-center. We could not, therefore, define a set of "free ion" states.

What we shall do is list some of the more important interactions and then consider several examples that represent rather different physical situations but which involve the major phenomena.

The principal terms in the electron Hamiltonian will consist of:

1. The electron kinetic energy.
2. The electron potential energy. Often it is convenient to divide this into a "free ion" potential energy plus one due to the crystalline surroundings, the so-called crystalline potential. Such a decomposition makes sense provided there is such a thing as a "free ion," but, as remarked above, it would not have meaning for an F-center.
3. The spin-orbit coupling. An electron moving in an electric field $\mathbf{E}$ experiences a coupling of the spin to the orbital motion $\mathcal{H}_{SO}$:

$$\mathcal{H}_{SO} = \frac{e\hbar}{2m^2c^2}\mathbf{S}\cdot(\mathbf{E}\times\mathbf{p}) \tag{1}$$

Often the electric field in an atom points radially outward and is a function of r only, so that

$$\mathbf{E}(\mathbf{r}) = \frac{\mathbf{r}}{r}E(r)$$

Then $\mathbf{E}\times\mathbf{p}$ becomes $(1/r)E(r)\mathbf{r}\times\mathbf{p} = (\hbar/r)E(r)\mathbf{L}$. This circumstance leads to the well-known form of the spin-orbit coupling, utilizing the spin-orbit coupling constant λ:

$$\mathcal{H}_{SO} = \lambda \mathbf{L} \cdot \mathbf{S} \tag{2}$$

For free atoms that obey Russell-Saunders coupling, the spin-orbit coupling gives rise to the splitting of states of given L and S and their classification according to the total angular moment $J = L + S, L + S - 1, \cdots, |L - S|$.

4. The coupling of the electron spin and orbital magnetic moments to an externally applied magnetic field.

5. The magnetic coupling of the nuclear spin to the electronic spin and orbital moments.

6. The coupling of the nuclear electrical quadrupole moment to the electronic charge.

Let us turn now to an example that will illustrate the role of some of the more important terms. We begin in the next section with a discussion of the role of the crystalline fields and spin-orbit coupling. In the Section 7.3 we shall consider the coupling to the nuclear magnetic moment.

7.2 EXAMPLE OF SPIN-ORBIT COUPLING AND CRYSTALLINE FIELDS

For our example we shall consider the case of an atom at the origin of a set of coordinates, possessing a single p-electron, acted on by four charges equidistant from the origin, two of the charges being positive, two negative, their magnitudes

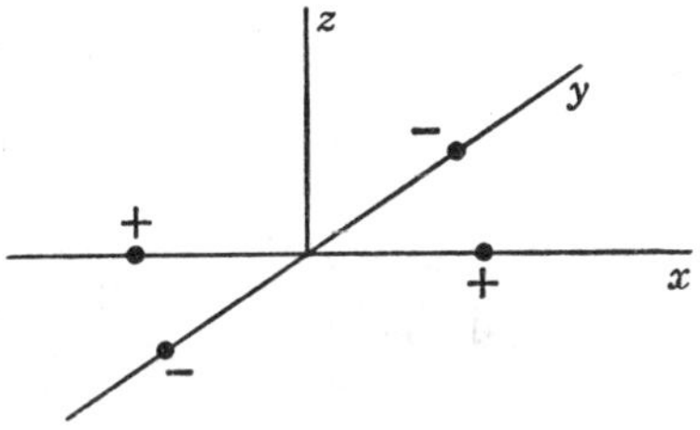

Fig. 7.1. Arrangement of two positive and two negative charges all equidistant from the origin.

all being the same. The details of the arrangement (see Fig. 7.1) are seen to be identical to those that we discussed earlier when we considered the phenomenon of chemical shifts.

Neglecting nuclear coupling, we have for the Hamiltonian of the electron of charge q (q negative):

$$\mathcal{H} = \frac{1}{2m}\left(\mathbf{p} - \frac{q}{c}\mathbf{A}\right)^2 + V_0 + V_1 + \lambda \mathbf{L} \cdot \mathbf{S} + 2\beta \mathbf{H} \cdot \mathbf{S} \tag{1}$$

where $\mathbf{A}$ is the vector potential associated with the applied static magnetic field $\mathbf{H}$, V_0 is the potential of the "free atom," V_1 is the potential due to the four charges, and $2\beta\mathbf{H} \cdot \mathbf{S}$ represents the coupling of the electron spin moment to the external field. We are here using β, the Bohr magneton, to express the electron magnetic moment. It is related to γ_e, the electron gyromagnetic ratio, and μ_e, the spin magnetic moment, by the equation:

$$\boldsymbol{\mu}_e = -\gamma_e \hbar \mathbf{S} = -2\beta \mathbf{S} \tag{2}$$

or

$$\gamma_e \hbar = 2\beta$$

the negative sign representing the fact that the spin and moment are oppositely directed.

Expanding the first term on the right of Eq. (1) gives us

$$\frac{1}{2m}\left(\mathbf{p} - \frac{q}{c}\mathbf{A}\right)^2 = \frac{p^2}{2m} - \frac{q}{2mc}(\mathbf{p}\cdot\mathbf{A} + \mathbf{A}\cdot\mathbf{p}) + \frac{q^2}{2mc^2}A^2 \tag{3}$$

It is convenient to specify the vector potential as

$$\mathbf{A} = \tfrac{1}{2}\mathbf{H}_0 \times \mathbf{r} \tag{4}$$

which gives us

$$\frac{1}{2m}\left(\mathbf{p} - \frac{q}{c}\mathbf{A}\right)^2 = \frac{p^2}{2m} - \frac{q\hbar}{2mc}\mathbf{H}_0\cdot\mathbf{L} + \frac{q^2}{8mc^2}H_0^2(x'^2 + y'^2) \tag{5}$$

where, as usual, $\mathbf{L} = (1/i)\mathbf{r} \times \nabla$, and where the axes x' and y' are perpendicular to the field direction z'. (We distinguish between the field direction z' and the crystalline axis z.) The term proportional to H_0^2 gives the usual diamagnetism. It turns out to be unimportant, compared to the term $\mathbf{H}_0 \cdot \mathbf{L}$, in influencing the electron spin resonance. By utilizing the fact that $\beta = e\hbar/2mc$, we have, accordingly, as the Hamiltonian:

$$\mathcal{H} = \frac{p^2}{2m} + \beta\mathbf{H}_0\cdot\mathbf{L} + V_0 + V_1 + \lambda\mathbf{L}\cdot\mathbf{S} + 2\beta\mathbf{H}\cdot\mathbf{S} \tag{6}$$

We shall consider that the principal energy terms are the kinetic energy and the "free atom" potential V_0. We shall treat the remaining terms by a perturbation method. For our example we shall think of the three degenerate p-states $xf(r)$, $yf(r)$, and $zf(r)$, which are solutions of the free atom potential V_0. We shall assume that the coupling to other free atom states is relatively unimportant, so that the effect of the remaining terms in the Hamiltonian can be found by considering only the submatrix of the Hamiltonian involving these three orbital states.

For practical laboratory fields the terms $\mathbf{H} \cdot \mathbf{L}$ and $\mathbf{H} \cdot \mathbf{S}$ are only about 1 cm^{-1}, whereas V_1 may be a substantial part of an electron volt (that is, 100 cm^{-1} to 10,000 cm^{-1}). The spin-orbit coupling constants vary substantially, some typical values of the coupling per electron being given in Table 7.1.

TABLE 7·1.
Spin-Orbit Coupling Constants per Electron for Several Atoms

Atom	Coupling Constant (cm^{-1})
B	10
C	28
F	271
Cl	440
Br	1842

We see that, under some circumstances, V_1 will dominate; under other circumstances the spin-orbit coupling will be the major effect. The latter situation is, for example, typical of the rare earths, whereas the former is typical of the iron group.

Let us first consider the case that V_1 is much larger than λ. At first, we consider the effect of V_1 only. For the situation of Fig. 7.1, the effect of V_1 will be to lift the orbital degeneracy. The resultant energy levels, shown in Fig. 7.2, are all

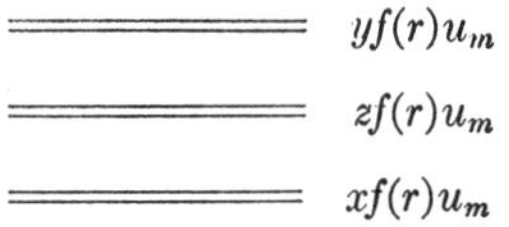

FIG. 7.2. Energy levels of the three p-states under the potential of Fig. 7.1.

two-fold degenerate because of the electron spin. We denote the wave functions as $xf(r)u_m$, and so on, where the function u_m is a spin function. If there were no spin-orbit coupling, the spin would be quantized independently of the orbital state so that the u_m's would be the usual eigenfunctions of $S_{z'}$, where z' is the magnetic field direction.

Let us consider, then, the effect of the two remaining terms:

$$\beta \mathbf{H} \cdot \mathbf{L} + \lambda \mathbf{L} \cdot \mathbf{S} \tag{7}$$

We examine the sorts of matrix elements these terms possess. There are two sorts, those that connect the same orbital state, and those that connect different orbital states. The former are clearly the more important, if they exist, since the orbital splittings are so large. We have, then, matrix elements such as

$$\int xf(r)u_m^* \beta H_z L_z xf(r)u_{m'}\, d\tau\, d\tau_s \tag{8}$$

or

$$\int xf(r)u_m^* \lambda L_z S_z xf(r)u_{m'}\, d\tau\, d\tau_s \tag{9}$$

where $d\tau$ stands for an integral over spatial coordinates, and $d\tau_s$, over spin variables. We see that both integrals of Eqs. (8) and (9) involve

$$\int xf(r)L_z xf(r)\, d\tau \tag{10}$$

Recalling our earlier discussion about the quenching of orbital angular momentum, we realize that the integral of Eq. (10) vanishes. Therefore the only non-vanishing matrix elements of terms $\beta\mathbf{H} \cdot \mathbf{L}$ and $\lambda\mathbf{L} \cdot \mathbf{S}$ connect states differing in the orbital energy. They have, therefore, no effect in first order.

We have discussed this very problem in the absence of spin, noting that there was no first-order term $\beta\mathbf{H} \cdot \mathbf{L}$, since the states $xf(r)$, and so forth, correspond to no net circulation of the electron. A similar remark applies to the spin-orbit coupling. The spin is coupled to states in which the electron has no preferential circulation. The average magnetic field due to orbital motion seen by the spin vanishes.

We know, however, from our discussion of chemical shifts that the term $\beta\mathbf{H} \cdot \mathbf{L}$ will induce some orbital circulation. The spin will not, therefore, experience a strictly zero field due to orbital motion.

We can think of solving exactly for the wave function under the influence of the applied field and of computing the matrix elements of $\lambda\mathbf{L}\cdot\mathbf{S}$, using the exact wave function. As a practical matter we use perturbation theory to compute the effect of $\beta\mathbf{H}\cdot\mathbf{L}$ on the wave function, keeping only the first term.† We have, then, for the modified wave function ψ_{xm},

$$\psi_{xm} = xf(r)u_m + \sum_{m'}\sum_{w=y,z} \frac{(wm'|\beta\mathbf{H}\cdot\mathbf{L}|xm)}{E_x - E_w} wf(r)u_{m'} \tag{11}$$

Since $\beta\mathbf{H}\cdot\mathbf{L}$ does not depend on spin, $m' = m$. By writing the interaction $\beta\mathbf{H}\cdot\mathbf{L}$ in component form, we find

$$\psi_{xm} = \left[xf(r) + \sum_{w=y,z}\sum_{q=x,y,z} \frac{(w|L_q|x)}{E_x - E_w} \beta H_q wf(r)\right]u_m \tag{12}$$

We now use this corrected function to compute matrix elements of $\lambda\mathbf{L}\cdot\mathbf{S}$ which involve the ground orbital state. There are actually matrix elements to the excited state, which in second order can couple back down to the ground state. However, they do not involve the applied field $\mathbf{H}$. By neglecting them, we are finding the field dependent coupling energy. (The second-order terms in spin-orbit coupling produce no splitting when the spin is $\frac{1}{2}$.)

$$\begin{aligned}\int \psi^*_{xm'}\lambda\mathbf{L}\cdot\mathbf{S}\psi_{xm}\,d\tau\,d\tau_s \\ = \lambda\beta \sum_{w=y,z}\ \sum_{q,q'=x,y,z} \frac{(m'|S_{q'}|m)[(x|L_{q'}|w)(w|L_q|x) + (x|L_q|w)(w|L_{q'}|x)]H_q}{E_x - E_w}\end{aligned} \tag{13}$$

For computing matrix elements internal to the ground orbital state, Eq. (13) is equivalent to our replacing the terms $\beta\mathbf{H}\cdot\mathbf{L}$ and $\lambda\mathbf{L}\cdot\mathbf{S}$ by an effective term in the Hamiltonian ($\mathcal{H}_{\text{eff}}$):

$$\begin{aligned}\mathcal{H}_{\text{eff}} &= \sum_{q,q'} S_q H_{q'}\lambda\beta \sum_{w} \frac{[(x|L_q|w)(w|L_{q'}|x) + (x|L_{q'}|w)(w|L_q|x)]}{E_x - E_w} \\ &= \beta\sum_{q,q'} S_q a_{qq'} H_{q'}\end{aligned} \tag{14}$$

Since the matrix elements that make up $a_{qq'}$ transform under coordinate rotations like L_q and $L_{q'}$, the $a_{qq'}$'s are components of a second-rank tensor. Examination of Eq. (14) shows that it is a symmetric tensor ($a_{qq'} = a_{q'q}$).

† We have two terms in the Hamiltonian, $\beta\mathbf{H}\cdot\mathbf{L}$ and $\lambda\mathbf{L}\cdot\mathbf{S}$, neither of which gives a first-order contribution. In second and higher orders, both terms perturb the wave function. Because of the similarity between the present problem and the chemical shift, first of all we treat the effect of the term $\beta\mathbf{H}\cdot\mathbf{L}$ on the wave function. It may seem more sensible to take the much larger $\lambda\mathbf{L}\cdot\mathbf{S}$ term first. As we shall see, however, our final answer involves an approximation that is proportional to the product $\beta\mathbf{H}\cdot\mathbf{L}$ and $\lambda\mathbf{L}\cdot\mathbf{S}$ (it is the interplay between the two energies that gives the effect). For this purpose it is immaterial which interaction we use to perturb the wave function.

For our particular case we can compute the matrix elements from the operators

$$L_x = \frac{1}{i}\left(y\frac{\partial}{\partial z} - z\frac{\partial}{\partial y}\right)$$
$$L_y = \frac{1}{i}\left(z\frac{\partial}{\partial x} - x\frac{\partial}{\partial z}\right) \tag{15}$$
$$L_z = \frac{1}{i}\left(x\frac{\partial}{\partial y} - y\frac{\partial}{\partial x}\right)$$

By using these expressions, we find that

$$L_x x f(r) = 0$$
$$L_y x f(r) = \frac{1}{i} z f(r) \tag{16}$$
$$L_z x f(r) = -\frac{1}{i} y f(r)$$

Thus the matrix elements of L_x vanish, those of L_y connect only to the state $zf(r)$, and those of L_z connect only to $yf(r)$. This gives us contributions only from terms with $q = q'$. That is, the x-, y-, z-axes are principal axes of the tensor $a_{qq'}$. Specifically we have, using Eqs. (14) and (16),

$$\mathcal{H}_{\text{eff}} = 2\beta\left[\frac{\lambda}{E_x - E_z} S_y H_y + \frac{\lambda}{E_x - E_y} S_z H_z\right] \tag{17}$$

By combining this result with the Zeeman term, $2\beta\mathbf{H} \cdot \mathbf{S}$, we obtain a spin Hamiltonian for the ground orbital state

$$\mathcal{H} = \beta(g_{xx}H_x S_x + g_{yy}H_y S_y + g_{zz}H_z S_z) \tag{18}$$

where

$$g_{xx} = 2$$
$$g_{yy} = 2\left(1 - \frac{\lambda}{E_z - E_x}\right) \tag{19}$$
$$g_{zz} = 2\left(1 - \frac{\lambda}{E_y - E_x}\right)$$

We may employ the dyadic notation $\mathbf{g}$, defined by

$$\mathbf{g} = \mathbf{i}g_{xx}\mathbf{i} + \mathbf{j}g_{yy}\mathbf{j} + \mathbf{k}g_{zz}\mathbf{k} \tag{20}$$

to write the interaction as

$$\mathcal{H} = \beta\mathbf{H} \cdot \mathbf{g} \cdot \mathbf{S} \tag{21}$$

in place of

$$\mathcal{H} = 2\beta\mathbf{H} \cdot \mathbf{S} \tag{22}$$

Comparison of Eqs. (21) and (22) shows that the combined effect of the spin-orbit coupling and orbital Zeeman energy is as though the real field $\mathbf{H}$ were replaced by an effective field $\mathbf{H}_{\text{eff}}$, given by

$$\mathbf{H}_{\text{eff}} = \frac{\mathbf{H} \cdot \mathbf{g}}{2} = \mathbf{i}H_x \frac{g_{xx}}{2} + \mathbf{j}H_y \frac{g_{yy}}{2} + \mathbf{k}H_z \frac{g_{zz}}{2} \tag{23}$$

with the resonance given by

$$\mathcal{H} = 2\beta \mathbf{H}_{\text{eff}} \cdot \mathbf{S} \tag{24}$$

Since g_{xx}, g_{yy}, and g_{zz} are in general different, the effective field differs from the actual field in both magnitude and direction. If we denote by z'' the direction of the effective field, it is clear that a coordinate transformation will put Eq. (24) into the form

$$\mathcal{H} = 2\beta H_{\text{eff}} S_{z''} \tag{25}$$

where H_{eff} is the magnitude of $\mathbf{H}_{\text{eff}}$. The resonant frequency ω_0 therefore satisfies the condition

$$\begin{aligned} \hbar\omega_0 &= 2\beta H_{\text{eff}} \\ &= \beta\sqrt{H_x^2 g_{xx}^2 + H_y^2 g_{yy}^2 + H_z^2 g_{zz}^2} \\ &= \beta H \sqrt{\alpha_1^2 g_{xx}^2 + \alpha_2^2 g_{yy}^2 + \alpha_3^2 g_{zz}^2} \end{aligned} \tag{26}$$

where α_1, α_2, and α_3 are the cosines of the angle between $\mathbf{H}$ and the x-, y-, and z-axes. Often one writes Eq. (26) as

$$\hbar\omega_0 = g\beta H \tag{27}$$

where the "g-factor" is defined by the equation

$$g = \sqrt{g_{xx}^2\alpha_1^2 + g_{yy}^2\alpha_2^2 + g_{zz}^2\alpha_3^2} \tag{28}$$

Eqs. (27) and (28) emphasize the fact that for a given orientation of $\mathbf{H}$, the splitting of the spin states is directly proportional to the magnitude of $\mathbf{H}$. Frequently one talks about the g-shift, a term that refers to the difference between g and the free spin value of 2. From Eqs. (19) and (28), recognizing that both $E_z - E_x$ and $E_y - E_x$ are positive, we see that positive values of λ make g less than or equal to 2, whereas negative λ's make g greater than or equal to 2. We associate positive λ's with atomic shells less than half-full, negative λ's with those more than half-full. Another terminology is to remark that electron resonances give positive λ and hole resonances give negative λ's. We shall return to this point in Section 7.4, where we shall find that a great deal of caution must be exercised in this simple interpretation as a general rule.

The size of the g-shift clearly increases with the nuclear charge, as we noted in Table 7.1. Its magnitude also depends on the magnitude of the splitting to the excited states to which the orbital angular momentum couples. Using an energy of about 1.3 ev (10,000 cm^{-1}) and a λ of 100 cm^{-1}, we see $2 - g \approx 0.02$, a readily observable effect.

We note that the g-shift arises because of the interplay between the spin-orbit and orbital Zeeman interactions. It is analogous to the chemical shift that arises from the interplay between nuclear spin-electron orbit coupling and the electron orbital Zeeman interaction. In both cases we say that the spin (electron or nuclear) experiences both the applied magnetic field and a sort of induced magnetic field. All such phenomena involving the interplay of two interactions can be viewed also as an application of a generalized form of second-order perturbation theory. This is in fact Ramsey's method for deriving the chemical shift formulas. We shall illustrate by computing the g-shift.

The problem is treated in general in Appendix D. There it is shown that the perturbation effectively adds a term, $\mathcal{H}_{\text{new}}$, to the Hamiltonian, which has matrix elements between states $|0)$ and $|0')$; for our example these elements have the same orbital part $xf(r)$ but may differ in spin function.

Defining a perturbation term, $\mathcal{H}_{\text{pert}}$, by

$$\mathcal{H}_{\text{pert}} = \lambda \mathbf{L} \cdot \mathbf{S} + \beta \mathbf{H} \cdot \mathbf{L} \tag{29}$$

we find a matrix element $(0|\mathcal{H}_{\text{new}}|0')$ between $|0)$ and $|0')$, as outlined in Appendix D, given by

$$(0|\mathcal{H}_{\text{new}}|0') = \sum_n \frac{(0|\mathcal{H}_{\text{pert}}|n)(n|\mathcal{H}_{\text{pert}}|0')}{E_0 - E_n} \tag{30}$$

By substituting from Eq. (29), we get

$$\begin{aligned}(0|\mathcal{H}_{\text{new}}|0') = \sum_n \bigg\{ & \frac{(0|\lambda\mathbf{L}\cdot\mathbf{S}|n)(n|\beta\mathbf{H}\cdot\mathbf{L}|0')}{E_0 - E_n} \\ & + \frac{(0|\beta\mathbf{H}\cdot\mathbf{L}|n)(n|\lambda\mathbf{L}\cdot\mathbf{S}|0')}{E_0 - E_n} \\ & + \frac{(0|\beta\mathbf{H}\cdot\mathbf{L}|n)(n|\beta\mathbf{H}\cdot\mathbf{L}|0')}{E_0 - E_n} + \frac{(0|\lambda\mathbf{L}\cdot\mathbf{S}|n)(n|\lambda\mathbf{L}\cdot\mathbf{S}|0')}{E_0 - E_n} \bigg\}\end{aligned} \tag{31}$$

The first two terms on the right give the g-shift we have calculated. The last two terms shift the two spin states equally. They do not, therefore, either produce a splitting of the doubly degenerate ground state or contribute to the g-shift. (If the spin were greater than $\frac{1}{2}$, however, such a term could give a splitting of the ground spin state even when $\mathbf{H} = 0$.) The last two terms are just what we should have had if either perturbation were present by itself. Our previous calculation of the g-shift did not give them because it treated the effect of one term of the perturbation ($\beta\mathbf{H} \cdot \mathbf{L}$) on the other ($\lambda\mathbf{L} \cdot \mathbf{S}$). The method could be extended to find all the terms included in Eq. (31), but we see that direct application of Eq. (30) gives us a systematic method of getting all terms. On the other hand, the physical principles of the first calculation are somewhat more apparent.

In the example we have discussed so far, we have considered the crystalline potential V_1 to be much larger than the spin-orbit coupling constant λ. As a result, the orbital angular momentum is largely quenched, and the g-value is very close to the spin-only value of 2. This situation corresponds to the iron group atoms as well as to many electron and hole centers. We turn now to the opposite case, one of strong spin-orbit coupling and relatively much weaker crystalline fields, as encountered in the case of rare earth atoms.

If the spin-orbit coupling is dominant, the situation is in first approximation similar to that of a free atom. In fact the Hamiltonian

$$\mathcal{H} = \frac{p^2}{2m} + V_0 + \lambda\mathbf{L}\cdot\mathbf{S} + \beta\mathbf{H}\cdot\mathbf{L} + 2\beta\mathbf{H}\cdot\mathbf{S} + V_1 \tag{32}$$

is identical to that of a free atom except for the term V_1. As a first approximation we consider just the effect of the term $\lambda\mathbf{L}\cdot\mathbf{S}$ on the state formed from spin functions and the three p-states $xf(r)$, $yf(r)$, and $zf(r)$. The sum of the angular momenta **L** and **S** is the total angular momentum **J**.

$$\mathbf{J} = \mathbf{L} + \mathbf{S} \tag{33}$$

By squaring **J**, we have

$$\lambda\mathbf{L}\cdot\mathbf{S} = \frac{\lambda}{2}[\mathbf{J}^2 - \mathbf{L}^2 - \mathbf{S}^2] \tag{34}$$

with eigenvalues E_{SO} given by

$$E_{SO} = \frac{\lambda}{2}[J(J+1) - L(L+1) - S(S+1)] \tag{35}$$

Since we are concerned with states all of which are characterized by an orbital quantum number L and spin quantum number S, the possible values of J are $L+S, L+S-1, \cdots |L-S|$. For our example, $L = 1$, $S = \frac{1}{2}$, so that $J = \frac{3}{2}$ or $\frac{1}{2}$. The $J = \frac{3}{2}$ and $\frac{1}{2}$ states are therefore split apart by an energy spacing

$$\Delta E = \tfrac{3}{2}\lambda \tag{36}$$

(More generally the state J is λJ above the state $J - 1$.) The energy levels are shown in Fig. 7.3 for a positive λ.

FIG. 7.3. Energy levels for $L = 1$, $S = \frac{1}{2}$ resulting from a spin orbit coupling $\lambda\mathbf{L}\cdot\mathbf{S}$.

We consider next the effect of V_1. Here it becomes convenient to assume a specific form. Assuming that the potential arises from charges external to the atom, the potential in the region of the atom can be expressed as a sum of the form

$$V_1 = \sum_{l,m} C_{lm} r^l Y_{lm} \tag{37}$$

where the Y_{lm}'s are spherical harmonics and the C_{lm}'s are constants. If the potential is due to the charges of Fig. 7.1, it vanishes on the z-axis and changes sign if we replace x by y and y by $-x$ (a coordinate rotation). It is a maximum on the x-axis and a minimum on the y-axis for a given distance from the origin. The lowest l in the series of Eq. (37) is clearly $l = 2$. Of the five $l = 2$ functions, xy, xz, yz, $3z^2 - r^2$, $x^2 - y^2$, only the last is needed. We have, therefore, as an approximation, insofar as terms for $l > 2$ are not required,

$$V_1 = A(x^2 - y^2) \tag{38}$$

where A is a constant. (We shall see shortly that no higher terms are needed for an exact treatment.) We have, then, to consider the effect of V_1 on the states of Fig. 7.3. Two sorts of matrix elements will be important: those entirely within a given J, such as $(JM_J|V_1|JM'_J)$ and those connecting the different J states. The former will be the more important because they connect degenerate states. We can compute the matrix elements internal to a given J by means of the Wigner-Eckart theorem, for we notice that, with respect to L_x, L_y, and L_z (hence with respect to J_x, J_y, and J_z), V_1 is a linear combination of T_{2M}'s. That is, the commutation relations of V_1 with J_z, $J_x \pm iJ_y$ show V_1 to be a linear combination of T_{2M}'s. (In fact V_1 is proportional to $T_{22} + T_{2-2}$). Thus we have

$$\begin{aligned}(JM_J|V_1|JM'_J) &= A(JM_J|x^2 - y^2|JM'_J) \\ &= C_J(JM_J|J_x^2 - J_y^2|JM'_J)\end{aligned} \tag{39}$$

This is equivalent to our replacing V_1 by the operator $\mathcal{H}_1$,

$$\mathcal{H}_1 = C_J(J_x^2 - J_y^2) \tag{40}$$

as long as we only compute matrix elements diagonal in J.

As an alternative, had the potential V_1 been $B(3z^2 - r^2)$, we should have used

$$\mathcal{H}_1 = C'_J(3J_z^2 - J^2) \tag{41}$$

We describe the calculation of C_J and C'_J below. This case of what is called the "axial field" is frequently encountered.

We have still to consider the effect of the magnetic field terms. Again let us consider only the matrix elements diagonal in J. This means that we wish to have

$$(JM_J|\beta\mathbf{H}\cdot\mathbf{L} + 2\beta\mathbf{H}\cdot\mathbf{S}|JM'_J) = \beta\mathbf{H}\cdot(JM_J|\mathbf{L} + 2\mathbf{S}|JM'_J) \tag{42}$$

We can apply the Wigner-Eckart theorem to the matrix element, which, with respect to $\mathbf{J}$, is a linear combination of T_{1M}'s. We can therefore write

$$(JM_J|\mathbf{L} + 2\mathbf{S}|JM'_J) = g_J(JM_J|\mathbf{J}|JM'_J) \tag{43}$$

where g_J is a constant for a given J, independent of M_J or M'_J. We recognize this problem to be the same as that of computing the Zeeman effect of free atoms, and the constant g_J is therefore the familiar Landé g-factor:

$$g_J = 1 + \frac{J(J+1) + S(S+1) - L(L+1)}{2J(J+1)} \tag{44}$$

Equation (43) is equivalent (as far as matrix elements diagonal in J are concerned) to our having a term $\mathcal{H}_Z$ replacing the two magnetic terms, where $\mathcal{H}_Z$ is given by

$$\mathcal{H}_Z = g_J\beta\mathbf{H}\cdot\mathbf{J} \tag{45}$$

By combining Eqs. (40) and (45) with Eq. (34), we obtain an effective spin Hamiltonian, $\mathcal{H}_{\text{eff}}$, which describes our problem accurately within a given J:

$$\mathcal{H}_{\text{eff}} = C_J(J_x^2 - J_y^2) + g_J\beta\mathbf{H}\cdot\mathbf{J} \tag{46}$$

or, for the axial field,

$$\mathcal{H}_{\text{eff}} = C'_J(3J_z^2 - J^2) + g_J\beta\mathbf{H}\cdot\mathbf{J} \tag{47}$$

The two terms on the right of Eqs. (46) and (47) lift the $(2J + 1)$-fold degeneracy of each J state. We shall not discuss the details of handling this problem other than to remark that clearly it is formally equivalent to the solution of the problem of a nucleus possessing a quadrupole moment acted on by an electric field gradient and a static magnetic field.

So far we have not computed the constants C_J or C'_J. We turn now to that task, illustrating the method by computing C'_J.

We have, using Eq. (41),

$$B(JM_J|3z^2 - r^2|JM'_J) = C'_J(JM_J|3J_z^2 - J^2|JM'_J) \tag{48}$$

By choosing $M_J = M'_J = J$, we have

$$B(JJ|3z^2 - r^2|JJ) = C'_J[3J^2 - J(J+1)] \tag{48a}$$

$$C'_J = \frac{B}{J(2J-1)}(JJ|3z^2 - r^2|JJ) \tag{49}$$

Now, for $J = \frac{1}{2}$, all matrix elements of $3J_z^2 - J^2$ vanish (analogous to the fact that a quadrupole coupling cannot split a pair of spin $\frac{1}{2}$ levels). For $J = \frac{3}{2}$, we have

$$|JJ) = \left(\frac{x + iy}{\sqrt{2}}\right) f(r) u_{1/2} \tag{51}$$

where we have denoted the spin function $S_z = +\frac{1}{2}$ by $u_{1/2}$. Therefore we find

$$C'_{3/2} = \frac{B}{3}\int\left(\frac{x^2 + y^2}{2}\right) f^2(r)(3z^2 - r^2)\, d\tau \tag{52}$$

The angular portions of the integral can be carried through, using spherical coordinates, to give

$$C'_{3/2} = -\frac{2B}{15}\overline{r^2} \tag{52a}$$

where $\overline{r^2}$ is the average value of r^2 for the p-states.

The spin Hamiltonians of Eqs. (46) and (47) do not include any matrix elements joining states of $J = \frac{3}{2}$ with those of $J = \frac{1}{2}$. If we wish to include such effects, we can actually apply the Wigner-Eckart theorem in an alternate manner. All matrix elements of V_1 are between states of $L = 1$. That is, we are concerned only with $(LM_L|V_1|LM'_L)$. However, the commutators of L_x, L_y, and L_z with V_1 show that V_1 is a linear combination of T_{2M}'s. Therefore all matrix elements are of the form

$$\begin{aligned} A(LM_L|x^2 - y^2|LM'_L) &= C_L(LM_L|L_x^2 - L_y^2|LM'_L) \\ B(LM_L|3z^2 - r^2|LM'_L) &= C'_L(LM_L|3L_z^2 - L^2|LM'_L) \end{aligned} \tag{53}$$

These matrix elements are equivalent to those we should have had by replacing V_1 by an equivalent Hamiltonian, $\mathcal{H}_1$:

$$\mathcal{H}_1 = C_L(L_x^2 - L_y^2)$$

or

$$\mathcal{H}_1 = C'_L(3L_z^2 - L^2) \tag{54}$$

In terms of $\mathcal{H}_1$, the effective Hamiltonian $\mathcal{H}_{\text{eff}}$, which will give all matrix elements formed from the three p-states $xf(r)$, $yf(r)$, and $zf(r)$, is

$$\mathcal{H}_{\text{eff}} = \lambda \mathbf{L} \cdot \mathbf{S} + C_L(L_x^2 - L_y^2) + \beta \mathbf{H} \cdot (2\mathbf{S} + \mathbf{L})$$

or (55)

$$\mathcal{H}_{\text{eff}} = \lambda(\mathbf{L} \cdot \mathbf{S}) + C'_L(3L_z^2 - L^2) + \beta \mathbf{H} \cdot (2\mathbf{S} + \mathbf{L})$$

Eq. (55) reduces to Eq. (46) or (47) for matrix elements diagonal in J.

In the absence of an external magnetic field, the energy levels of the Hamiltonian of Eq. (55) would remain at least doubly degenerate, according to Kramer's theorem, stated in Section 6.5 since $L = 1$, $S = \frac{1}{2}$.

It is interesting to note that the derivation of Eq. (43)

$$(JM_J|\mathbf{L} + 2\mathbf{S}|JM'_J) = g_J(JM_J|\mathbf{J}|JM'_J) \tag{43}$$

using the Wigner-Eckart theorem, is quite analogous to the statement about the nuclear magnetic moment $\boldsymbol{\mu}$ and spin $\mathbf{I}$

$$\boldsymbol{\mu} = \gamma \hbar \mathbf{I} \tag{56}$$

which, stated more precisely, is

$$(IM|\boldsymbol{\mu}|IM') = \gamma \hbar (IM|\mathbf{I}|IM') \tag{57}$$

We expressed the potential of Fig. 7.1 by means of only *one* term in the expansion of the potential, that with $l = 2$. We might have supposed also that terms $l = 4$, 6, and so on, would have been needed. (The odd l's are not needed for this example, owing to the inversion symmetry of the charges.) If we had included an $l = 4$ term, we should have then needed to compute matrix elements such as

$$(LM_L|r^l Y_{lm}|LM'_L) \tag{58}$$

with $l = 4$. However, with respect to L_x, L_y, and L_z, $r^l Y_{lm}$ is a T_{lm}. Therefore we can apply the Wigner-Eckart theorem to evaluate it. Recognizing that such an integral is closely related to the combination of angular momentum (by means of the Clebsch-Gordan coefficients), we note that it will vanish unless L and l can couple to form an angular momentum L (the triangle rule). For the case $L = 1$, $l = 4$, we can see that L and l could combine to give angular momenta of 5, 4, or 3, so that the integral must vanish. In fact, for $L = 1$, only $l = 2$ gives non-vanishing matrix elements. We need not, therefore, bother with $l = 4$, 6, and so on, in the expansion of the potential.

7.3 HYPERFINE STRUCTURE

We have not as yet considered the magnetic coupling of the electron to the nearby nuclei. The basic form of the interaction has been discussed in Chapter 4. We distinguish between s-states and non s-states.

s-states:

$$\mathcal{H}_{ISr} = \frac{8\pi}{3} \gamma_e \gamma_n \hbar^2 \mathbf{I} \cdot \mathbf{S}\, \delta(\mathbf{r}) \tag{1}$$

Non s-states:

$$\mathcal{H}_{ISr} = \frac{\gamma_e \gamma_n \hbar^2}{r^3}\left[\frac{3(\mathbf{I}\cdot\mathbf{r})(\mathbf{S}\cdot\mathbf{r})}{r^2} - \mathbf{I}\cdot\mathbf{S}\right] \tag{2}$$

The effect of the hyperfine coupling can be illustrated by considering the example of the preceding section in which the orbital angular momentum was quenched (corresponding to a crystalline potential V_1 much larger than the spin-orbit coupling λ). In the Hamiltonian matrix there will then be elements of the hyperfine coupling diagonal in the electron orbital energy as well as those connecting states of different crystalline energy such as $xf(r)$ and $yf(r)$. We shall neglect the elements that are off-diagonal. We have, then, only matrix elements such as

$$(xm_Sm_I|\mathcal{H}_{ISr}|xm_S'm_I') = \int \phi^*_{m_I}u^*_{m_S}xf(r)\mathcal{H}_{ISr}\phi_{m_I'}u_{m_S'}xf(r)\,d\tau\,d\tau_S\,d\tau_I \tag{3}$$

where m_S and m_I stand for eigenvalues of S_z and I_z, ϕ_{m_I} and u_{m_S} are nuclear and electron spin functions, and where $d\tau$ and $d\tau_S$ stand for integration, respectively, over electron spatial and spin coordinates, and $d\tau_I$ over nuclear spin coordinate. It is, as usual, convenient to leave the specification of the quantization of both electron and nuclear spin till later, since the appropriate quantum states will depend on other parts of the Hamiltonian. We therefore omit the electron and nuclear spin functions and integrations, computing only $\int xf(r)\mathcal{H}_{ISr}xf(r)\,d\tau$. This integral leaves the nuclear and electron spin coordinates as operators. We shall therefore denote it by $\mathcal{H}_{IS}$.

$$\mathcal{H}_{IS} = \int xf(r)\mathcal{H}_{ISr}xf(r)\,d\tau \tag{4}$$

By substituting Eq. (2), we obtain

$$\mathcal{H}_{IS} = \gamma_e\gamma_n\hbar^2 \int \frac{1}{r^3}\left[3\left(\frac{\mathbf{I}\cdot\mathbf{r}}{r^2}\right)(\mathbf{S}\cdot\mathbf{r}) - \mathbf{I}\cdot\mathbf{S}\right] x^2f^2(r)\,d\tau \tag{5}$$

The terms such as I_xxS_yy will contribute nothing, since for them the integrand is an odd function of x or y. The other terms can be expressed as the product of angular and radial integrals, giving

$$\mathcal{H}_{IS} = \gamma_e\gamma_n\hbar^2\left(\overline{\frac{1}{r^3}}\right)\frac{2}{5}\,[3I_xS_x - \mathbf{I}\cdot\mathbf{S}] \tag{6}$$

where, as usual, $(\overline{1/r^3})$ denotes the value of $1/r^3$ averaged over the state $xf(r)$.

If instead of a p-state we had an s-state, or more generally a wave function ψ containing some s-state, we could compute a corresponding term $\mathcal{H}_{IS}$ arising from the δ-function coupling:

$$\mathcal{H}_{IS} = \int \psi^*(\mathbf{r})\mathcal{H}_{ISr}\psi(\mathbf{r})\,d\tau$$

$$= \frac{8\pi}{3}\gamma_e\gamma_n\hbar^2|\psi(0)|^2\mathbf{I}\cdot\mathbf{S} \tag{7}$$

The most general interaction is, of course, the sum of the couplings to the interactions of Eqs. (1) and (2):

$$\mathcal{H}_{IS} = \int |\psi(\mathbf{r})|^2\left\{\frac{8\pi}{3}\gamma_e\gamma_n\hbar^2\mathbf{I}\cdot\mathbf{S}\,\delta(\mathbf{r}) + \frac{\gamma_e\gamma_n}{r^3}\hbar^2\left[3\,\frac{(\mathbf{I}\cdot\mathbf{r})(\mathbf{S}\cdot\mathbf{r})}{r^2}\right] - \mathbf{I}\cdot\mathbf{S}\right\}d\tau \tag{8}$$

It will be linear in the spin variables I_x, I_y, I_z and S_x, S_y, and S_z, being of the general form,

$$\mathcal{H}_{IS} = \sum_{\alpha,\alpha'=x,y,z} A_{\alpha\alpha'} S_\alpha I_{\alpha'} \tag{9}$$

but with the A's symmetric (that is, $A_{\alpha\alpha'} = A_{\alpha'\alpha}$). One can therefore always find the principal axes such that $A_{\alpha\alpha'}$ is diagonal, with values A_α and the hyperfine coupling given as

$$\begin{aligned}\mathcal{H}_{IS} &= A_x I_x S_x + S_y A_y I_y + A_z I_z S_z \\ &= \mathbf{S} \cdot \mathbf{A} \cdot \mathbf{I}\end{aligned} \tag{10}$$

where the dyadic $\mathbf{A}$ is given by

$$\mathbf{A} = \mathbf{i}A_x\mathbf{i} + \mathbf{j}A_y\mathbf{j} + \mathbf{k}A_z\mathbf{k} \tag{11}$$

If we did not have quenched orbital angular momentum, it would be necessary to include the coupling of the nuclear moment to the magnetic field arising from the orbital motion of the electron. We should also need to choose a new set of basic electronic states to obtain the "spin" Hamiltonian, such as, for example, states that are eigenfunctions of J^2.

We can combine Eq. (10) with Eq. (21) of the preceding section to obtain the spin Hamiltonian that includes both nucleus and electron for a case of quenched orbital angular momentum:

$$\mathcal{H} = \beta \mathbf{H} \cdot \mathbf{g} \cdot \mathbf{S} - \gamma_n \hbar \mathbf{H} \cdot \mathbf{I} + \mathbf{I} \cdot \mathbf{A} \cdot \mathbf{S} \tag{12}$$

(If the nucleus experiences a quadrupolar coupling, a term $\mathcal{H}_Q$ should be added.)

We shall examine the sorts of effects that the couplings of Eq. (12) produce by a simple example. We note first that there is no reason for the principal axes of $\mathbf{g}$ and $\mathbf{A}$ to coincide, although they do in fact for many simple cases. (Experimental situations have been reported in which they differ.) We shall assume that they do, for our example. We begin, moreover, with the assumption that H is parallel to one of the principal axes, the z-axis, so that

$$\mathcal{H} = \beta H g_{zz} S_z - \gamma_n \hbar H I_z + A_x I_x S_x + A_y I_y S_y + A_z I_z S_z \tag{13}$$

We cannot solve this Hamiltonian in closed form without making some approximations. We shall assume that the electron spin Zeeman energy, $\beta H g_{zz}$, is much bigger than the hyperfine coupling energies A_x, A_y, and A_z. This approximation is frequently good when one has strong magnetic fields ($2\beta H = 10^{10}$ cycles for $H =$ 3300 gauss, whereas A is often 10^9 cycles or less). If we take the electron Zeeman term to be large, we see that $\mathcal{H}$ commutes with S_z to a good approximation. We take the eigenfunctions to be eigenfunctions of S_z, with eigenvalue m_S. The terms $A_x S_x I_x$ and $A_y S_y I_y$ then have no matrix elements that are diagonal in m_S. We drop them from the Hamiltonian in first order. On the other hand, $A_z S_z I_z$ is diagonal in m_S and must be kept. This gives us an approximate Hamiltonian:

$$\mathcal{H} = \beta g_{zz} H S_z - \gamma_n \hbar H I_z + A_z S_z I_z \tag{14}$$

We see that I_z commutes with Eq. (14). We therefore take the states to be eigenfunctions of I_z with eigenvalues m_I. The first-order energy is therefore

$$E = \beta g_{zz} H m_S - \gamma_n \hbar H m_I + A_z m_S m_I \tag{15}$$

Since I^2, S^2, and I_z and S_z all commute with the Hamiltonian of Eq. (14), we can take the eigenfunctions to be a product of a nuclear spin and electron spin function:

$$\psi_{m_I m_S} = \phi_{I m_I} u_{S m_S} \tag{16}$$

The possible transitions produced by an alternating field are found by considering the matrix elements of the magnetic operator $\mathcal{H}_m(t)$:

$$\mathcal{H}_m(t) = (\gamma_e \hbar S_x - \gamma_n \hbar I_x) H_x \cos \omega t \tag{17}$$

between states such as those of Eq. (16). We find in this way that the S_x part of $\mathcal{H}_m(t)$ connects states with $\Delta m_S = \pm 1$, $\Delta m_I = 0$, whereas the I_x portion connects $\Delta m_S = 0$, $\Delta m_I = +1$. We can consider these respectively to represent electron resonance and nuclear resonance. The transitions are allowed only if ω satisfies the conservation of energy, which, by using Eq. (15) and the selection rules, gives for electron resonance:

$$\omega_e = \frac{g_{zz}\beta H_0 + A_z m_I}{\hbar} \tag{18}$$

and for nuclear resonance:

$$\omega_n = \gamma_n H_0 + \frac{A_z m_s}{\hbar} \tag{19}$$

The effect of the hyperfine coupling on the electron resonance is seen to be equivalent to the addition of an extra magnetic field proportional to the z-component of the nuclear spin. Since the nucleus can take up only quantized orientation, the electron resonance is split into $2I + 1$ (equally spaced) lines. If the nuclei have no preferential orientation, the lines corresponding to various values of m_I occur with equal probability, and the resonance pattern looks like that of Fig. 7.4.

FIG. 7.4. Absorption versus frequency for the electron resonance for the case of a nucleus of spin $\frac{3}{2}$. The lines are, in first approximation, equally spaced.

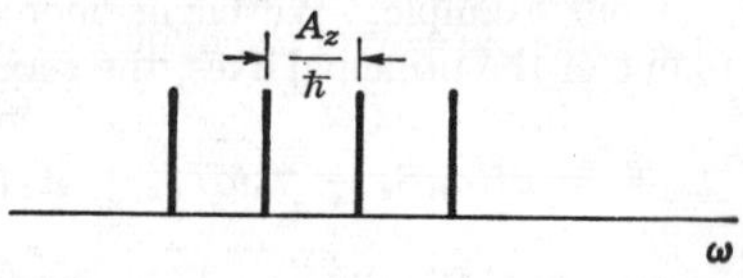

If one looks at the nuclear resonance, the frequencies are given by Eq. (19). To interpret the expression, we must know whether the nuclear Zeeman energy $\gamma_n \hbar H_0$ is larger or smaller than the hyperfine coupling $A_z m_S$, since Eq. (19) gives

FIG. 7.5. Nuclear resonance when the nuclear Zeeman energy is larger than $A_z m_S$, drawn on the assumption of an electron spin of $\frac{1}{2}$.

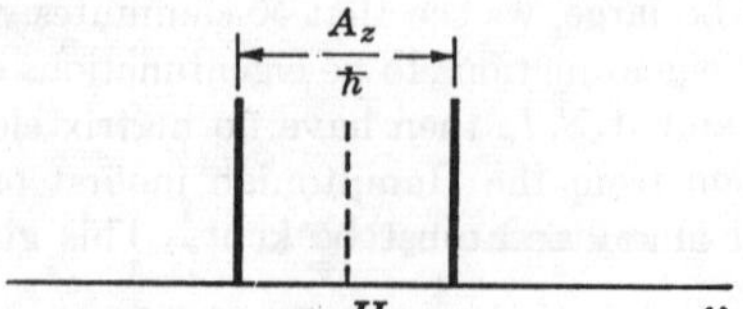

both positive and negative frequencies. In the former case (Fig. 7.5) the resonance is split into $2S + 1$ lines spaced $A_z/\hbar$ apart and centered on the angular frequency $\gamma_n H_0$.

If the nuclear Zeeman energy is smaller than $A_z m_S$, the two values of m_S, m_S and $-m_S$ give rise to two lines occurring at

$$\omega = \frac{A_z|m_S|}{\hbar} \pm \gamma_n H_0 \tag{20}$$

For an electron with spin ½, the result is shown in Fig. 7.6.

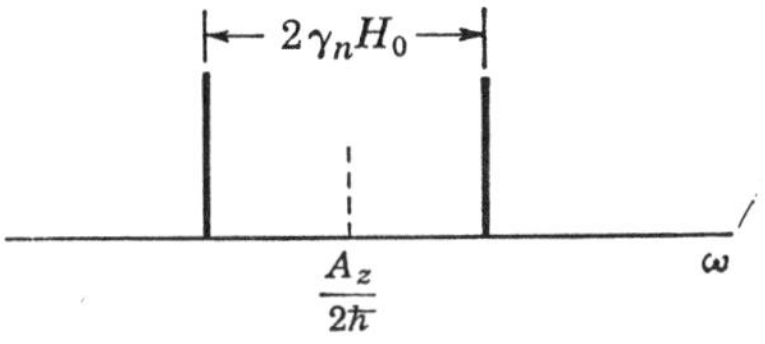

FIG. 7.6. Nuclear resonance for an electronic spin of $\frac{1}{2}$ when the hyperfine coupling is larger than the nuclear Zeeman coupling.

An examination of Figs. 7.4, 7.5, and 7.6 shows that the electron resonance will enable one to measure the hyperfine coupling tensor and the nuclear spin, but will not by itself enable one to measure the nuclear moment. When combined with the results of a nuclear resonance, even the nuclear magnetic moment can be found. This latter feature is of particular importance in the study of color centers because it enables one to identify the nuclear species that gives rise to the hyperfine splitting, since the nuclear γ's are known from other experiments. The nuclear resonance, on the other hand, enables one to measure the spin of the electron system.

We have so far restricted ourselves to an orientation of the static field along one of the principal axes of the g- and hyperfine tensors. Interesting new effects arise when the field lies along other directions: The axis of quantization of the nucleus becomes different from that of the electron and in fact depends on whether the electron is oriented parallel or antiparallel to the field. For the sake of simplicity we shall illustrate these effects for the case where the electronic g-factor is isotropic. We shall take the field direction, z', to lie in the x–z plane, where x, y, and z are the principal axes of the hyperfine coupling. The orientation is illustrated in Fig. 7.7.

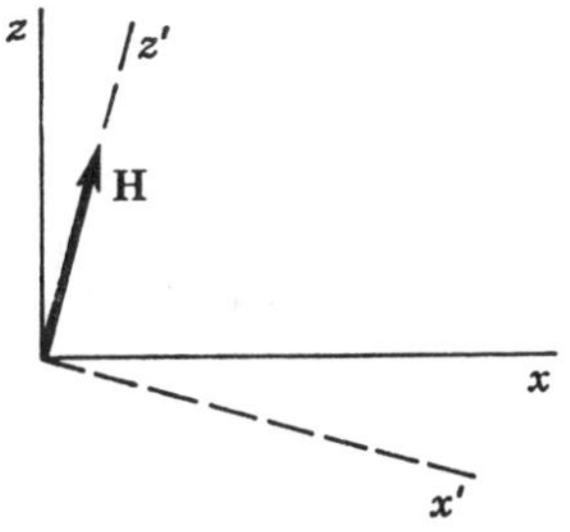

FIG. 7.7. Orientation of axes x, z, principal axes of the hyperfine tensor A, relative to the direction of the static field z'.

The Hamiltonian becomes

$$\mathcal{H} = 2\beta H_{z'} S_{z'} - \gamma_n \hbar H_{z'} I_{z'} + A_x I_x S_x + A_y I_y S_y + A_z I_z S_z \tag{21}$$

We shall continue to assume $2\beta H_0 \gg A_x$, A_y, and A_z so that, to a good approximation, the Hamiltonian commutes with $S_{z'}$. We now seek to find those other parts of the Hamiltonian that will be diagonal in a representation in which $S_{z'}$ is diagonal. To do this, we espress the spin components I_x, I_y, I_z, and S_x, S_y, and S_z in terms of the primed axes. (Actually it would be sufficient to express S_x, S_y, and S_z in terms of $S_{x'}$, $S_{y'}$, and $S_{z'}$. However, the transformation of the nuclear axes enables us to see more readily that the nuclear quantization direction is not parallel to that of the electron.) Noting that $y = y'$, we have

$$\begin{aligned} S_x &= S_{x'} \cos\theta + S_{z'} \sin\theta \\ S_y &= S_{y'} \\ S_z &= S_{z'} \cos\theta - S_{x'} \sin\theta \\ I_x &= I_{x'} \cos\theta + I_{z'} \sin\theta \\ I_y &= I_{y'} \\ I_z &= I_{z'} \cos\theta - I_{x'} \sin\theta \end{aligned} \tag{22}$$

By substituting these expressions into Eq. (21), we find

$$\begin{aligned} \mathcal{H} = 2\beta H_0 S_{z'} &- \gamma_n \hbar H_0 I_{z'} + I_{x'} S_{x'}(A_x \cos^2\theta + A_z \sin^2\theta) \\ &+ I_{y'} S_{y'} A_y + I_{z'} S_{z'}(A_x \sin^2\theta + A_z \cos^2\theta) \\ &+ (I_{x'} S_{z'} + I_{z'} S_{x'})(A_x - A_z) \sin\theta \cos\theta \end{aligned} \tag{23}$$

To first order, those terms in the hyperfine coupling involving $S_{x'}$ or $S_{y'}$ possess zero diagonal elements in the $S_{z'}$ scheme of quantization and therefore may be omitted. In second order, they will contribute energy shifts of the order of $A^2/2\beta H_0$, where by A^2 we mean the square of a matrix element of order A_x, A_y, or A_z, and the $2\beta H_0$ comes in because the "excited state" differs in electron spin orientation in the static field. The reduced Hamiltonian, $\mathcal{H}_{\text{red}}$, which results from dropping all terms involving S_x or S_y, is then

$$\begin{aligned} \mathcal{H}_{\text{red}} = 2\beta H_0 S_{z'} &- \gamma_n \hbar H_0 I_{z'} \\ &+ [I_{z'}(A_x \sin^2\theta + A_z \cos^2\theta) \\ &+ I_{x'}(A_x - A_z) \sin\theta \cos\theta] S_{z'} \end{aligned} \tag{24}$$

Of course $S_{z'}$ commutes with $\mathcal{H}_{\text{red}}$. However, $I_{z'}$ does not. As far as the nucleus is concerned, $\mathcal{H}_{\text{red}}$ corresponds to a nucleus coupled to a magnetic field with components $H_{x'}$, $H_{y'}$, and $H_{z'}$ of

$$\begin{aligned} H_{x'} &= \frac{1}{\gamma_n \hbar} (A_z - A_x) \sin\theta \cos\theta \, S_{z'} \\ H_{y'} &= 0 \\ H_{z'} &= H_0 - \left(\frac{A_x \sin^2\theta + A_z \cos^2\theta}{\gamma_n \hbar} \right) S_{z'} \end{aligned} \tag{25}$$

These expressions involve the operator $S_{z'}$, by which we mean, of course, that the effective field depends on the electron quantum state. By denoting the eigenvalue of $S_{z'}$ by m_S, we have

$$H_{x'}(m_S) = \frac{1}{\gamma_n \hbar}(A_z - A_x)\sin\theta\cos\theta\, m_S$$

$$H_{y'}(m_S) = 0$$

$$H_{z'}(m_S) = H_0 - \left(\frac{A_x \sin^2\theta + A_z \cos^2\theta}{\gamma_n \hbar}\right) m_S \qquad (26)$$

The direction of quantization of the nucleus is clearly along the resultant of the effective field of Eq. (26) and *not* along the static field. The direction differs for the different m_S values. The magnitude of the nuclear energy separation, $\Delta E_{\text{nuclear}}$, is as usual:

$$\Delta E_{\text{nuclear}} = \gamma_n \hbar H_{\text{eff}}(m_S) \qquad (27)$$

where $H_{\text{eff}}(m_S)$ is the magnitude of the fields of Eq. (26) and depends on m_S. The total energy of electron and nucleus is therefore

$$E = 2\beta H_0 m_S - \gamma_n \hbar H_{\text{eff}}(m_S) m_I \qquad (28)$$

We may note another interesting side effect of the tilt in the nuclear quantization axis as one varies m_S. The nuclear functions u_{m_I} for one value of m_S are different from those for another value of m_S, owing to the change in the direction of nuclear quantization. We write them as $u_{m_I}(m_S)$ to emphasize this point. We can express the $2I + 1$ functions $u_{m_I}(m_S + 1)$ in terms of the $2I + 1$ functions of $u_{m_I}(m_S)$ by the relationship

$$u_{m_I}(m_S + 1) = \sum_{m_I'} a_{m_S m_I m_I'} u_{m_I'}(m_S) \qquad (29)$$

where the a's are constants. We have, then, the possibility of transitions m_S, m_I to $m_S + 1$, m_I' where $m_I' \neq m_I$ (since $a_{m_S m_I m_I'}$ is in general not zero). Such a transition represents a simultaneous nuclear and electron spin transition.

Actually it does not really represent a nuclear orientation change. Equation (29) simply expresses the fact that a nucleus of given m_I relative to $H_{\text{eff}}(m_S)$ must (since its spatial orientation is fixed during the electron flip) go to a mixture of m_I''s when the electron orientation changes, the m_I''s referring as they do to a different quantization direction.

7.4 V_k CENTER

A particularly interesting example of the application of the ideas of the previous sections is the discovery and identification of the so-called V_k center by Känzig and Castner.† The detailed analysis of the spectra will enable us to discuss the g-shift more thoroughly, including the effects of having several electrons and more than one force center.

† T. G. Castner and W. Känzig, *J. Phys. Chem. Solids.*, **3**: 178 (1957).

Känzig and Castner's first work in electron spin resonance was followed by a set of beautiful experiments by Delbecq, Smaller, and Yuster,† who combined optical techniques with electron resonance to determine (1) the optical absorptions associated with the center and (2) the energies of the excited states. A full account of all the work on V_k centers would take us too far afield. We shall remark on the method of identification of the center, and on certain features associated with the g-shift, which are not found in "one-atom" one-electron centers.

It is helpful to begin by, so to speak, giving the answer. The V_k center is formed in alkali halides by X-raying crystals at a temperature near that of liquid nitrogen. In this process, electrons are ejected from the negative halogen ion, changing it from a closed-shell configuration to one with one electron missing from the p-shell. The ejected electron may have a variety of fates. We shall simply assume that not all recombine with neutral halogens. As an example, consider Cl; the neutral chlorine atom is unstable and pulls together with a neighboring Cl^- to form what may be conveniently called a Cl_2^- molecule. The Cl–Cl axis turns out to lie in 110 or equivalent crystal directions, as illustrated in Fig. 7.8.

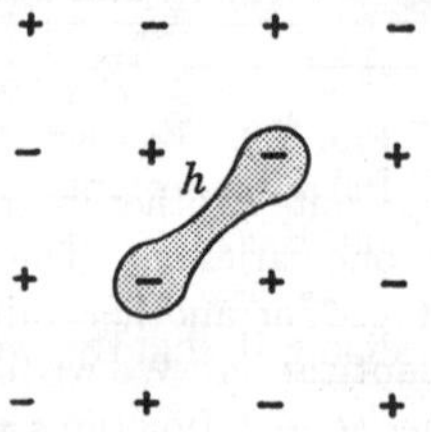

FIG. 7.8. A Cl_2^- molecule, or V_k center, in KCl. The center may be thought of as a hole, denoted by h, trapped on a pair of Cl^- ions.

The electronic structure turns out to be very similar to that of the p-electrons with quenched orbital angular momentum, discussed in Section 7.2, the electron with the unpaired spin being in an orbit whose axis is parallel to the bond direction of the Cl_2^- molecule. Coupling to excited states gives a g-shift that varies as the magnetic field orientation is varied with respect to the crystal axes, and the coupling of the unpaired spin with the nuclear moments of the *two* chlorines gives rise to a hyperfine coupling.

As we have remarked, this center was first discovered by electron spin resonance. A pattern observed for a case where the static magnetic field is along the 100-crystal direction is shown in Fig. 7.9.

At first sight the spectrum seems too hopelessly complicated to unravel, but fortunately a convenient starting point is the set of seven prominent lines. They are nearly equally spaced and are of intensities 1: 2: 3: 4: 3: 2: 1. These were recognized to arise from the coupling of the unpaired electron spin with magnetic moments of a pair of cholorine nuclei.

Let us explain. There are two isotopes of chlorine: Cl^{35}, which is 75 percent abundant; and Cl^{37}, 25 percent abundant. Both are of spin $\frac{3}{2}$, but have slightly different magnetic moments ($\gamma_{37}/\gamma_{35} = 0.83$). As we shall show, the seven-line pattern arises from a pair of Cl^{35}'s. Let us assume that H_0 lies along a principal axis of the Cl_2^-; call it the z-axis. By recalling our discussion of the preceding section

† C. J. Delbecq, B. Smaller, and P. H. Yuster, *Phys. Rev.*, **111**: 1235 (1958).

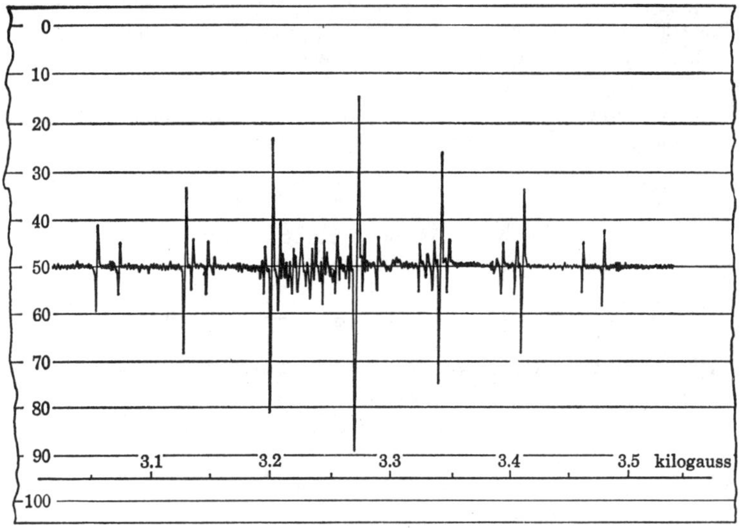

FIG. 7.9. V_k resonance in KCl for the static field parallel to a 100 crystallographic axis. (This figure kindly supplied by Castner and Känzig.)

and generalizing it slightly, we see that the electron resonance condition will be

$$\omega = \frac{1}{\hbar} [g_{zz}\beta H_0 + A_z(m_1 + m_2)] \tag{1}$$

where m_1 and m_2 are the m-values of the two Cl nuclei. Therefore the frequency depends on m_1 and m_2 only through their sum $m_1 + m_2$. The largest $m_1 + m_2$ is $\frac{3}{2} + \frac{3}{2} = 3$. The next largest is $\frac{1}{2} + \frac{3}{2} = 2$. This value of $m_1 + m_2$ is also found if $m_1 = \frac{3}{2}$, $m_2 = \frac{1}{2}$. Since we assume the nuclei to be distributed at random among their m-states, the line at $m_1 + m_2 = 2$ will be twice as strong as that for $m_1 + m_2 = 3$. We indicate the possible combinations of m_1 and m_2 in Table 7.2.

TABLE 7·2.

Combinations (m_1, m_2) to Make the Same Total Value $m_1 + m_2$, and the Corresponding Frequency and Statistical Weight.

(m_1, m_2)	$A(m_1 + m_2)$	Statistical Weight
$(\frac{3}{2}, \frac{3}{2})$	$3A$	1
$(\frac{3}{2}, \frac{1}{2})(\frac{1}{2}, \frac{3}{2})$	$2A$	2
$(\frac{3}{2}, -\frac{1}{2})(\frac{1}{2}, \frac{1}{2})(-\frac{1}{2}, \frac{3}{2})$	$1A$	3
$(\frac{3}{2}, -\frac{3}{2})(\frac{1}{2}, -\frac{1}{2})(-\frac{1}{2}, \frac{1}{2})(-\frac{3}{2}, \frac{3}{2})$	$0A$	4
$(-\frac{3}{2}, \frac{1}{2})(-\frac{1}{2}, -\frac{1}{2})(\frac{1}{2}, -\frac{3}{2})$	$-1A$	3
$(-\frac{3}{2}, -\frac{1}{2})(-\frac{1}{2}, -\frac{3}{2})$	$-2A$	2
$(-\frac{3}{2}, -\frac{3}{2})$	$-3A$	1

The recognition that the seven main lines could arise from a scheme such as we have described was the first clue as to the nature of the resonance. If one accepts this clue, that the electron spends equal time on two Cl atoms, one must next consider what happens for Cl_2^- molecules in which the nuclei are both Cl^{37}'s or one is a Cl^{35} and the other is a Cl^{37}. The probability of finding a single atom of Cl^{35} is $\frac{3}{4}$; that of finding a Cl^{37} is $\frac{1}{4}$. Therefore the probability of finding pairs is as follows:

$$\begin{aligned} Cl^{35} - Cl^{35}&: \quad \tfrac{3}{4} \times \tfrac{3}{4} = \tfrac{9}{16} \\ \left.\begin{aligned} Cl^{35} - Cl^{37}&: \quad \tfrac{3}{4} \times \tfrac{1}{4} = \tfrac{3}{16} \\ Cl^{37} - Cl^{35}&: \quad \tfrac{1}{4} \times \tfrac{3}{4} = \tfrac{3}{16} \end{aligned}\right\} &\tfrac{6}{16} \\ Cl^{37} - Cl^{37}&: \quad \tfrac{1}{4} \times \tfrac{1}{4} = \tfrac{1}{16} \end{aligned}$$

The generalization of Eq. (1) for unlike nuclei may be written as

$$\omega = \frac{1}{\hbar}\,[g_{zz}\beta H_0 + (A_z^{35} m_{35} + A_z^{37} m_{37})] \tag{2}$$

in an obvious notation. The hyperfine coupling, as we have seen, is proportional to the nuclear γ's, so that

$$\frac{A^{35}}{A^{37}} = \frac{\gamma_{35}}{\gamma_{37}} \tag{3}$$

The result of having non-equivalent nuclei is that configurations such as $(\frac{3}{2}, \frac{1}{2})$ and $(\frac{1}{2}, \frac{3}{2})$ no longer give the same frequency. If we call the $(\frac{3}{2}, \frac{3}{2})$ intensity "unity," the line that for like nuclei would have intensity 2 splits into two lines of unit intensity when the nuclei differ; that of intensity 3 splits into three lines of unit intensity, and so on. The positions are all predictable, using the measured A_z^{35} and Eq. (3). The intensity of the 35–37 lines is $\frac{6}{9}$ that of the outermost line of the 35–35 spectrum. There is in addition a set of seven lines from the Cl^{37} pairs, also having a predicted position, with an intensity $\frac{1}{9}$ that of the Cl^{35} pairs. All these lines are found at the proper positions and with the proper intensity. In this way many of the lines are accounted for.

An additional factor in determining the spectrum is the fact that the g-shift displaces the position of the center of the hyperfine patterns. The principal axes of the g-tensor with respect to the molecule are shown in Fig. 7.10. As we see in

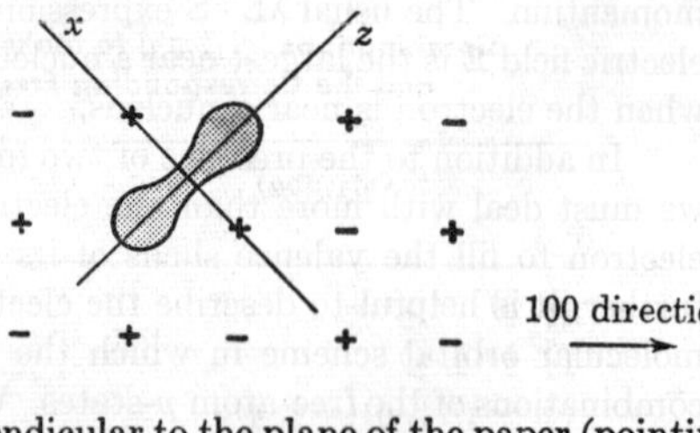

FIG. 7.10. Principal axes x, y, z of the g-tensor for the V_k center. The y-axis points out of the paper.

Fig. 7.10, if the magnetic field were perpendicular to the plane of the paper (pointing in a (001) direction), it would be parallel to the y-axis of the center. If it were along the 100 or 010 directions, it would make an angle of 45 deg with respect to the z-axis of the molecule in Fig. 7.10. For any given orientation of the magnetic field with respect to the crystal axes, there are in general several classes of V_k centers in terms of the angles made by H_0, with the principal axes of the center. If H_0 is parallel to a 111 direction, there are two classes of molecules. If H_0 is parallel to the 100 direction, $\frac{1}{3}$ of the centers have their bond axes perpendicular to H_0 and $\frac{2}{3}$ have a bond axis making a 45 deg angle with H_0. We can see that in general there will be several hyperfine patterns whose centers of gravity are displaced because of the anisotropy of the g-factor. Moreover, the hyperfine splitting is itself strongly anisotropic, A_z being much bigger than either A_x or A_y (z being the bond axis). The anisotropy is interpreted as indicating that on each atom the individual bond function is a linear combination of an s-function $g(r)$ and a p-function $zf(r)$.†

The hyperfine coupling becomes, then, using Eqs. (6) and (7) of the preceding section,

$$\mathcal{H}_{IS} = \alpha^2\gamma_e\gamma_n\hbar^2\left(\overline{\frac{1}{r^3}}\right)\frac{3}{5}\,3(I_{1z}+I_{2z})S_z + \left[(1-\alpha^2)\frac{4\pi}{3}|g(0)|^2 - \alpha^2\frac{1}{5}\left(\overline{\frac{1}{r^3}}\right)\right]\gamma_e\gamma_n\hbar^2(\mathbf{I}_1+\mathbf{I}_2)\cdot\mathbf{S} \tag{4}$$

where α^2 is the fraction of p-function, $(\overline{1/r^3})$ the average of $(1/r^3)$ for the state $zf(r)$, and where a factor of $\frac{1}{2}$ multiplies the expression of Eq. (8) of the preceding section, since the wave function spreads over two atoms. (We have neglected renormalization due to overlap of atomic functions.) There is a near cancellation of the two terms multiplying $(\mathbf{I}_1 + \mathbf{I}_2) \cdot \mathbf{S}$, leading to a strong anisotropy.

The fact that the electron ranges over more than one atom presents a new problem in calculating the g-shift. In the example we studied, we represented the spin-orbit coupling by a form $\lambda\mathbf{L} \cdot \mathbf{S}$ appropriate to a free atom. The origin about which the angular momentum was measured was, of course, the nuclear charge, since it is motion of the spin with respect to this charge that produces the spin-orbit coupling. When there is more than one nucleus, it is not apparent which nucleus to choose as the origin. The dilemma is resolved by using the more basic form of the spin-orbit coupling:

$$\mathcal{H}_{SO} = \frac{e\hbar}{2m^2c^2}\,\mathbf{S}\cdot(\mathbf{E}\times\mathbf{p}) \tag{5}$$

In this expression $\mathbf{E}$ is the electric field through which the electron is moving, and $\mathbf{p}$ is the momentum operator of the electron, $(\hbar/i)\nabla$. Since for an isolated atom, $\mathbf{E}$ is directed along the radius vector from the origin, $\mathbf{E} \times \mathbf{p} \propto \mathbf{r} \times \mathbf{p}$, the angular momentum. The usual $\lambda\mathbf{L} \cdot \mathbf{S}$ expression therefore follows from Eq. (5). Since the electric field $\mathbf{E}$ is the largest near a nucleus, the principal contribution to $\mathcal{H}_{SO}$ comes when the electron is near a nucleus.

In addition to the presence of two force centers, we have the complication that we must deal with more than one electron. In fact the V_k center lacks only one electron to fill the valence shells of its two chlorine atoms. In order to proceed further, it is helpful to describe the electronic states. We shall describe them in a molecular orbital scheme in which the molecular orbitals are made up as linear combinations of the free-atom p-states. We shall denote by x_1 an atomic p-function $xf(r)$ centered on atom 1 of the center. The atomic functions are thus x_1, y_1, z_1, x_2, y_2, and z_2, the z-axis lying along the bond. The functions $z_1 + z_2$ and $z_1 - z_2$

† The electronic wave functions are discussed in the subsequent text. We may remark that the bond function referred to here is the function $z_1 + z_2$ mentioned in the later discussion.

are shown schematically in Fig. 7.11. A study of the figure shows that $z_1 - z_2$ corresponds to a lower energy than does $z_1 + z_2$, since it has fewer nodes and tends to concentrate the electronic density between the two atoms where it can share

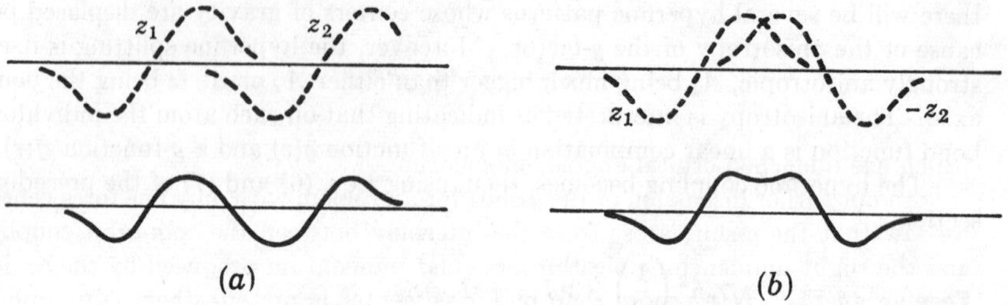

FIG. 7.11. Functions (a) $z_1 + z_2$ and (b) $z_1 - z_2$ shown schematically. The function of (a) is higher in energy, since (1) it has more nodes and (2) the node lies at a region of attractive potential for the electron.

their attractive potential. The states are in fact referred to as bonding ($z_1 - z_2$) and antibonding ($z_1 + z_2$). In a similar manner it turns out that $x_1 + x_2$ and $y_1 + y_2$ are bonding, and $x_1 - x_2$ and $y_1 - y_2$ are antibonding. (The z-states are the so-called σ-states and the x or y states are the π-states.) The energy levels of these states are shown schematically in Fig. 7.12. Actually the states $x_1 + x_2$ and $y_1 + y_2$, which are degenerate in the free molecule, are not degenerate in a crystal, but we neglect that splitting.

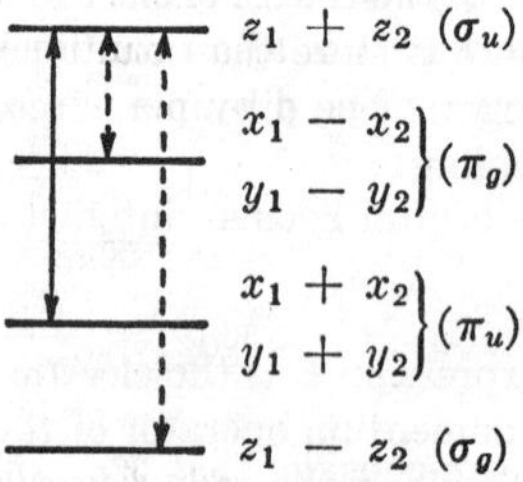

FIG. 7.12. Molecular orbitals formed from p-states in a halogen molecule ion. The allowed optical transitions into the unfilled σ_u orbit are shown by dashed lines. The g-shift "transitions" are shown by a solid line.

Since there are 6 orbital functions, there is room for 12 p-electrons. The V_k center, which has only 11, therefore has a hole in the $z_1 + z_2$ state. That is, there is an unpaired electron in that state. We have introduced, in Fig. 7.12, a labeling u or g (ungerade or gerade) that describes the parity of the orbital state.

One may expect to observe an optical absorption due to V_k centers. Since electrical dipole transitions are allowed only for transitions u to g or g to u, the optical absorption will arise from transitions of an electron in either the states $z_1 - z_2$ or $x_1 - x_2$, $y_1 - y_2$ to the empty $z_1 + z_2$. The strongest optical transition is from the $z_1 + z_2$ to $z_1 - z_2$, since the electronic dipole matrix element here is the largest (in fact, corresponding to a dipole moment arm of the length of the molecule).

We see, therefore, that we must generalize our previous discussion to account for two new features: the lack of a single force center, and the fact that more than one electron is involved.

In order to illustrate the first point (more than one force center) without the complications of the second (more than one electron), let us consider an example in which we have only one electron occupying the V_k center orbitals. Then the ground-orbital state function Ψ_0, is, neglecting overlap,

$$\Psi_0 = \frac{1}{\sqrt{2}}(z_1 - z_2) \tag{6}$$

which has quenched orbital angular momentum.

In our earlier discussion of the g-shift for a problem with only one force center, we saw that the g-shift arose from the interplay between the spin-orbit coupling and the slight unquenching of orbital angular momentum produced by the orbital Zeeman energy. When more than one force center is present, there is no unique point about which to measure angular momentum, and it is natural to return to the more basic form of the spin-orbit coupling:

$$\mathcal{H}_{SO} = \frac{e\hbar}{2m^2c^2}\mathbf{S}\cdot(\mathbf{E}\times\mathbf{p}) \tag{7}$$

In the absence of an applied magnetic field, this expression is correct, but in the presence of a magnetic field described by a vector potential $\mathbf{A}$, we must modify it to obtain a gauge invariant result:

$$\mathcal{H}_{SO} = \frac{e\hbar}{2m^2c^2}\mathbf{S}\cdot\left[\mathbf{E}\times\left(\mathbf{p}+\frac{e}{c}\mathbf{A}\right)\right] \tag{8}$$

where $-e$ is the charge of the electron. Equation (8) follows directly from the Dirac equation, but it is also intuitively obvious because, as we have discussed earlier we always replace $\mathbf{p}$ by $\mathbf{p} - (q/c)\mathbf{A}$ in the presence of a magnetic field where, in our case, $q = -e$.

The orbital Zeeman interaction, $\mathcal{H}_{OZ}$ is

$$\mathcal{H}_{OZ} = \frac{e}{2mc}(\mathbf{p}\cdot\mathbf{A} + \mathbf{A}\cdot\mathbf{p}) + \frac{e^2}{2mc^2}A^2 \tag{9}$$

We can consider that $\mathcal{H}_{OZ}$ and $\mathcal{H}_{SO}$ together constitute a perturbation $\mathcal{H}_{\text{pert}}$:

$$\mathcal{H}_{\text{pert}} = \mathcal{H}_{SO} + \mathcal{H}_{OZ} \tag{10}$$

We are concerned with calculating matrix elements designated by an orbital quantum number n and a spin quantum number σ. In particular the effect of $\mathcal{H}_{\text{pert}}$ is, according to Appendix D, equivalent to our having an additional interaction, $\mathcal{H}_{\text{new}}$, whose matrix elements diagonal in the ground orbital state $|0)$ are

$$(0\sigma|\mathcal{H}_{\text{new}}|0\sigma') = (0\sigma|\mathcal{H}_{\text{pert}}|0\sigma') + \sum_{n,\sigma''}{}' \frac{(0\sigma|\mathcal{H}_{\text{pert}}|n\sigma'')(n\sigma''|\mathcal{H}_{\text{pert}}|0\sigma')}{E_0 - E_n} \tag{11}$$

where the prime on the summation means omitting $n = 0$, and where we have neglected the spin contributions to the energy denominators. The g-shift arises from keeping just those terms of Eq. (11) that are linear in the vector potential and the electron spin. Thus we get $(0\sigma|\mathcal{H}_{\Delta g}|0\sigma')$ as

$$(0\sigma|\mathcal{H}_{\Delta g}|0\sigma') = \frac{e\hbar}{2m^2c^2}\left(0\sigma\left|\mathbf{S}\cdot\mathbf{E}\times\frac{e}{c}\mathbf{A}\right|0\sigma'\right) + \frac{e^2\hbar}{4m^3c^3}\sum_{n,\sigma''}{}' \frac{\begin{array}{c}(0\sigma|\mathbf{S}\cdot\mathbf{E}\times\mathbf{p}|n\sigma'')(n\sigma''|\mathbf{p}\cdot\mathbf{A}+\mathbf{A}\cdot\mathbf{p}|0\sigma') \\ +(0\sigma|\mathbf{p}\cdot\mathbf{A}+\mathbf{A}\cdot\mathbf{p}|n\sigma'')(n\sigma''|\mathbf{S}\cdot\mathbf{E}\times\mathbf{p}|0\sigma')\end{array}}{E_0 - E_n} \tag{12}$$

Since $\mathbf{p}\cdot\mathbf{A}+\mathbf{A}\cdot\mathbf{p}$ does not depend on spin,

$$(n\sigma''|\mathbf{p}\cdot\mathbf{A}+\mathbf{A}\cdot\mathbf{p}|0\sigma') = (n|\mathbf{p}\cdot\mathbf{A}+\mathbf{A}\cdot\mathbf{p}|0)\,\delta_{\sigma'\sigma''} \tag{13}$$

Therefore we get

$$(0\sigma|\mathcal{H}_{\Delta g}|0\sigma') = \frac{e^2\hbar}{2m^2c^3}(\sigma|\mathbf{S}|\sigma')\cdot\left[(0|\mathbf{E}\times\mathbf{A}|0) + \frac{1}{2m}\sum_n{}'\left\{\frac{(0|\mathbf{E}\times\mathbf{p}|n)(n|\mathbf{p}\cdot\mathbf{A}+\mathbf{A}\cdot\mathbf{p}|0)+c.c.}{E_0 - E_n}\right\}\right] \tag{14}$$

This expression is the basis for a proper treatment of the problem of several force centers. However, in order to proceed with that problem, we should first understand some aspects of the single force center problem that we have not discussed. In particular, what is the best choice of the gauge for the vector potential, and what happens when we change gauge?

Suppose the atom in question is located at the origin. Then the wave functions $|n)$ are in general either classified by angular momentum about the origin or are perhaps linear combinations of such atomic orbitals. If we took as the vector potential $\mathbf{A}(\mathbf{R})$, defined as

$$\mathbf{A}(\mathbf{R}) \equiv \tfrac{1}{2}\mathbf{H}_0 \times (\mathbf{r}-\mathbf{R}) \tag{15}$$

where $\mathbf{R}$ is an arbitrary constant vector, then, using the fact that div $\mathbf{A}(\mathbf{R}) = 0$, we could write the matrix elements $(n|\mathbf{p}\cdot\mathbf{A}+\mathbf{A}\cdot\mathbf{p}|0)$ as

$$\begin{aligned}(n|\mathbf{p}\cdot\mathbf{A}+\mathbf{A}\cdot\mathbf{p}|0) &= \int u_n^*\mathbf{H}_0\times(\mathbf{r}-\mathbf{R})\cdot\mathbf{p}u_0\,d\tau \\ &= \hbar\mathbf{H}_0\cdot\int u_n^*\mathbf{L}(\mathbf{R})u_0\,d\tau\end{aligned} \tag{16}$$

where

$$\mathbf{L}(\mathbf{R}) \equiv \frac{1}{i}(\mathbf{r}-\mathbf{R})\times\nabla \tag{17}$$

is the dimensionless angular momentum operator about the arbitrary point $\mathbf{R}$. Integrals such as the lower one on the right of Eq. (16) are readily evaluated by the methods of Eqs. (15) and (16) of Section 7.2, provided $\mathbf{R}$ is chosen as zero so that the angular momentum is measured about the natural origin of the atomic orbitals that make up the functions $|n)$. We shall call this the "natural" gauge.

An even more important point is seen by examining the first-order term of Eq. (14):

$$\frac{e^2\hbar}{2m^2c^3}(\sigma|\mathbf{S}|\sigma')\cdot(0|\mathbf{E}\times\mathbf{A}(\mathbf{R})|0) = \frac{e^2\hbar}{4m^2c^3}(\sigma|\mathbf{S}|\sigma')\cdot(0|\mathbf{E}\times(\mathbf{H}_0\times(\mathbf{r}-\mathbf{R}))|0) \tag{18}$$

By using the fact that the electric field **E** is large only near the nucleus, where it is in fact to a good approximation radial, we have

$$\mathbf{E}(\mathbf{r}) = \frac{\mathbf{r}}{r}E(r) \tag{19}$$

Then, taking the z-axis to lie along the direction of the static field, we find

$$\begin{aligned}\frac{e^2\hbar}{2m^2c^3}&(\sigma|\mathbf{S}|\sigma')\cdot(0|\mathbf{E}\times\mathbf{A}|0)\\ &= H_0\frac{e^2\hbar}{4m^2c^3}(\sigma|\mathbf{S}|\sigma')\cdot\left\{\left(0\left|\frac{E(r)}{r}[\mathbf{k}(x^2+y^2)-\mathbf{i}xz-\mathbf{j}yz]\right|0\right)\right.\\ &\qquad\left.-\left(0\left|\frac{E(r)}{r}[\mathbf{k}(xX+yY)-\mathbf{i}Xz-\mathbf{j}Yz]\right|0\right)\right\}\end{aligned} \tag{20}$$

where X and Y are two of the components of **R**.

If the wave function $|0)$ has a definite parity, the second term on the right vanishes. If $|0)$ does not have a definite parity (as, for example, if it were an s–p hybrid), the second term does not vanish. Since this term depends on the choice of **R**, it can in the latter case be made to take on any value. In order that the g-shift be independent of the gauge, there must be a compensating change in the terms of Eq. (12) that have the energy denominators. Such is in fact the case.

If we take the "natural" gauge for which $\mathbf{R} = 0$, the order of magnitude of the right-hand side of Eq. (20) is approximately $\beta H_0 r_0/a_H$, where r_0 is the classical electron radius $e^2/mc^2(\cong 10^{-13}\text{ cm})$ and a_H is the Bohr radius $(0.5\times10^{-8}\text{ cm})$. The matrix element is therefore $\cong 10^{-5}\beta H_0$ and is in general negligible. It is for this reason that one is justified in omitting the first-order term, as is ordinarily done.

We have seen that the "natural" gauge makes for simple evaluation of the matrix elements such as those in Eq. (16). When there is more than one force center, no single gauge appears natural, and we should like, in fact, to be able to use a mixture of gauges, one gauge when in the vicinity of one nucleus, the other in the vicinity of a second nucleus. Such a trick is actually possible, provided we can neglect certain overlap integrals. Let us state a theorem; then we shall outline its proof and then show how the theorem enables us to use such a technique of several "natural" gauges to treat the problem of multiple force centers.

Let us therefore consider a system with two atoms. The ground state $|0)$ will be a linear combination

$$|0) = u_0 + v_0 \tag{21}$$

where u_0 is a linear combination of atomic orbitals on the first atom and v_0 is a linear combination of atomic orbitals on the second atom. The excited states $|n)$ are also linear combinations:

$$|n) = u_n + v_n \tag{21a}$$

We shall neglect all contributions to matrix elements involving a product of a u and a v. This approximation is often good, but can lead to errors in some cases.

We have, then, as our theorem that the combined effect of the spin-orbit and orbital Zeeman coupling is to give a g-shift characterized by

$$(0\sigma|\mathcal{H}_{\Delta g}|0\sigma') = \frac{e^2\hbar}{2m^2c^3}(\sigma|\mathbf{S}|\sigma')\cdot\Bigg\{(u_0|\mathbf{E}\times\mathbf{A}'|u_0) + (v_0|\mathbf{E}\times\mathbf{A}''|v_0) + \frac{1}{2m}\sum_n{}' \frac{(0|\mathbf{E}\times\mathbf{p}|n)[(u_n|\mathbf{A}'\cdot\mathbf{p}+\mathbf{p}\cdot\mathbf{A}'|u_0) + (v_n|\mathbf{A}''\cdot\mathbf{p}+\mathbf{p}\cdot\mathbf{A}''|v_0)] + c.c.}{E_0 - E_n}\Bigg\} \tag{22}$$

where $\mathbf{A}'$ and $\mathbf{A}''$ are any vector potentials that give the static field $\mathbf{H}_0$ (they differ therefore, at most by a gauge transformation), and where

$$(u_n|\mathbf{A}'\cdot\mathbf{p}+\mathbf{p}\cdot\mathbf{A}'|u_0) \equiv \int u_n^*(\mathbf{A}'\cdot\mathbf{p}+\mathbf{p}\cdot\mathbf{A}')u_0\,d\tau \tag{23}$$

The beauty of Eq. (22) is that it allows us to choose the vector potential $\mathbf{A}'$ used to evaluate the integrals with the u's independently of the vector potential $\mathbf{A}''$ used for integrals involving v's. (We shall discuss handling the matrix elements $(0|\mathbf{E}\times\mathbf{p}|n)$ shortly.)

In particular, as we shall see, if the two nuclei are at $\mathbf{R}_1$ and $\mathbf{R}_2$, respectively, we can evaluate the matrix elements readily by choosing

$$\begin{aligned}\mathbf{A}' &= \mathbf{A}_1 \equiv \tfrac{1}{2}\mathbf{H}_0\times(\mathbf{r}-\mathbf{R}_1)\\ \mathbf{A}'' &= \mathbf{A}_2 \equiv \tfrac{1}{2}\mathbf{H}_0\times(\mathbf{r}-\mathbf{R}_2)\end{aligned} \tag{24}$$

To prove the theorem of Eq. (22), we start with Eq. (14). We express the matrix elements involving $\mathbf{A}$ in terms of the u's and v's, and neglect overlap terms. For example,

$$(0|\mathbf{E}\times\mathbf{A}|0) = (u_0|\mathbf{E}\times\mathbf{A}|u_0) + (v_0|\mathbf{E}\times\mathbf{A}|v_0) \tag{25}$$

Then we introduce two vector potentials, $\mathbf{A}'$ and $\mathbf{A}''$, which differ by a gauge transformation:

$$\mathbf{A}' = \mathbf{A}'' + \nabla\phi \tag{26}$$

defining the function ϕ. (That Eq. (26) is simply a gauge transformation follows, of course, from the fact that it satisfies the requirement $\nabla\times\mathbf{A}' = \nabla\times\mathbf{A}''$.) We then substitute $\mathbf{A}'$ for $\mathbf{A}$ in integrals involving u's, and $\mathbf{A}''+\nabla\phi$ for $\mathbf{A}$ in integrals involving v's. By collecting terms, we get

$$\begin{aligned}(0\sigma|\mathcal{H}_{\Delta g}|0\sigma') = \frac{e^2\hbar}{2m^2c^3}(\sigma|\mathbf{S}|\sigma')\cdot\Bigg\{&(u_0|\mathbf{E}\times\mathbf{A}'|u_0) + (v_0|\mathbf{E}\times\mathbf{A}''|v_0)\\ &+ \frac{1}{2m}\sum_n{}' \frac{(0|\mathbf{E}\times\mathbf{p}|n)[(u_n|\mathbf{p}\cdot\mathbf{A}'+\mathbf{A}'\cdot\mathbf{p}|u_0) + (v_n|\mathbf{p}\cdot\mathbf{A}''+\mathbf{A}''\cdot\mathbf{p}|v_0)] + c.c.}{E_0 - E_n}\\ &+ (v_0|\mathbf{E}\times\nabla\phi|v_0)\\ &+ \frac{1}{2m}\sum_n{}' \frac{(0|\mathbf{E}\times\mathbf{p}|n)(v_n|\mathbf{p}\cdot\nabla\phi+\nabla\phi\cdot\mathbf{p}|v_0) + c.c.}{E_0 - E_n}\Bigg\}\end{aligned} \tag{27}$$

To derive our theorem, Eq. (22), we must show that the terms involving ϕ add to zero. By making use of the fact that we are neglecting overlap terms, our proof is equivalent to showing that the quantity $(0\sigma|\mathcal{H}_{\Delta g}(\phi)|v_0\sigma')$, defined below, vanishes:

$$(0\sigma|\mathcal{H}_{\Delta g}(\phi)|v_0\sigma') \equiv \frac{e^2\hbar}{2m^2c^3}(\sigma|\mathbf{S}|\sigma') \cdot \left\{(0|\mathbf{E} \times \nabla\phi|v_0) + \frac{1}{2m}\sum_n{}' \frac{\{(0|\mathbf{E} \times \mathbf{p}|n)(n|\mathbf{p} \cdot \nabla\phi + \nabla\phi \cdot \mathbf{p}|v_0) + c.c.\}}{E_0 - E_n}\right\} = 0 \tag{28}$$

The integral I, defined as

$$I \equiv \int \psi_n^*(\mathbf{p} \cdot \nabla\phi + \nabla\phi \cdot \mathbf{p})v_0 \, d\tau \tag{29}$$

can be transformed, making use of the fact that the wave functions are real and utilizing partial integrations, to be

$$I = \frac{\hbar}{i}\int [v_0\phi\nabla^2\psi_n - \psi_n\phi\nabla^2 v_0] \, d\tau \tag{30}$$

It is simple to re-express the first term on the right, since

$$\nabla^2\psi_n = \frac{2m}{\hbar^2}(V - E_n)\psi_n \tag{31}$$

where V is the potential acting on the electron. We evaluate the second term by noting that, neglecting overlap,

$$\begin{aligned}\int \psi_n\phi\nabla^2 v_0 \, d\tau &= \int v_n\phi\nabla^2 v_0 \, d\tau \\ &= \int v_n\phi\nabla^2\psi_0 \, d\tau\end{aligned} \tag{32}$$

By utilizing Eq. (31) in Eq. (32) and again neglecting overlap, we obtain finally

$$(n|\mathbf{p} \cdot \nabla\phi + \nabla\phi \cdot \mathbf{p}|v_0) = \frac{\hbar}{i} \cdot \frac{2m}{\hbar^2}(E_0 - E_n)\int \psi_n\phi v_0 \, d\tau \tag{33}$$

We can substitute this expression into Eq. (28) and collect terms to obtain

$$(0\sigma|\mathcal{H}_{\Delta g}(\phi)|v_0\sigma') = \frac{e^2\hbar}{2m^2c^3}(\sigma|\mathbf{S}|\sigma') \cdot \left\{(0|\mathbf{E} \times \nabla\phi|v_0) - 2\sum_n{}'(0|\mathbf{E} \times \nabla|n)(n|\phi|v_0)\right\} \tag{34}$$

The prime can be removed from the summation, since the diagonal spin-orbit matrix elements vanish, giving

$$\begin{aligned}(0\sigma|\mathcal{H}_{\Delta g}(\phi)|v_0\sigma') &= \frac{e^2\hbar}{2m^2c^3}(\sigma|\mathbf{S}|\sigma') \cdot \{(0|\mathbf{E} \times \nabla\phi - 2(\mathbf{E} \times \nabla)\phi|v_0)\} \\ &= -\frac{e^2\hbar}{2m^2c^3}(\sigma|\mathbf{S}|\sigma') \cdot \int \mathbf{E} \times \nabla(\phi v_0^2) \, d\tau\end{aligned} \tag{35}$$

where $(\mathbf{E} \times \nabla)$ signifies that $\mathbf{E} \times \nabla$ is to operate on all functions to its right, that is, on both ϕ and v_0.

But the integral can be shown to vanish, utilizing the fact that $\nabla \times \mathbf{E} = 0$ and transforming the integral $\int \nabla \times (\mathbf{E}\phi v_0^2)\, d\tau$ into a surface integral. We omit these details, since they are quite standard. Our theorem is thus proved.

We have not as yet said anything about the spin-orbit matrix elements to excited states. By utilizing the fact that the electric field $\mathbf{E}$ is large only near the nuclei, we are *always* able to neglect overlap when evaluating spin-orbit matrix elements. Thus

$$(0|\mathbf{E} \times \mathbf{p}|n) = (u_0|\mathbf{E} \times \mathbf{p}|u_n) + (v_0|\mathbf{E} \times \mathbf{p}|v_n) \tag{36}$$

To see the full import of Eq. (36) as well as to illustrate our theorem Eq. (22) concretely, we now turn to the evaluation of the specific problem of molecular complex in which only one electron occupies the V_k center orbitals. The ground state is therefore given by Eq. (6), $\psi_0 = (1/\sqrt{2})(z_1 - z_2)$. We are concerned with excited states such as $(1/\sqrt{2})(x_1 \pm x_2)$. We have, using Eq. (36),

$$\begin{aligned}(0|\mathbf{E} \times \mathbf{p}|n) &= \left(\frac{z_1 - z_2}{\sqrt{2}}\,\middle|\mathbf{E} \times \mathbf{p}\middle|\,\frac{x_1 \pm x_2}{\sqrt{2}}\right) \\ &= \tfrac{1}{2}[(z_1|\mathbf{E} \times \mathbf{p}|x_1) \mp (z_2|\mathbf{E} \times \mathbf{p}|x_2)]\end{aligned} \tag{37}$$

Since the two atoms are identical and since $\mathbf{E}$ is large only near a nucleus,

$$(z_1|\mathbf{E} \times \mathbf{p}|x_1) = (z_2|\mathbf{E} \times \mathbf{p}|x_2) \tag{38}$$

Therefore, when the upper sign applies, the two terms in the square bracket Eq. (37) cancel, and $(0|\mathbf{E} \times \mathbf{p}|n)$ vanishes. On the other hand, for the lower sign, the terms add, giving twice either one. Thus the state $(x_1 + x_2)/\sqrt{2}$ does not contribute to the g-shift, but the state $(x_1 - x_2)/\sqrt{2}$ does. Of course a similar argument shows that $(y_1 + y_2)/\sqrt{2}$ also makes no contribution although $(y_1 - y_2)/\sqrt{2}$ does. The states involved in the g-shift are shown in Fig. 7.13 by the solid arrow.

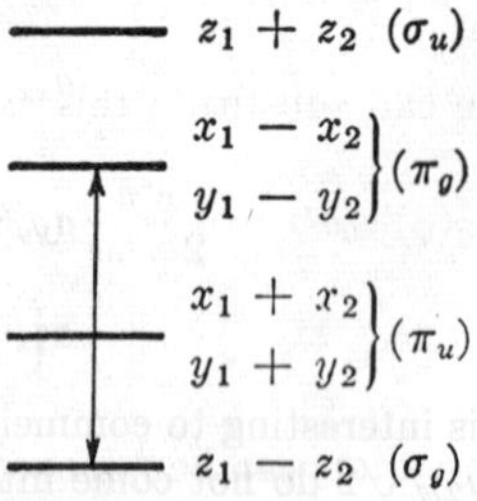

FIG. 7.13. The solid line indicates the states joined to the ground state $z_1 - z_2$ by the spin-orbit coupling.

If we had a free atom, the spin-orbit matrix elements could be expressed in terms of the free-atom spin-orbit coupling constant λ according to the equation

$$\left(k\,\middle|\frac{e\hbar}{2m^2c^2}\mathbf{S} \cdot \mathbf{E} \times \mathbf{p}\middle|\,l\right) = \lambda(k|\mathbf{L} \cdot \mathbf{S}|l) \tag{39}$$

where k and l denote free-atom states associated with the particular λ. For our example, x_1, y_1, and z_1 are being taken as free-atom p-states. Therefore we can write

$$\frac{e\hbar}{2m^2c^2}(\sigma|\mathbf{S}|\sigma')\cdot(z_1|\mathbf{E}\times\mathbf{p}|x_1) = \lambda(\sigma|\mathbf{S}|\sigma')\cdot(z_1|\mathbf{L}_1|x_1) \tag{40}$$

where $\hbar\mathbf{L}_1$ is the angular momentum about the nucleus of the first atom, and where λ is the spin-orbit coupling constant appropriate to the (np) electron configuration of the outer electron. Evaluation of the matrix element $(z_1|\mathbf{L}_1|x_1)$ proceeds as in Eqs. (15) and (16) of Section 7.2.

We now turn to evaluation of the matrix elements $(u_n|\mathbf{A}'\cdot\mathbf{p}+\mathbf{p}\cdot\mathbf{A}'|u_0)$ of Eq. (22). We have that $u_n = x_1/\sqrt{2}$ or $y_1/\sqrt{2}$, $u_0 = z_1/\sqrt{2}$. By utilizing Eq. (16) and the fact that the u's are real, we have

$$\begin{aligned}(u_n|\mathbf{A}_1\cdot\mathbf{p}+\mathbf{p}\cdot\mathbf{A}_1|u_0) &= \hbar\mathbf{H}_0\cdot\int u_n\mathbf{L}_1u_0\,d\tau \\ &= \frac{\hbar\mathbf{H}_0}{2}\cdot(x_1|\mathbf{L}_1|z_1) \quad \text{or} \quad \frac{\hbar\mathbf{H}_0}{2}\cdot(y_1|\mathbf{L}_1|z_1)\end{aligned} \tag{41}$$

But, by the symmetry of the atoms,

$$(u_n|\mathbf{A}_1\cdot\mathbf{p}+\mathbf{p}\cdot\mathbf{A}_1|u_0) = (v_n|\mathbf{A}_2\cdot\mathbf{p}+\mathbf{p}\cdot\mathbf{A}_2|v_0) \tag{42}$$

so that we have, neglecting the first-order terms such as given by Eq. (22),

$$(0\sigma|\mathcal{H}_{\Delta g}|0\sigma') = 2\beta\lambda(\sigma|\mathbf{S}|\sigma')\cdot\left[\frac{(z_1|\mathbf{L}_1|x_1)(x_1|\mathbf{L}_1|z_1)}{E_{z_1-z_2}-E_{x_1-x_2}} + \frac{(z_1|\mathbf{L}_1|y_1)(y_1|\mathbf{L}_1|z_1)}{E_{z_1-z_2}-E_{y_1-y_2}}\right]\cdot\mathbf{H}_0 \tag{43}$$

This is equivalent to having

$$\mathcal{H}_{\Delta g} = \sum_{\substack{q=x,y,z\\ q'=x,y,z}} 2\beta S_q a_{qq'} H_{q'} \tag{44}$$

By evaluating the matrix elements, we get that $a_{qq'} = 0$ if $q \neq q'$, and

$$\begin{aligned} a_{xx} &= -\frac{\lambda}{E_{y_1-y_2}-E_{z_1-z_2}} \\ a_{yy} &= -\frac{\lambda}{E_{x_1-x_2}-E_{z_1-z_2}} \\ a_{zz} &= 0 \end{aligned} \tag{45}$$

It is interesting to comment a bit more on why the states $(x_1+x_2)/\sqrt{2}$ and $(y_1+y_2)/\sqrt{2}$ do not come into the g-shift. We note not only that the spin-orbit matrix elements to those states vanish, but also that the orbit-Zeeman terms cancel. Mixture of these excited states corresponds to production of a current flow in the ground state, shown in Fig. 7.14.

According to Eq. (8), the gauge-invariant spin-orbit interaction is between the spin and the gauge-invariant current density $\mathbf{j}(\mathbf{r})$. With a current flow such as that given by Fig. 7.14, flowing in opposite senses on the two atoms, the net spin-orbit coupling vanishes. That is the significance of the vanishing of the spin-orbit matrix element. The vanishing of the orbit-Zeeman terms represents the fact that the

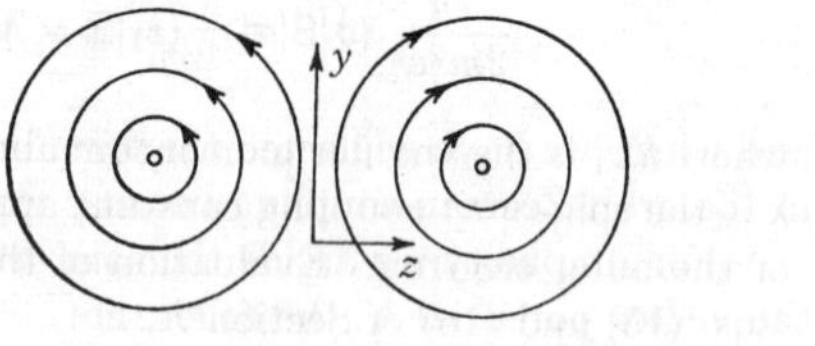

FIG. 7.14. Current flow produced by mixing some of the function $(x_1 + x_2)/\sqrt{2}$ into the ground state $(z_1 - z_2)\sqrt{2}$.

applied field would never induce a current flow oppositely directed on the two atoms. Rather, it gives a flow such as that shown in Fig. 7.15.

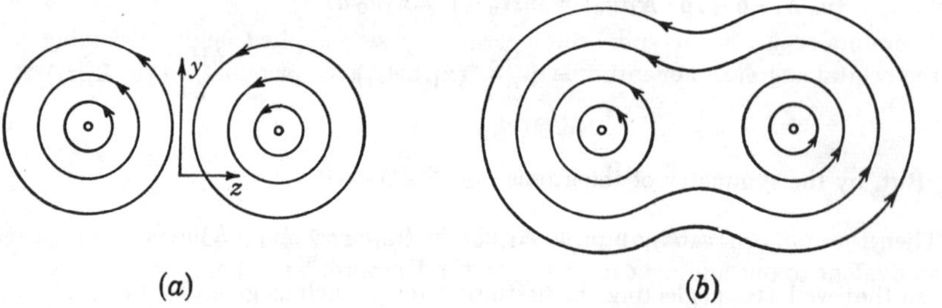

FIG. 7.15. (a) Current flow produced by the external field H_0 in the molecular complex. The fact that no current crosses the boundary between the two atoms results from the neglect of overlap. If overlap is included, the pattern is shown in (b).

We see that the technique of handling the problem of several force centers is to break the integrals into terms that are large only near the individual force centers, thereby converting the problem to a sum of single force center problems.

The second problem with which we must grapple in order to analyze the V_k center is how to compute the g-shift when we have a system with more than one electron. Since the spin and orbit are uncoupled in the absence of spin-orbit coupling, let us assume that we can characterize the multi-electron states by a total spin quantum number S with eigenvalues M for some component. An extra quantum number n will also be needed to define the energy. We designate the ground state, then, as $|oSM)$ and excited states by $|nS'M')$. We are concerned as before with the spin-orbit and the orbital Zeeman couplings, $\mathcal{H}_{OS}$ and $\mathcal{H}_{OZ}$, respectively. The same expressions will apply as for the case of one electron, except that we must now label the coordinates by a symbol j, to specify which of the N-electrons is involved.

We have, then,

$$\begin{aligned} \mathcal{H}_{SO} &= \sum_j \mathcal{H}_{SO}^{(j)} \\ \mathcal{H}_{OZ} &= \sum_j \mathcal{H}_{OZ}^{(j)} \end{aligned} \tag{46}$$

where

$$\begin{aligned}\mathcal{H}_{SO}^{(j)} &= \frac{e\hbar}{2m^2c^2}\,\mathbf{S}_j\cdot\left[\mathbf{E}_i\times\left(\mathbf{p}_j+\frac{e}{c}\,\mathbf{A}_j\right)\right]\\ \mathcal{H}_{OZ}^{(j)} &= \frac{e}{2mc}\,(\mathbf{p}_j\cdot\mathbf{A}_j+\mathbf{A}_j\cdot\mathbf{p}_j)\end{aligned} \tag{47}$$

and where we have neglected the term involving the square of the vector potential in the orbit-Zeeman coupling because we seek terms linear in H_0.

For simplicity we divide the spin-orbit coupling into two terms, one involving the vector potential **A**; the other, not.

$$\begin{aligned}\mathcal{H}_{SO\mathbf{A}}^{(j)} &= \frac{e\hbar}{2m^2c^2}\,\mathbf{S}_j\cdot\left[\mathbf{E}_j\times\frac{e}{c}\,\mathbf{A}_j\right]\\ \mathcal{H}_{SOO}^{(j)} &= \frac{e\hbar}{2m^2c^2}\,\mathbf{S}_j\cdot[\mathbf{E}_j\times\mathbf{p}_j]\end{aligned} \tag{48}$$

Therefore $\mathcal{H}_{SOO}$ is the spin-orbit operator in zero-applied field. Assuming that the orbital angular momentum is quenched, we have, therefore, that

$$\begin{aligned}(oSM|\mathcal{H}_{OZ}|oSM') &= 0\\ (oSM|\mathcal{H}_{SOO}|oSM') &= 0\end{aligned} \tag{49}$$

Then the spin-orbit and orbital Zeeman coupling combine to give matrix elements equivalent to our adding a term $\mathcal{H}_{\Delta g}$ to the Hamiltonian, where

$$\begin{aligned}(oSM|\mathcal{H}_{\Delta g}|oSM') = (oSM|\mathcal{H}_{SO\mathbf{A}}|oSM')\\ + \sum_{nS'M''}\frac{(oSM|\,\mathcal{H}_{SOO}\,|nS'M'')(nS'M''|\,\mathcal{H}_{OZ}\,|oSM')}{E_0-E_n}\\ + \frac{(oSM|\,\mathcal{H}_{OZ}\,|nS'M'')(nS'M''|\,\mathcal{H}_{SOO}\,|oSM')}{E_0-E_n}\end{aligned} \tag{50}$$

where we have neglected the spin in the energy denominators, and where we are also keeping only the terms that give rise to a g-shift.

In the case of the V_k center, we may take the wave functions $|nSM)$ to be a product of one-electron molecular orbital states, properly antisymmetrized. The calculation proceeds along lines similar to that of the indirect nuclear coupling in Section 4.8. Let us denote the state $(z_1 - z_2)/\sqrt{2}$ containing electron number 1 with spin-up ($m = +\frac{1}{2}$) as

$$u_{z_1-z_2,+}(1) \tag{51}$$

Since the total spin of the V_k center is ½, the state $|oSM) = |o\ ½\ ½)$ is then

$$\left|o\,\frac{1}{2}\,\frac{1}{2}\right) = \frac{1}{\sqrt{11!}}\sum_P(-1)^P P u_{z_1-z_2,+}(1)u_{z_1-z_2,-}(2)u_{x_1+x_2,+}(3)\cdots u_{z_1+z_2,+}(11) \tag{52}$$

That is, all the orbitals except $u_{z_1+z_2,-}$ are occupied by an electron.

It is convenient to denote functions such as $(z_1 - z_2)/\sqrt{2}$ by a symbol l and the spin quantum number by σ (since m is also used for the mass of an electron). In this notation the individual electron orbitals are denoted as $|l\sigma)$. As discussed in Section 4.8, all matrix elements of Eq. (50) arise from one-electron operators, so that the states joined by the operators can at most differ in the occupation of one orbital. Thus we find that we can express $(oSM|\mathcal{H}_{SOA}|oSM')$ in terms of the one-electron operator $\mathcal{H}_{SOA}^{(1)}$:

$$(oSM|\mathcal{H}_{SOA}|oSM') = \sum_{\substack{l\sigma \\ l\sigma'}} (l\sigma|\mathcal{H}_{SOA}^{(1)}|l\sigma') \tag{53}$$

where $l\sigma$ goes over all values occupied in $|oSM)$ and where $l\sigma'$ goes over all values occupied in $|oSM')$. We do not include matrix elements $(l\sigma|\mathcal{H}_{SOA}|l'\sigma')$ where $l' \neq l$, since these states imply a change in the occupation of molecular orbitals. That would imply that the ground state possessed orbital degeneracy, a circumstance we do not wish to consider.

The second-order terms are handled in a similar manner. The sum over electrons can be converted to a sum over orbitals occupied in the ground state and the sum over n to a sum over orbitals not occupied in the ground state. Therefore we get

$$\begin{aligned}(oSM|\mathcal{H}_{\Delta g}|oSM') = &\sum_{\substack{l\sigma \text{ in } |oSM) \\ l\sigma' \text{in } |oSM')}} (l\sigma|\mathcal{H}_{SOA}^{(1)}|l\sigma') \\ &+ \sum_{\text{restriction } A}{}' \frac{(l\sigma|\mathcal{H}_{OZ}^{(1)}|l'\sigma)(l'\sigma|\mathcal{H}_{SOO}^{(1)}|l\sigma')}{E_l - E_{l'}} \\ &+ \sum_{\text{restriction } B}{}' \frac{(l\sigma|\mathcal{H}_{SOO}^{(1)}|l'\sigma')(l'\sigma'|\mathcal{H}_{OZ}^{(1)}|l\sigma')}{E_l - E_{l'}}\end{aligned} \tag{54}$$

where, by restriction A, we mean:

$|l\sigma)$ is occupied in $|oSM)$.
$|l\sigma')$ is occupied in $|oSM')$.
$|l'\sigma)$ is occupied in neither $|oSM)$ nor $|oSM')$.

and by restriction B we mean

$|l\sigma)$ is occupied in $|oSM)$.
$|l\sigma')$ is occupied in $|oSM')$.
$|l'\sigma')$ is occupied in neither $|oSM)$ nor $|oSM')$.

Equation (54) will hold for any system in which the wave function can be taken as a product of individual spin functions.

We wish, of course, to incorporate our earlier theorem, Eq. (22), to enable us to use the "natural" gauges. This can be done readily by noting two things: The first is that, since $\mathcal{H}_{OZ}^{(1)}$ is independent of spin,

$$\begin{aligned}(l\sigma|\mathcal{H}_{OZ}^{(1)}|l'\sigma) &= (l|\mathcal{H}_{OZ}^{(1)}|l') \\ &= (l\sigma'|\mathcal{H}_{OZ}^{(1)}|l'\sigma')\end{aligned} \tag{55}$$

By utilizing this fact, we can see the second point. If we remove the condition that $|l'\sigma)$ be unoccupied in $|oSM)$ or $|oSM')$ from restriction A, and that $|l'\sigma')$ be unoccupied in $|oSM)$ or $|oSM')$ from restriction B, the extra terms we acquire will exactly cancel in pairs. We can therefore write

$$(oSM|\mathcal{H}_{\Delta g}|oSM') = \sum_{\substack{l\sigma \\ l\sigma'}}' (l\sigma|\mathcal{H}_{SOA}^{(1)}|l\sigma')$$
$$+ \sum_{\substack{l\sigma \\ l\sigma' \\ l'}}' \frac{(l\sigma|\mathcal{H}_{OZ}^{(1)}|l'\sigma)(l'\sigma|\mathcal{H}_{SOO}^{(1)}|l\sigma') + (l\sigma|\mathcal{H}_{SOO}^{(1)}|l'\sigma')(l'\sigma'|\mathcal{H}_{OZ}^{(1)}|l\sigma')}{E_l - E_{l'}} \tag{56}$$

where now we require only that $|l\sigma)$ be occupied in $|oSM)$ and $|l\sigma')$ be occupied in $|oSM')$.

Consider now all the terms on fixed $l\sigma$ and $l\sigma'$:

$$(l\sigma|\mathcal{H}_{SOA}^{(1)}|l\sigma') + \sum_{l'}' \frac{(l\sigma|\mathcal{H}_{OZ}^{(1)}|l'\sigma)(l'\sigma|\mathcal{H}_{SOO}^{(1)}|l\sigma') + (l\sigma|\mathcal{H}_{SOO}^{(1)}|l'\sigma')(l'\sigma'|\mathcal{H}_{OZ}^{(1)}|l\sigma')}{E_l - E_{l'}} \tag{57}$$

This is identical in form to Eq. (14). It can therefore be converted to the expression involving the mixed gauge. Let us therefore define

$$(l\sigma|V^{(1)}|l\sigma') = \frac{e^2\hbar}{2m^2c^3} (\sigma|\mathbf{S}_1|\sigma') \cdot [(u_l|\mathbf{E}_1 \times \mathbf{A}'_1|u_l) + (v_l|\mathbf{E}_1 \times \mathbf{A}''_1|v_l)]$$

and

$$(l\sigma|U^{(1)}|l'\sigma') = \frac{e^2\hbar}{2m^3c^3} (\sigma|\mathbf{S}_1|\sigma') \cdot [(u_l|\mathbf{A}'_1 \cdot \mathbf{p}_1 + \mathbf{p}_1 \cdot \mathbf{A}'_1|u_{l'})$$
$$+ (v_l|\mathbf{A}''_1 \cdot \mathbf{p}_1 + \mathbf{p}_1 \cdot \mathbf{A}''_1|v_{l'})] \tag{58}$$

In terms of these definitions we can rewrite the expression of Eq. (57) as

$$(l\sigma|V^{(1)}|l\sigma') + \sum_{l'}' \frac{(l\sigma|U^{(1)}|l'\sigma)(l'\sigma|\mathcal{H}_{SOO}^{(1)}|l\sigma') + (l\sigma|\mathcal{H}_{SOO}^{(1)}|l'\sigma')(l'\sigma'|U^{(1)}|l\sigma')}{E_l - E_{l'}} \tag{59}$$

Therefore we find

$$(oSM|\mathcal{H}_{\Delta g}|oSM') = \sum_{\substack{l\sigma \\ l\sigma'}} (l\sigma|V^{(1)}|l\sigma')$$
$$+ \sum_{\substack{l\sigma \\ l\sigma' \\ l'}}' \frac{(l\sigma|U^{(1)}|l'\sigma)(l'\sigma|\mathcal{H}_{SOO}^{(1)}|l\sigma') + (l\sigma|\mathcal{H}_{SOO}^{(1)}|l'\sigma')(l'\sigma'|U^{(1)}|l\sigma')}{E_l - E_{l'}} \tag{60}$$

where $l\sigma$ includes all values occupied in $|oSM)$ and $l\sigma'$ includes all values occupied in $|oSM')$. As we have remarked, allowing $l'\sigma$ or $l'\sigma'$ of the excited states to include values occupied in either $|oSM)$ or $|oSM')$ introduces pairs of terms that cancel. It is therefore simplest in practice to reimpose conditions A and B so that no superfluous terms arise in the summation.

By means of the Wigner-Eckart theorem, it is possible to show that Eq. (60) implies that all matrix elements $(oSM|\mathcal{H}_{\Delta g}|oSM')$ can be obtained from a Hamiltonian of the form

$$\mathcal{H}_{\Delta g} = 2\beta \sum_{\substack{q=x,y,z \\ q'=x,y,z}} H_q a_{qq'} S_{q'} \tag{61}$$

where the components S_q are, for example,

$$S_x = \sum_{i=1}^{N} S_{xi} \quad \text{etc.} \tag{62}$$

For the V_k center, however, rather than employ the Wigner-Eckart theorem, we shall simply evaluate Eq. (60). Symmetry tells us that the principal axes of the g-tensor are the x-, y-, z-axes of the molecule, where the z-axis lies along the bond. Suppose, therefore, that the static field lies along the x-axis and that M is taken as the eigenvalue of S_x. Since this is a principal axis, the only non-vanishing matrix elements have $M = M'$. Of course we can verify this by explicit evaluation of Eq. (60). S is, of course, $\frac{1}{2}$. Let us compute Eq. (60) for $M = M' = \frac{1}{2}$. The simplest way to discuss the matrix elements is, then, in terms of a diagram of the states. Since we are computing a diagonal term in $(oSM|\mathcal{H}_{\Delta g}|oSM')$, the states labeled $|l\sigma)$ and $|l\sigma')$ of Eq. (60) must be identical (we must return the electron to the state from which it was virtually excited). Setting $\sigma' = \sigma$ and neglecting the terms involving $(l\sigma|V^{(1)}|l\sigma)$, we have

$$(oSM|\mathcal{H}_{\Delta g}|oSM) = \sum_{\substack{|l\sigma)\ \text{occupied} \\ |l'\sigma)\ \text{unoccupied}}} \left[\frac{(l\sigma|U^{(1)}|l'\sigma)(l'\sigma|\mathcal{H}^{(1)}_{SOO}|l\sigma) + c.c.}{E_l - E_{l'}}\right] \tag{63}$$

where $|l\sigma)$ occupied or $|l'\sigma)$ unoccupied refer respectively to whether or not $|l\sigma)$ is occupied or $|l'\sigma)$ is unoccupied in the ground state. For $S = \frac{1}{2}$, $M = \frac{1}{2}$, the states $|l'\sigma)$ and $|l\sigma)$ can be summarized by a diagram in which solid arrows designate states occupied by electrons, an arrow pointing up, ↑, referring to $\sigma = +\frac{1}{2}$, and so on; and dashed arrows, ↓ or ↑, referring to unoccupied states. The ground state is shown in Fig. 7.16.

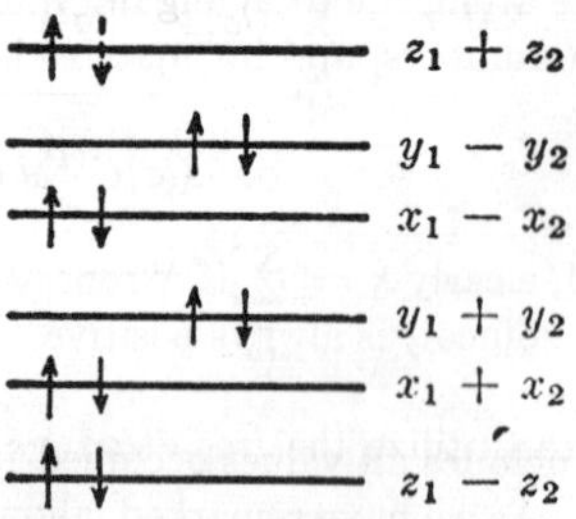

FIG. 7.16. Ground state $|o\ \frac{1}{2}\ \frac{1}{2})$ of the V_k center. We assume that the crystal field splits the states $x_1 \pm x_2$ slightly from $y_1 \pm y_2$. The solid arrows indicate an occupied state (↑↓); the dashed ones (↑↓) are unoccupied.

An excited state is obtained by transferring an electron from an occupied to a vacant orbital. For a field in the x-direction, the orbital Zeeman term couples only the state $y_1 + y_2$ to $z_1 + z_2$, as can be seen by an argument similar to that for deriving Eq. (15). The states joined in the g-shift are shown on Fig. 7.17.

FIG. 7.17. The double arrow indicates states joined by the matrix elements of Eq. (32) for a field in the x-direction. The arrows indicate the electron spin quantization, ↑ signifying spin parallel to the static field and ↓ signifying spin antiparallel. The dashed arrow ↓ state is vacant in the ground state.

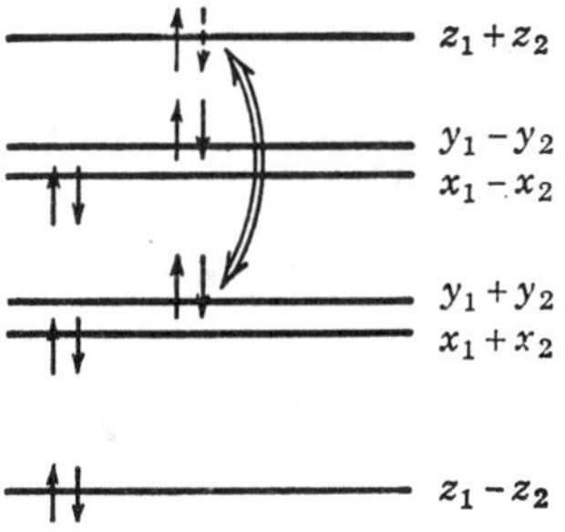

The explicit evaluation of the matrix elements follows the discussion relating to Eqs. (36) and (41), giving

$$\left(o\ \frac{1}{2}\ \frac{1}{2}\ |\mathcal{H}_{\Delta g}|o\ \frac{1}{2}\ \frac{1}{2}\right) = 2\beta H_x \frac{(y_1|L_x^{(1)}|z_1)(z_1 - \frac{1}{2}|\mathcal{H}_{soox}^{(1)}|y_1 - \frac{1}{2})}{E_{y_1+y_2} - E_{z_1+z_2}} \tag{64}$$

where $\mathcal{H}_{soox}$ is the one-electron, spin-orbit coupling associated with the x-component of spin and is given by

$$\left(z_1 - \frac{1}{2}\ |\mathcal{H}_{soox}^{(1)}|y_1 - \frac{1}{2}\right) = \frac{e\hbar}{2m^2c^2}\left[\int z_1^*(\mathbf{E} \times \mathbf{p})_x y_1\, d\tau\right]\left(-\frac{1}{2}\ |S_x^{(1)}| - \frac{1}{2}\right) \tag{65}$$

where $d\tau$ indicates integration over the electron position coordinate.

The expression of Eq. (65) involves functions on one atom only, and can therefore be related to the free-atom expression. In fact, for a free atom, if one neglects the coupling of one spin to the orbit of another electron, one can write the spin-orbit coupling of N-electrons as

$$\mathcal{H}_{SO} = \sum_{i=1}^{N} \zeta_i \mathbf{L}^i \cdot \mathbf{S}^i \tag{66}$$

For equivalent electrons, the ζ_i's are all equal. If one has Russell-Saunders coupling in the free atom, the total angular momentum quantum numbers L and S are good quantum numbers, and for matrix elements internal to a given L and S, we have

$$\mathcal{H}_{SO} = \lambda \mathbf{L} \cdot \mathbf{S} \tag{67}$$

If $N = 1$, clearly $\lambda = \zeta$. If N represents a shell that has only one missing electron, $\lambda = -\zeta$. Since ζ is always positive, we obtain in this way the fact that holes have negative λ.

We can utilize the free-atom ζ's to evaluate Eq. (65), since it enables us to write

$$\frac{e\hbar}{2m^2c^2}\left[\int z_1^*(\mathbf{E} \times \mathbf{p})_x y_1\, d\tau\right]\left(-\frac{1}{2}\ |S_x| - \frac{1}{2}\right) = \zeta(z_1|l_x^{(1)}|y_1)\left(-\frac{1}{2}\ |S_x^{(1)}| - \frac{1}{2}\right) \tag{68}$$

We obtain in this manner

$$\left(o\,\frac{1}{2}\,\frac{1}{2}\,|\mathcal{H}_{\Delta g}|o\,\frac{1}{2}\,\frac{1}{2}\right) = -\frac{2\beta H_x\zeta(-\frac{1}{2}|S_x^{(1)}|-\frac{1}{2})}{E_{z_1+z_2}-E_{y_1-y_2}} \tag{69}$$

Since the spin Zeeman energy, $(0\,\frac{1}{2}\,\frac{1}{2}|\mathcal{H}_{SZ}|0\,\frac{1}{2}\,\frac{1}{2})$, is

$$(o\,\tfrac{1}{2}\,\tfrac{1}{2}|\mathcal{H}_{SZ}|o\,\tfrac{1}{2}\,\tfrac{1}{2}) = 2\beta H_x(\tfrac{1}{2}|S_x^{(1)}|\tfrac{1}{2}) \tag{70}$$

being just that of the one unpaired spin, we have

$$\begin{aligned} g_{xx} &= 2\left(1+\frac{\zeta}{E_{z_1+z_2}-E_{y_1-y_2}}\right) \\ &= 2\left(1-\frac{\lambda}{E_{z_1+z_2}-E_{y_1-y_2}}\right) \end{aligned} \tag{71}$$

where λ is the free Cl atom spin-orbit coupling constant. We note $g_{xx} > 2$.

In a similar manner we get

$$\begin{aligned} g_{yy} &= 2\left(1+\frac{\zeta}{E_{z_1+z_2}-E_{x_1-x_2}}\right) \\ g_{zz} &= 2 \end{aligned} \tag{72}$$

It is interesting to note in our calculation that the origin of the positive g-shift rather than the negative one that we would have for a single electron is the spin matrix element $(-\frac{1}{2}|S_x^{(1)}|-\frac{1}{2})$ of Eq. (69). The $|-\frac{1}{2})$ states come in because we have excited one of the paired spins into an originally unpaired state. We deal with a spin that points opposite to M.

We may contrast the situation with one in which only five electrons fill the states, as shown in Fig. 7.18. We shall assume the degeneracy of the states $y_1 + y_2$ and $x_1 + x_2$ is lifted, as shown, and likewise for $y_1 - y_2$ and $x_1 - x_2$. A field

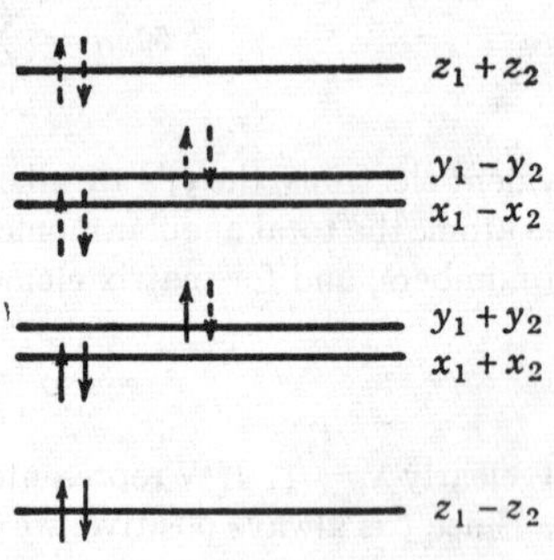

FIG. 7.18. Filled states when the V center orbitals contain only five electrons.

in the x-direction would join states $|y_1 + y_2, \frac{1}{2})$ and $|z_1 + z_2, \frac{1}{2})$ and would make $g < 2$ (an "electron" shift). On the other hand, a field in the z-direction joins the nearly degenerate $|y_1 + y_2, -\frac{1}{2})$ and $|x_1 + x_2, -\frac{1}{2})$ states. It would have $g > 2$ (a "hole" shift). The close proximity of these two states would make $|\Delta g_{zz}| \gg |\Delta g_{xx}|$, and g_{yy}, of course, is still 2, since the pertinent matrix elements vanish.

It is clear that the 12 states are less than half-full, yet the predominant g-shift is that of a "hole." We see, therefore, that we must use extreme caution in characterizing centers as "electron" or "hole" centers simply from the g-shift data.

We should also comment that we have assumed very simple functions with no overlap between atoms, to compute the matrix elements. In general, we would need to make corrections both for overlap and for the possibility that the functions x_1, y_1, z_1, and so on are linear combinations of atomic orbitals, as we did in discussing the hyperfine coupling. However, these corrections do not alter the principles, although they do complicate the numerical calculations.

CHAPTER 8

SUMMARY

We have considered a variety of effects — line widths, chemical shifts, Knight shifts, hyperfine splittings — a bewildering array of seemingly special cases. As we look back, we see some effects that occur in first-order perturbation theory, others that require a higher order. Since we have discussed the phenomena one by one, it is appropriate to summarize by writing a single Hamiltonian that includes everything. As we contemplate it, we should remind ourselves of the significance of each term. We write below the Hamiltonian describing a nucleus interacting with an electron in the presence of a magnetic field $\mathbf{H}_0$. We define the vector potentials $\mathbf{A}_0$, associated with the field $\mathbf{H}_0$, and $\mathbf{A}_n$, associated with the field at the electron owing to the nuclear moment ($\mathbf{A}_n = \boldsymbol{\mu} \times \mathbf{r}/r^3$ normally). We also define the quantity

$$\boldsymbol{\pi} = \frac{\hbar}{i}\nabla + \frac{e}{c}\mathbf{A}_0 \tag{1}$$

Then we have the following Hamiltonian:

$$\mathcal{H} = -\frac{\hbar^2}{2m}\nabla^2 \qquad + V_0 + V_{\text{cryst}}$$

electron kinetic energy; electron potential energy in the field of the nucleus and other electrons; electron potential energy due to charges outside the atom

$$+ \frac{e\hbar}{2m^2c^2}\mathbf{S}\cdot\left[\mathbf{E}\times\left(\mathbf{p}+\frac{e}{c}\mathbf{A}_0\right)\right] + \gamma_e\hbar\mathbf{H}_0\cdot\mathbf{S}$$

electron spin-orbit coupling; electron spin Zeeman energy

$$+ \frac{e}{2mc}(\mathbf{p}\cdot\mathbf{A}_0 + \mathbf{A}_0\cdot\mathbf{p}) + \frac{e^2}{2mc^2}A_0^2$$

coupling of electron orbital motion to H_0

$$+ \frac{e}{2mc}(\boldsymbol{\pi}\cdot\mathbf{A}_n + \mathbf{A}_n\cdot\boldsymbol{\pi}) + \frac{\gamma_e\gamma_n\hbar^2}{r^3}\left[\frac{3(\mathbf{I}\cdot\mathbf{r})(\mathbf{S}\cdot\mathbf{r})}{r^2} - \mathbf{I}\cdot\mathbf{S}\right]$$

coupling of nuclear moment to electron orbital motion; coupling of nuclear moment with electron spin moment for non *s*-states

$$+ \frac{8\pi}{3}\gamma_e\gamma_n\hbar^2\mathbf{I}\cdot\mathbf{S}\,\delta(\mathbf{r}) + \mathcal{H}_q$$

coupling of nuclear moment with electron spin moment for *s*-states; coupling of nuclear quadrupole moment to field gradient due to electron and external charges

$$- \gamma_n\hbar\mathbf{H}_0\cdot\mathbf{I}$$

nuclear Zeeman energy

We can add to this the coupling of nuclei with each other and the magnetic coupling of electrons with each other.

PROBLEMS

CHAPTER 2

1. Consider an Hermitian operator F which is an explicit function of time. (For example, $F = -\gamma\hbar I_x H_x \cos\omega t$, the interaction energy of a spin with an alternating magnetic field in the x-direction.) Prove that

$$\frac{dF}{dt} = \frac{i}{\hbar}[\mathcal{H}, F] + \frac{\partial F}{\partial t}$$

where $\partial F/\partial t$ represents an actual derivative of $F(t)$ with respect to time.

2. Equation (14a), Section 2.2, gives an expression for $\langle u_x(t)\rangle$ for a particle of spin $\frac{1}{2}$. Generalize the expression for a spin I.

3. A magnet has an inhomogeneous static magnetic field. The fraction of spins, df, that experience a magnetic field between H and $H + dH$ is

$$df = p(H)\,dH$$

where

$$\int_0^\infty p(H)\,dH = 1$$

Assume the inhomogeneity is slight and that it simply gives a spread in field with no change in the direction.

Compute the magnetization in the x-direction, perpendicular to the static field, as a function of time, assuming that at $t = 0$ the total magnetization was $\mathbf{M}_0$, pointing in the x-direction, for the three forms of $p(H)$:

(a) $p(H)$ is a constant for $H_0 - a < H < H_0 + a$ and is zero for all other fields.

(b) $p(H) \alpha\, e^{-(H-H_0)^2/a^2}$

(c) $p(H) \alpha \dfrac{1}{1 + (H - H_0)^2/a^2}$

4. A nucleus of spin $\frac{1}{2}$ is quantized by a field H_0 in the z-direction. It is in the $m = +\frac{1}{2}$ state at $t = 0$ when a rotating magnetic field of amplitude H_1 is applied for a time t_w, producing a 90 degree pulse.

(a) Compute the wave function of the spin in the rotating reference system as a function of time during and after the pulse.

(b) Compute the wave function in the laboratory reference system during and after the pulse.

(c) Compute the $\langle \mu_x(t)\rangle$ during and after the pulse.

5. A coil of length 1, cross-sectional area A, and n turns is wound in the form of a solenoid. The axis of the coil is in the x-direction, and a static field, H_0 is in the z-direction.

(a) Assuming the nuclear moments are in thermal equilibrium, what is the nuclear magnetization per unit volume, M_0, produced by H_0, in terms of H_0 and the static nuclear susceptibility χ_0?

(b) Compute a numerical value of χ_0 for protons in water at room temperature, using the formula

$$\chi_0 = \frac{N\gamma^2\hbar^2 I(I+1)}{3kT}$$

where N is the number of spins per unit volume. (For protons, γ can be found from the fact that the resonance occurs at 42 Mc for $H_0 = 10^4$ gauss.)

(c) The magnetization, $\mathbf{M}_0$, is turned by a 90 degree pulse. Derive an expression for the amplitude V_0 of the voltage induced in the coil by the precessing $\mathbf{M}_0$.

(d) Make a numerical estimate of V_0 for protons, assuming a 10-turn coil 2 cm long, 1 cm in diameter, and an H_0 of 5000 gauss.

6. Suppose the coil of Problem 5 has inductance L_0 and resistance R_0 and is in series resonance with a condenser C.

(a) Derive an expression for the voltage across the condenser in terms of the induced voltage V_0 of Problem 5, L_0, R_0, C, and $Q(=L_0\omega/R)$.

(b) Using the numerical estimate of Problem 5(d), and assuming the coil has a Q of 100, compute the size of the voltage across C.

7. From Eq. (18) of Section 2.9 we have that

$$\chi_0 = \frac{2}{\pi}\frac{1}{\omega_0}\int_0^\infty \chi''(\omega')\,d\omega'$$

Show that if $\chi''_{\max}$ is the maximum value of χ'' in an absorption line,

$$\chi''_{\max} = \frac{\pi}{2}\chi_0\frac{\omega_0}{\Delta\omega}$$

where $\Delta\omega$ is a suitably defined line breadth.

Assuming that the line width of the nuclear resonance of protons in water is 0.1 gauss broad (because of magnet inhomogeneity) and that $H_0 = 10^4$ gauss, compute $\chi''_{\max}$ for water, and also compute the maximum fractional change in coil resistance for a coil of $Q = 100$.

8. The response of a certain piece of material to a step of magnetic field of unit height, applied at $t = 0$, is

$$M_{\text{step}}(t) = \chi_0(1 - e^{-t/T})$$

(a) Compute $\chi'(\omega)$ and $\chi''(\omega)$.

(b) Show that χ' and χ'' satisfy the Kramers-Kronig relations.

CHAPTER 3

1. A pair of identical spins of $I_1 = I_2 = \frac{1}{2}$ are coupled by their magnetic dipole moments. Assuming zero external static magnetic field, show that the proper eigenstates of the spins are the singlet and triplet states, and then find the energies of the different states.

2. Suppose in Problem 1 that a static magnetic field H_0 is applied parallel to the internuclear axis.
   (a) Find the energy levels and eigenfunctions as a function of H_0.
   (b) An alternating magnetic field is applied perpendicular to the internuclear axis. Find the allowed transitions, their frequencies, and relative intensities: (1) for H_0 much less than the dipolar coupling; (2) for H_0 much larger than the dipolar coupling.

3. Equation (28) of Section 3.3 involves $\text{Tr}[\mathcal{H}_d^0, \mu^-]\mu^+$. Prove that this trace vanishes.

4. Consider two identical spin $\frac{1}{2}$ nuclei. Let $I_z \equiv I_{1z} + I_{2z}$ be the total z-component of angular momentum. Evaluate $\text{Tr}I_z^2$ by explicit evaluation of the diagonal matrix elements for two schemes of quantization: (a) the m_1, m_2 scheme and (b) the I, M scheme. Show that the answers agree with each other.

5. Consider a nucleus of spin I. Compute $\text{Tr}(I_zI_x)$ and $\text{Tr}(I^2I_x^2)$.

6. Consider a group of N non-interacting spins of spin I and gyromagnetic ratio γ. The total wave function can be taken as a product of the individual spin states, and the total energy as the sum of the individual eigen-energies. Evaluate the expression for $\chi''(\omega)$ of Eq. (18), Section 2.10, to give the absorption. For simplicity, let $Z = (2I + 1)^N$ and $e^{-E_a/kT} = 1$, the expressions for the high-temperature limit.

7. The electrostatic exchange coupling between two electrons can be represented by adding a term $A\mathbf{S}_1 \cdot \mathbf{S}_2$ to the Hamiltonian.
   (a) Prove that this term commutes with the Zeeman energy.
   (b) Prove that addition of such a term to the direct dipole coupling does not affect the second moment computed when assuming dipolar coupling alone

8. Consider three operators, A, B, and C. Prove that

$$\text{Tr}ABC = \text{Tr}CAB = \text{Tr}BCA$$

9. Consider a nucleus with spin $\frac{3}{2}$ whose Hamiltonian is $\mathcal{H} = \mathcal{H}_Z + \mathcal{H}_Q$, where

$$\mathcal{H}_Z = \gamma_n\hbar H_0 I_z$$

$$\mathcal{H}_Q = A(3I_z^2 - I^2)$$

The form of $\mathcal{H}_Q$ is similar to the one that sometimes arises when a nucleus has an electrical quadrupole moment. An alternating field is applied to the system to produce absorption.
   (a) Prove that $\mathcal{H}_Z$ and $\mathcal{H}_Q$ commute.
   (b) Treating $\mathcal{H}_Q$ as analogous to $\mathcal{H}_d^0$ in Section 3.3, and assuming $A \ll \gamma_n\hbar H_0$, prove that

$$\langle\omega\rangle = \gamma_n H_0$$

   and find $\langle\Delta\omega^2\rangle$.

10. Derive Eq. (5) of Section 3.4 for the case of a uniformly rotating pair of nuclei.

CHAPTER 4

1. In Section 4.4, gauge transformations are discussed.
(a) Using Eq. (3), show that Eq. (4) is true.
(b) Prove that the operator

$$\mathbf{r} \times \left(\frac{\hbar}{i} \nabla - \frac{q}{c} \mathbf{A}\right)$$

for the angular momentum is gauge-invariant.
(c) Consider an s-state $\psi(\mathbf{r}) = u(r)$ in the absence of a magnetic field. A uniform magnetic field with vector potential $\mathbf{A}_0 = \frac{1}{2}\mathbf{H}_0 \times \mathbf{r}$ is applied. Derive an expression for the resulting angular-momentum expectation value, and evaluate the answer in units of $\hbar$ for the ground state of hydrogen, assuming $H_0 = 10{,}000$ gauss.

2. Calculate the numerical size of the magnetic field produced by the orbital motion of an electron in the $n = 2$, $l = 1$, $m = +1$ state at the nucleus of a hydrogen atom. (Neglect all effects associated with the electron spin.)

3. The hyperfine coupling for s-states may be found simply in the approximation that a nucleus is a uniformly magnetized sphere. In this problem, we derive the famous s-state formula for that model.

A uniformly magnetized sphere of magnetization $\mathbf{M}$ per unit volume can be represented by current distribution flowing on the surface, the current being proportional to $\mathbf{M} \cdot \mathbf{n}$, where $\mathbf{n}$ is the unit outer normal. We shall represent a nucleus by such a sphere of radius R. Consider the current to flow in circles about the z-axis; the surface current density $J(\theta)$ is then

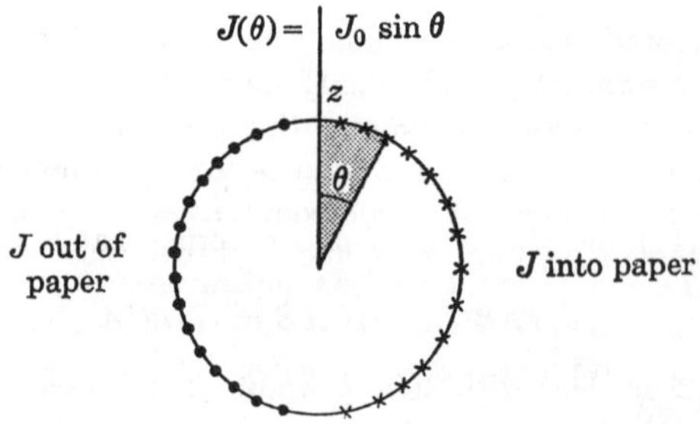

(a) Show that the magnetic field $\mathbf{H}$ inside the sphere is uniform and that outside the sphere it is a pure dipole field.
(b) Show that the field inside is

$$\mathbf{H} = \frac{8\pi}{3} J_0 \mathbf{k}$$

(c) Show that the magnetic moment μ of the sphere is $(4\pi/3)R^3 J_0$.
(d) Show that

$$\overline{H}_z = \int H_z |u^2(r)| \, d\tau = \frac{8\pi}{3} |u(0)|^2 \mu$$

where $u(r)$ is a spherically symmetric function that does not vary too rapidly within R of the origin and where H_z is the z-component of field due to the sphere.

4. An atom has a single valence electron in an s-state and a nucleus of spin I. The electron spin-lattice relaxation time is so short that the nucleus experiences only the time-average magnetic field of the electron. Derive an expression for the resonance frequency of the nucleus when a static field H_0 is applied, giving your answer in terms of the electron susceptibility χ_e. Discuss the temperature and field dependence: (a) at high temperature (where $kT \gg \gamma_e \hbar H_0$) and (b) at low temperature (where $\gamma_e \hbar H_0 \sim kT$).

5. In the text the Knight shift was calculated by first-order perturbation theory, using the fact that the static magnetic field H_0 causes a repopulation of the electrons among their spin states.

It is possible to obtain an expression for the Knight shift by using second-order perturbation theory and by assuming that the applied field varies spatially in such a manner that there is no repopulation.

Thus, suppose the applied field is in the z-direction, varying with x as

$$H_z = H_0 \cos qx \tag{1}$$

Consider a nucleus at $x = 0$. Using second-order perturbation, show that the electron wave function is perturbed in such a manner that a Knight shift is produced and that, in the limit of $q \approx 0$, the answer agrees with the result found in the text.

6. The electronic structure of the hydrogen molecule can be described in terms of the molecular orbital model, using molecular orbitals that are a linear combination of atomic orbitals.† The lowest molecular orbital is the bonding one formed by a linear combination of free-hydrogen $1s$-states. Compute an expression for the indirect coupling of the proton spins. As an approximation consider that the only excited state is the antibonding orbital formed from a linear combination of the free-hydrogen $1s$-states.

CHAPTER 5

From Eqs. (11) and (12) of Section 5.3, verify that $W_{mn} = W_{nm}e^{(E_n - E_m)\beta_L}$, where $\beta_L = 1/kT_L$ and T_L is the lattice temperature.

2. Consider a system of N spins that interact with one another via a dipole-dipole coupling and with an external static field H in the z-direction. Assuming a density matrix ρ, given by

$$\rho = \frac{e^{-\mathcal{H}/kT}}{Z}$$

corresponding to thermal equilibrium (where Z is the partition function), show that the thermal equilibrium expectation value of the total magnetization is

$$\overline{\langle M_x \rangle} = \overline{\langle M_y \rangle} = 0$$

$$\overline{\langle M_z \rangle} = \frac{N\gamma_n^2 \hbar^2 I(I+1)}{3kT} H$$

in the high-temperature approximation.

---

† See, for example, H. Eyring, J. Walter, and G. E. Kimball, *Quantum Chemistry*, chaps. xi and xii. New York: John Wiley & Sons, Inc.

It is interesting to note that these equations are of the form $\mathbf{M} = C\mathbf{H}/T$, Curie's law, and that the constant C does not depend on whether H is large or small compared with the local field due to neighboring dipoles — in contrast to one's naïve expectation.

3. Consider in a metal a system of nuclear spins that interact with a dipolar coupling only. By means of Eq. (21) of Section 5.3, prove that the spin-lattice relaxation time is one-half its value in a strong static field ($T_1 = 1/a_{00}$).

4. A nucleus of spin 3/2 has a static Hamiltonian $\mathcal{H}_0 = -\gamma_n \hbar H_0 I_z$. It is acted on by a time-dependent interaction $\mathcal{H}_1(t)$, given by

$$\mathcal{H}_1(t) = A(t)(I_x^2 - I_y^2)$$

where $A(t)$ is a random function of time. Assume that the correlation function $A(t)$ is

$$\overline{A(t)A(t+\tau)} = \overline{A(t)^2}e^{-|\tau|/\tau_0}$$

(a) Express $\mathcal{H}_1(t)$ in terms of the raising and lower operators, I^+ and I^-.
(b) Compute the probability per second of transitions from the $m = \frac{3}{2}$ state to the other three m-states induced by $\mathcal{H}_1(t)$.

5. Consider Problem 4. Assuming that the relative populations of the m-states always correspond to a spin temperature, compute the spin-lattice relaxation time due to the $\mathcal{H}_1(t)$.

6. In Section 5.8, the effect of an alternating field is included in the density matrix formalism.

(a) Show that the solutions of Eq. (14) are correct for low V.
(b) Carry out the solution for $\langle M_x(t)\rangle$, assuming large V, thereby obtaining the results for saturation.

7. Consider a system with three energy levels 1, 2, and 3. An alternating interaction $V(t) = V\cos\omega t$ is applied nearly at resonance with the transition between states 1 and 2.

(a) Write down the differential equations for the density matrix analagous to Eqs. (10) and (11) of Section 5.8.
(b) In the limit of negligible saturation, compute $\langle M_x(t)\rangle$ and show that the width of the resonance is affected by the relaxation to level 3. (This is the phenomenon of lifetime broadening due to transitions to a level that is not directly involved in the spectral line.)

CHAPTER 6

1. It is stated in Section 6.1 that Eqs. (25b) and (29) provide a set of recursion relations among the elements $(JM_J\eta|T_{LM}|J'M_{J'}\eta')$ for the various possible values of M_J, M', and $M_{J'}$, and a fixed set J, L, J', η, η'. For the case that $J = J'$, show that it is indeed true that specifying one matrix element (for example, that for which $M_J = M_{J'} = J$) enables all others to be computed by using the recursion relations.

2. Verify that the functions $T_{2M}(\mathbf{J})$ of Table 6.1 in Section 6.1 satisfy the commutation relations of a T_{2M} with respect to $\mathbf{J}$.

3. Consider an axially symmetric potential and a weak static field. The Hamiltonian is then

$$\mathcal{H} = \frac{e^2qQ}{4I(2I-1)}(3I_z^2 - I^2) - \gamma_n \hbar H I_{z'}$$

If $H = 0$, the spins are quantized by the quadrupole coupling as shown in Fig. 6.3. The states $m = \pm\frac{1}{2}$ are degenerate. Show that when H is weak, these states are split, the energy difference going from $\gamma_n\hbar H$ when z' is parallel to z to $(I+\frac{1}{2})\gamma_n\hbar H$ when z' is perpendicular to z.

4. Consider the Hamiltonian and energies given by Eqs. (6) and (7) of Section 6.5. An alternating field $H_x \cos \omega t$ is applied perpendicular to the z-axis. Find the allowed transitions, their frequencies, and the relative intensities.

Work out numerical answers for the cases $I = \frac{3}{2}$ and $\frac{5}{2}$.

5. Show that a charge e located at a point x_0, y_0, z_0 produces a field gradient

$$V_{zz} \equiv \left.\frac{\partial^2 V}{\partial z^2}\right)_{x,y,z=0}$$

of

$$V_{zz} = e\,\frac{3z_0^2 - r_0^2}{r_0^5}$$

6. A nucleus of spin $\frac{5}{2}$ experiences an electrical quadrupole coupling

$$\mathcal{H} = A(I_x^2 - I_y^2)$$

(a) Show that the energy eigenvalues are 0, $\pm 2\sqrt{7}A$.

(b) Show that the eigenfunctions are

$$E = 0 \begin{cases} \psi_1 = (\frac{9}{14})^{1/2}[\phi_{5/2} - (\frac{5}{9})^{1/2}\phi_{-3/2}] \\ \psi_2 = (\frac{9}{14})^{1/2}[\phi_{-5/2} - (\frac{5}{9})^{1/2}\phi_{3/2}] \end{cases}$$

$$E = 2(7)^{1/2}A \begin{cases} \psi_3 = (\frac{5}{28})^{1/2}[\phi_{5/2} + (\frac{14}{5})^{1/2}\phi_{1/2} + (\frac{9}{5})^{1/2}\phi_{-3/2}] \\ \psi_4 = (\frac{5}{28})^{1/2}[\phi_{-5/2} + (\frac{14}{5})^{1/2}\phi_{-1/2} + (\frac{9}{5})^{1/2}\phi_{3/2}] \end{cases}$$

$$E = -2(7)^{1/2}A \begin{cases} \psi_5 = (\frac{5}{28})^{1/2}[\phi_{5/2} - (\frac{14}{5})^{1/2}\phi_{1/2} + (\frac{9}{5})^{1/2}\phi_{-3/2}] \\ \psi_6 = (\frac{5}{28})^{1/2}[\phi_{-5/2} - (\frac{14}{5})^{1/2}\phi_{-1/2} + (\frac{9}{15})^{1/2}\phi_{3/2}] \end{cases}$$

where $\phi_{5/2}$ is an eigenfunction of I_z with $m = \frac{5}{2}$, and so on.

(c) Show that application of a *small* static field H_0 in the z'-direction splits the degenerate $E = 0$ states, the splitting being $\gamma_n\hbar H_0(\frac{15}{7})$ *independent* of the orientation of z' with respect to x, y, or z.

7. Prove that the eigenvalues E_1, E_2, and so on of a Hamiltonian $\mathcal{H} = A(I_x^2 - I_y^2)$ come in pairs $\pm E_1$, $\pm E_2$, or else are zero. (*Hint:* Consider the effect of an operator R that changes x into y and y into $-x$.)

CHAPTER 7

1. Evaluate the coefficient C_J, defined by Eq. (39) of Section 7.2, to obtain an answer analogous to Eq. (52a) of that section.

2. In the notation of Section 7.2 prove that, with respect to L_x, L_y, and L_z, the function $x^2 - y^2$ is a linear combination of T_{2M}'s.

3. Equation (6) of Section 7.3 says

$$\mathcal{H}_{IS} = \gamma_e \gamma_n \hbar^2 \left(\overline{\frac{1}{r^3}}\right) \frac{2}{5} [3I_x S_x - \mathbf{I} \cdot \mathbf{S}]$$

Show that this follows from Eq. (5):

$$\mathcal{H}_{IS} = \gamma_e \gamma_n \hbar^2 \int \frac{1}{r^3} \left[3 \frac{(\mathbf{I} \cdot \mathbf{r})(\mathbf{S} \cdot \mathbf{r})}{\mathbf{r}^2} - \mathbf{I} \cdot \mathbf{S}\right] x^2 f^2(r)\, d\tau$$

4. In Section 7.3 the hyperfine splitting was worked out for the case of an isotropic electron g-factor. Generalize the result to the case of a Hamiltonian for a field with x- and y-components only:

$$\mathcal{H} = \beta(g_{xx}H_x + g_{zz}H_z) + A_x I_x S_x + A_y I_y S_y + A_z I_z S_z - \gamma_n \hbar (H_x I_x + H_z I_z)$$

5. Consider an atom with a single p-electron, the orbital angular momentum being quenched by a crystalline field such as that of Fig. 7.1.

By using second-order perturbation, show that the interplay of the spin-orbit coupling $\lambda \mathbf{L} \cdot \mathbf{S}$ and the coupling $(e/2mc)(\mathbf{p} \cdot \mathbf{A}_n + \mathbf{A}_n \cdot \mathbf{p})$ between the nuclear moment and the electron orbit give an effective spin-spin coupling between the nucleus and electron.

6. Consider a single p-electron whose spin and orbit are strongly coupled so that the JM_J scheme of quantization applies. The nuclear moment and electron orbital motion are coupled by a Hamiltonian

$$\mathcal{H} = \frac{e}{2mc} (\mathbf{p} \cdot \mathbf{A}_n + \mathbf{A}_n \cdot \mathbf{p}) \tag{1}$$

where $\mathbf{A}_n = \gamma_n \hbar \mathbf{I} \times \mathbf{r}/r^3$ is the vector potential due to the nucleus.

(a) Using the Wigner-Eckart theorem, show that for matrix elements diagonal in the electron quantum number, J, Eq. (1) is equivalent to an effective Hamiltonian

$$\mathcal{H}_{\text{eff}} = A_J \mathbf{J} \cdot \mathbf{I} \tag{2}$$

where A_J is a constant for a given J, independent of M_J.

(b) Find A_J for the $J = \frac{3}{2}$ state.

APPENDIXES

APPENDIX A: A THEOREM ABOUT EXPONENTIAL OPERATORS

We wish to prove a theorem about the exponential function of two operators, A and B, and their commutator C:

$$C \equiv [A, B] \tag{1}$$

The theorem states that when both A and B commute with C, then

$$e^{A+B} = e^{A}e^{B}e^{-C/2} \tag{2}$$

or

$$e^{A+B} = e^{B}e^{A}e^{C/2} \tag{3}$$

We shall prove Eq. (2).

The problem is most readily solved by considering the function $e^{\lambda(A+B)}$. We seek the function $G(\lambda)$ such that

$$e^{\lambda(A+B)} = e^{\lambda A}e^{\lambda B}G(\lambda) \tag{4}$$

To find $G(\lambda)$, we seek a differential equation in λ which it satisfies. In essence this amounts to finding the way in which the function $e^{\lambda(A+B)}$ changes for small changes in λ, and then integrating from $\lambda = 0$ to $\lambda = 1$.

By taking the derivative of both sides of Eq. (4), we get

$$(A + B)e^{\lambda(A+B)} = e^{\lambda A}(A + B)e^{\lambda B}G(\lambda) + e^{\lambda A}e^{\lambda B}\frac{dG}{d\lambda} \tag{5}$$

By utilizing Eq. (4) and multiplying from the left by $e^{-\lambda B}e^{-\lambda A}$, we can rewrite Eq. (5) as

$$e^{-\lambda B}e^{-\lambda A}Be^{\lambda A}e^{\lambda B}G - BG = \frac{dG}{d\lambda} \tag{6}$$

We can evaluate the expression

$$e^{-\lambda A}Be^{\lambda A} \equiv R(\lambda) \tag{7}$$

as follows: by taking the derivative of both sides of Eq. (6) with respect to λ, we find

$$e^{-\lambda A}(BA - AB)e^{\lambda A} = \frac{dR}{d\lambda} \tag{8}$$
$$-C =$$

since $AB - BA \equiv C$ commutes with A.

Integrating Eq. (8) we have

$$R(\lambda) = -C\lambda + \text{constant} \tag{9}$$

We can evaluate the constant by setting $\lambda = 0$ and by noting from Eq. (7) that $R(0) = B$. Therefore

$$R(\lambda) = -C\lambda + B \tag{10}$$

By substituting Eq. (10) into Eq. (6) and using the fact that C commutes with B, we get

$$-\lambda CG = \frac{dG}{d\lambda} \tag{11}$$

which can be interpreted to give

$$G = e^{-(\lambda^2 C/2 + \text{const.})} \tag{12}$$

The constant must be zero because, from Eq. (4), $G(0) = 1$.

Therefore

$$e^{(A+B)} = e^A e^B e^{-C/2} \tag{13}$$

Q.E.D.

APPENDIX B: SOME FURTHER EXPRESSIONS FOR THE SUSCEPTIBILITY

(This Appendix requires familiarity with Chapters 2, 3, and 5.)

Equation (18) of Section 2.10 gives an expression for χ''. Another expression is frequently encountered in the literature. It provides an alternative derivation for the moments of the shape function. It can be obtained from Eq. (18) of Section 2.10,

$$\chi'' = \frac{\hbar\omega\pi}{kTZ} \sum_{a,b} e^{-E_a/kT} |(a|\mu_x|b)|^2 \, \delta(E_a - E_b - \hbar\omega) \tag{1}$$

by use of the integral representation of the δ-function:

$$\delta(x) = \frac{1}{2\pi} \int_{-\infty}^{+\infty} e^{ix\tau} \, d\tau \tag{2}$$

By substituting into Eq. (1), we obtain

$$\chi''(\omega) = \frac{\hbar\omega}{2kTZ} \int_{-\infty}^{+\infty} \sum_{E_a, E_b} e^{-E_a/kT} \cdot (a|\mu_x|b)(b|\mu_x|a) e^{i(E_a - E_b - \hbar\omega)\tau}\, d\tau \tag{3}$$

and substituting for the variable τ a new variable t that has the dimensions of time,

$$\frac{t}{\hbar} = \tau \tag{4}$$

we get

$$\chi''(\omega) = \frac{\omega}{2kTZ} \int_{-\infty}^{+\infty} \sum_{a,b} e^{-E_a/kT} \cdot (a|\mu_x|b)(b|\mu_x|a) e^{[i(E_a - E_b)t]/\hbar} e^{-i\omega t}\, dt \tag{5}$$

We can use the fact that the states $|a)$ and $|b)$ are eigenfunctions of the Hamiltonian $\mathcal{H}$, to express the expression more compactly as

$$\chi''(\omega) = \frac{\omega}{2kTZ} \int_{-\infty}^{+\infty} \sum_{a,b} (a|e^{-\mathcal{H}/kT} e^{i(\mathcal{H}t/\hbar)} \mu_x e^{-(i/\hbar)\mathcal{H}t}|b)(b|\mu_x|a) e^{-i\omega t}\, dt \tag{6}$$

But the summation over a and b is clearly just a trace, so that

$$\chi''(\omega) = \frac{\omega}{2kTZ} \int_{-\infty}^{+\infty} \mathrm{Tr}[e^{-\mathcal{H}/kT} e^{i(\mathcal{H}t/\hbar)} \mu_x e^{-(i/\hbar)\mathcal{H}t} \mu_x] e^{-i\omega t}\, dt \tag{7}$$

In the high-temperature approximation, we replace $\exp(-\mathcal{H}/kT)$ by unity. If we then define the operator $\mu_x(t)$ by

$$\mu_x(t) = e^{i(\mathcal{H}t/\hbar)} \mu_x e^{-i(\mathcal{H}t/\hbar)} \tag{8}$$

we can also express Eq. (7) as

$$\chi''(\omega) = \frac{\omega}{2kTZ} \int_{-\infty}^{+\infty} \mathrm{Tr}[\mu_x(t)\mu_x] e^{-i\omega t}\, dt \tag{9}$$

The quantity $\mathrm{Tr}[\mu_x(t)\mu_x]$ is a form of correlation function, and Eq. (9) states that $\chi''(\omega)$ is given by the Fourier transform of that correlation function.

By using this expression for $\chi''(\omega)$, it is easy to show that omission of the dipolar terms C, D, E, and F of Chapter 3 gives one absorption at the Larmor frequency only, but that their inclusion gives absorption at 0 and $2\omega_0$.

We get also a very compact expression for the shape function $f(\omega)$:

$$f(\omega) = \frac{\chi''(\omega)}{\omega} = \frac{1}{2kTZ} \int_{-\infty}^{+\infty} \mathrm{Tr}[\mu_x(t)\mu_x] e^{-i\omega t}\, dt \tag{10}$$

We can prove another interesting theorem by taking the Fourier transform of Eq. (10):

$$\frac{1}{2kTZ} \mathrm{Tr}[\mu_x(t)\mu_x] = \frac{1}{2\pi} \int_{-\infty}^{+\infty} f(\omega) e^{i\omega t}\, d\omega \tag{11}$$

We see that, setting $t = 0$,

$$\frac{1}{2kTZ}\operatorname{Tr}[\mu_x(0)\mu_x] = \frac{1}{2\pi}\int_{-\infty}^{+\infty} f(\omega)\,d\omega \tag{12}$$

By taking the nth derivative of Eq. (11) with respect to t, and evaluating at $t = 0$, we find

$$\frac{1}{2kTZ}\frac{d^n}{dt^n}\operatorname{Tr}[\mu_x(t)\mu_x]\bigg|_{t=0} = \frac{(i)^n}{2\pi}\int_{-\infty}^{+\infty} \omega^n f(\omega)\,d\omega \tag{13}$$

We get, therefore, a compact expression for the nth moment of the shape function $f(\omega)$:

$$\begin{aligned}\langle\omega^n\rangle &= \frac{\displaystyle\int_{-\infty}^{+\infty} \omega^n f(\omega)\,d\omega}{\displaystyle\int_{-\infty}^{+\infty} f(\omega)\,d\omega} \\ &= \frac{(i)^{-n}(d^n/dt^n)\operatorname{Tr}[\mu_x(t)\mu_x]|_{t=0}}{\operatorname{Tr}[\mu_x(0)\mu_x]}\end{aligned} \tag{14}$$

As an illustration let us derive an expression for the second moment, $\langle\omega^2\rangle$. Taking the derivative of $\mu_x(t)$ gives

$$\begin{aligned}\frac{d^2}{dt^2}\operatorname{Tr}\{e^{i(\mathcal{H}t/\hbar)}\mu_x e^{-i(\mathcal{H}t/\hbar)}\mu_x\} &= \left(\frac{i}{\hbar}\right)^2 \operatorname{Tr}\{e^{i(\mathcal{H}/\hbar)t}[\mathcal{H},[\mathcal{H},\mu_x]]e^{i(\mathcal{H}/\hbar)t}\mu_x\} \\ &= \frac{1}{\hbar^2}\operatorname{Tr}\{e^{i(\mathcal{H}t/\hbar)}[\mathcal{H},\mu_x]e^{-(i/\hbar)\mathcal{H}t}[\mathcal{H},\mu_x]\}\end{aligned} \tag{15}$$

Therefore

$$\langle\omega^2\rangle = -\frac{1}{\hbar^2}\frac{\operatorname{Tr}[\mathcal{H},\mu_x]^2}{\operatorname{Tr}(\mu_x{}^2)} \tag{16}$$

This formalism provides a very simple way of generating expressions for the higher moments. Note, however, that the odd moments all vanish, since $f(\omega)$ is an even function of ω.

So far, apart from assuming the high-temperature approximation, we have left the specification of the Hamiltonian completely general. We can proceed further if we assume that it consists of the sum of a Zeeman term $\mathcal{H}_z$ and a term $\mathcal{H}_p$, often a perturbation, which commutes with $\mathcal{H}_z$. A typical $\mathcal{H}_p$ is the terms A and B of the dipolar coupling. Then, since $\mathcal{H}_p$ and $\mathcal{H}_z$ commute,

$$\begin{aligned}\mu_x(t) &= e^{(i/\hbar)(\mathcal{H}_z+\mathcal{H}_p)t}\mu_x e^{-(i/\hbar)(\mathcal{H}_z+\mathcal{H}_p)t} \\ &= e^{(i/\hbar)\mathcal{H}_pt}e^{-i\omega_0 I_z t}\mu_x e^{i\omega_0 I_z t}e^{-(i/\hbar)\mathcal{H}_pt} \\ &= e^{+(i/\hbar)\mathcal{H}_pt}(\mu_x\cos\omega_0 t + \mu_y\sin\omega_0 t)e^{-(i/\hbar)\mathcal{H}_pt}\end{aligned} \tag{17}$$

where we have used Eq. (13) of Section 2.5. We have, then,

$$\begin{aligned}\operatorname{Tr}[\mu_x(t)\mu_x] = {}& \cos\omega_0 t\operatorname{Tr}[e^{(i/\hbar)\mathcal{H}_pt}\mu_x e^{-(i/\hbar)\mathcal{H}_pt}\mu_x] \\ &+ \sin\omega_0 t\operatorname{Tr}[e^{(i/\hbar)\mathcal{H}_pt}\mu_y e^{(i/\hbar)\mathcal{H}_pt}\mu_x]\end{aligned} \tag{18}$$

In general, if $\mathcal{H}_p$ is invariant under a rotation of 180 deg about the x- or y-axes (as is usually the case), the second term vanishes. This can be shown by evaluating the trace, using coordinates $x' = x$, $y' = -y$, $z' = -z$, which differ only by a 180 deg rotation about x. Then $\mathcal{H}_p = \mathcal{H}'_p$ by our postulate, so that

$$\begin{aligned}\mathrm{Tr}(e^{i(\mathcal{H}_p/\hbar)t}\mu_y e^{-i(\mathcal{H}_p/\hbar)t}\mu_x) &= \mathrm{Tr}(e^{i(\mathcal{H}'_p/\hbar)t}(-\mu_{y'})e^{-i(\mathcal{H}'_p/\hbar)t}\mu_{x'}) \\ &= -\mathrm{Tr}(e^{i(\mathcal{H}'_p/\hbar)t}\mu_{y'}e^{(i/\hbar)\mathcal{H}'_p t}\mu_{x'}) \qquad (19)\end{aligned}$$

But the last trace is clearly the same as the first. Therefore the trace is equal to its own negative and must vanish.

We have, then, that the correlation function $\mathrm{Tr}(\mu_x(t)\mu_x)$ is given as

$$\mathrm{Tr}(\mu_x(t)\mu_x) = \cos\omega_0 t\;\mathrm{Tr}(e^{i(\mathcal{H}_p/\hbar)t}\mu_x e^{-(i/\hbar)\mathcal{H}_p t}\mu_x) \qquad (20)$$

Since this is the Fourier transform of the shape function $f(\omega)$, we see that the transient behavior consists of a term $\cos\omega_0 t$ multiplied by an envelope function.

If we define $\mu_x^*(t)$ as

$$\mu_x^*(t) = e^{(i/\hbar)\mathcal{H}_p t}\mu_x e^{-(i/\hbar)\mathcal{H}_p t} \qquad (21)$$

we can say that the envelope function is $\mathrm{Tr}(\mu_x^*(t)\mu_x)$.

By writing the $\cos\omega_0 t$ as

$$\cos\omega_0 t = \tfrac{1}{2}[e^{i\omega_0 t} + e^{-i\omega_0 t}] \qquad (22)$$

we can say that the two exponentials correspond to lines at $+\omega_0$ and $-\omega_0$. If we wish to discuss only the line at $+\omega_0$, $f_+(\omega)$, we can therefore write

$$f_+(\omega) = \frac{1}{4kTZ}\int_{-\infty}^{+\infty}\mathrm{Tr}(\mu_x^*(t)\mu_x)e^{+i\omega_0 t}e^{-i\omega t}\,dt \qquad (23)$$

and obtain its transform:

$$\frac{1}{4kTZ}\,e^{+i\omega_0 t}\,\mathrm{Tr}(\mu_x^*(t)\mu_x) = \frac{1}{2\pi}\int_{-\infty}^{+\infty} f_+(\omega)e^{+i\omega t}\,d\omega \qquad (24)$$

This can be rewritten as

$$\frac{1}{4kTZ}\,\mathrm{Tr}(\mu_x^*(t)\mu_x) = \frac{1}{2\pi}\int_{-\infty}^{+\infty} f_+(\omega)e^{i(\omega-\omega_0)t}\,d\omega \qquad (25)$$

By taking derivatives as before, we now get

$$\begin{aligned}\frac{(d^n/dt^n)\,\mathrm{Tr}(\mu_x^*(t)\mu_x)]_{t=0}}{\mathrm{Tr}(\mu_x^*(0)\mu_x)} &= (i^n)\frac{\displaystyle\int_{-\infty}^{+\infty}(\omega-\omega_0)^n f_+(\omega)\,d\omega}{\displaystyle\int_{-\infty}^{+\infty} f_+(\omega)\,d\omega} \qquad (26) \\ &= i^n\langle(\omega-\omega_0)^n\rangle\end{aligned}$$

This, then, gives the nth moment with respect to the frequency ω_0. This formalism has surpressed the line at $-\omega_0$, which would, of course, make an inordinately large contribution to $\langle(\omega - \omega_0)^n\rangle$ were it included!

By following steps similar to those of Eq. (15), we now find

$$\langle(\omega - \omega_0)^2\rangle = \frac{1}{\hbar^2} \frac{\mathrm{Tr}([\mathcal{H}_p, \mu_x]^2)}{\mathrm{Tr}\mu_x^2} \tag{27}$$

We also see that

$$\langle\omega - \omega_0\rangle = \frac{1}{\hbar} \mathrm{Tr}([\mathcal{H}_p, \mu_x]\mu_x) \tag{28}$$

which can be shown to vanish if $\mathcal{H}_p$ consists of the dipolar terms A and B, as shown in Chapter 3.

APPENDIX C: DERIVATION OF THE CORRELATION FUNCTION FOR A FIELD THAT JUMPS RANDOMLY BETWEEN $\pm h_0$

We shall assume the field jumps randomly between the two values $\pm h_0$, which we shall label as states 1 and 2. We shall call

$$\begin{aligned} +h_0 &= H_1 \\ -h_0 &= H_2 \end{aligned} \tag{1}$$

Then we wish to know the correlation function $G(\tau)$:

$$G(\tau) = \overline{H(t)H(t + \tau)} \tag{2}$$

where the bar indicates an ensemble average.

If the field is H_1 at time $t = 0$, then we can write for a single member of the ensemble:

$$H(0)H(\tau) = H_1[P_1(\tau)H_1 + P_2(\tau)H_2] \tag{3}$$

where $P_1(\tau)$ and $P_2(\tau)$ are either zero or one, depending on whether at time τ the field is H_1 or H_2. We now perform an ensemble average of Eq. (3) over the various histories. This replaces the quantities $P_1(\tau)$, $P_2(\tau)$ by their ensemble averages $p_1(\tau)$ and $p_2(\tau)$, which are the *probabilities* that in an ensemble in which the field was H_1 at $\tau = 0$, it will be H_1 or H_2 at time τ.

Thus we have

$$\overline{H(0)H(\tau)} = H_1[H_1p_1(\tau) + H_2p_2(\tau)] \tag{4}$$

This equation, of course, assumes that at $\tau = 0$, $H(\tau) = H_1$, so that as $\tau \to 0$, $p_1(\tau) \to 1$, $p_2(\tau) \to 0$. Equally likely is the situation that the field is H_2 at $\tau = 0$, which will give a similar equation except that 1 and 2 are interchanged.

We shall assume the behavior of p_1 and p_2 as a function of τ to be given by a rate equation:

$$\frac{dp_1}{d\tau} = W(p_2 - p_1)$$
$$\frac{dp_2}{d\tau} = W(p_1 - p_2) \tag{5}$$

This is a "normal modes" problem, with solutions obtained by adding or subtracting:

$$p_1(\tau) + p_2(\tau) = \text{const. } (= 1 \text{ from normalization})$$
$$p_1(\tau) - p_2(\tau) = Ce^{-2W\tau} \tag{6}$$

where $C = p_1(0) - p_2(0) = p_1(0)$. Since $p_2(0)$ vanishes and since $p_1(0) = 1$, $C = 1$.

By making use of Eqs. (1), (4), and (6), we have

$$\begin{aligned}\overline{H(0)H(\tau)} &= H_1[H_1p_1(\tau) + p_2(\tau)H_2] \\ &= h_0^2e^{-2W\tau}\end{aligned} \tag{7}$$

An identical answer is found for $\overline{H(0)H(\tau)}$ if the field is assumed to be H_2 at $\tau = 0$. We must weigh these equally (that is, average the answers over the *initial* fields) to get the final ensemble average. We denote this by a double bar, to indicate the fact that we have average over an ensemble of initial conditions as well as a variety of histories for a given initial condition:

$$\overline{\overline{H(0)H(\tau)}} = h_0^2e^{-2W\tau} = G(\tau)$$

This is the correlation time assumed in Chapter 5, with $2W \cong 1/\tau_0$.

APPENDIX D: A THEOREM FROM PERTURBATION THEORY

In this Appendix we shall derive from perturbation theory a theorem that has wide utility in magnetic resonance. It is closely related to second-order perturbation theory but gives the results in a form particularly useful when there is degeneracy. A typical situation in which the theorem has great use is illustrated by the g-shift calculation of Section 7.2. We may divide the Hamiltonian into three terms;

$$\mathcal{H} = \mathcal{H}_0 + \mathcal{H}_1 + \mathcal{H}_2 \tag{1}$$

where

$$\mathcal{H}_0 = \frac{p^2}{2m} + V_0 + V_1$$
$$\mathcal{H}_1 = 2\beta\mathbf{H}\cdot\mathbf{S} \tag{2}$$
$$\mathcal{H}_2 = \lambda\mathbf{L}\cdot\mathbf{S} + \beta\mathbf{H}\cdot\mathbf{L}$$

Since $\mathcal{H}_0$ does not depend on spin, its eigenstates may be taken as products of an orbital and a spin function. We denote the orbital quantum numbers by l and the spin quantum numbers by α. Then

$$\mathcal{H}_0|l\alpha) = E_l|l\alpha) \tag{3}$$

The states $|l\alpha)$ are degenerate for a given l because of the spin quantum numbers. The term $\mathcal{H}_1$ lifts the spin degeneracy. Since it depends on spin only, it has no matrix elements between different orbital states:

$$(l\alpha|\mathcal{H}_1|l'\alpha') = \delta_{ll'}(l\alpha|\mathcal{H}_1|l\alpha') \tag{4}$$

In general the matrix elements of $\mathcal{H}_1$ between states $|l\alpha)$ and $|l\alpha')$ where $\alpha \neq \alpha'$ will be non-zero. Therefore the presence of $\mathcal{H}_1$ still leaves us a group of submatrices $(l\alpha|\mathcal{H}_1|l\alpha')$ to diagonalize. For our example, since the spin was 1/2, these submatrices are only 2×2 and are easily handled.

The presence of the term $\mathcal{H}_2$ spoils things, since $\mathcal{H}_2$ joins states of different l. However, as a result of the quenching of the orbital angular momentum, the matrix elements of $\mathcal{H}_2$ that are diagonal in l vanish:

$$(l\alpha|\mathcal{H}_2|l\alpha') = 0 \tag{5}$$

We may schematize things as shown in the accompanying figure, where the Hamiltonian matrix is illustrated and where we have labeled which terms $\mathcal{H}_1$ or $\mathcal{H}_2$ have non-vanishing matrix elements.

Hamiltonian matrix. The regions in which non-vanishing elements of $\mathcal{H}_1$ or $\mathcal{H}_2$ may be found are labeled by the cross-hatching. The quantum numbers l_1, l_2, and l_3 designate different eigenvalues of $\mathcal{H}_0$.

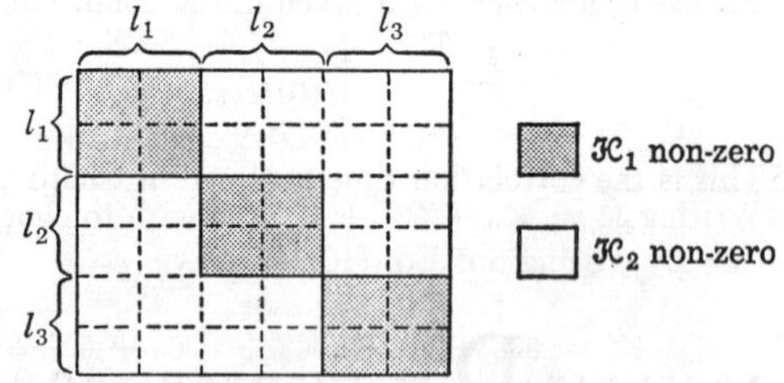

The technique that we shall describe below in essence provides a transformation which reduces the size of the matrix elements of $\mathcal{H}_2$ joining states of different l. In the process, new elements are added which are diagonal in l. In this way states of different l are, so to speak, uncoupled, and we are once again faced with diagonalizing only the smaller submatrices diagonal in l.

The basic technique may be thought of formally as follows. The set of basis functions $\psi_{l\alpha}$ form a complete set, but have the troublesome $\mathcal{H}_2$ matrix elements between states of different l. We seek a transformed set of functions $\phi_{l\alpha}$ given by

$$\phi_{l\alpha} = e^{iS}\psi_{l\alpha} \tag{6}$$

where S is a Hermitian operator that reduces the size of the troublesome matrix elements. In terms of the ϕ's, the Hamiltonian matrix elements are

$$\int \phi_{l\alpha}^* \mathcal{H} \phi_{l'\alpha'} \, d\tau \, d\tau_s \tag{7}$$

where $d\tau$ and $d\tau_s$ represent integration over spatial and spin variables, respectively. By utilizing Eq. (6) and the Hermitian property of S, we have

$$\int \phi_{l\alpha}^* \mathcal{H} \phi_{l'\alpha'}\, d\tau\, d\tau_s = \int \psi_{l\alpha}^* e^{-iS} \mathcal{H} e^{iS} \psi_{l'\alpha'}\, d\tau\, d\tau_s$$
$$= (l\alpha|e^{-iS}\mathcal{H}e^{iS}|l'\alpha') \tag{8}$$

where we have used the notation $|l\alpha)$ for matrix elements calculated using the ψ's. We may interpret Eq. (8) as saying that we can look either for transformed functions or a transformed Hamiltonian.

If we define $\mathcal{H}'$ as

$$\mathcal{H}' = e^{-iS}\mathcal{H}e^{iS} \tag{9}$$

we may state as our goal the determination of a Hermitian operator S that generates a transformed Hamiltonian $\mathcal{H}'$ such that $\mathcal{H}'$ has no matrix elements between states of different l.

Presumably S must be small, since the original Hamiltonian $\mathcal{H}$ has small matrix elements off-diagonal in l. Therefore we may approximate by expanding the exponentials in Eq. (9):

$$\begin{aligned}\mathcal{H}' &= e^{-iS}\mathcal{H}e^{iS} \\ &= \left(1 - iS - \frac{S^2}{2!} + \cdots\right)\mathcal{H}\left(1 + iS - \frac{S^2}{2!} + \cdots\right) \\ &= \mathcal{H} + i[\mathcal{H}, S] + \left[S\mathcal{H}S - \frac{S^2}{2}\mathcal{H} - \frac{\mathcal{H}S^2}{2}\right] \\ &= \mathcal{H} + i[\mathcal{H}, S] - \tfrac{1}{2}[[\mathcal{H}, S]S]\end{aligned} \tag{10}$$

Writing $\mathcal{H} = \mathcal{H}_0 + \mathcal{H}_1 + \mathcal{H}_2$, we wish to choose S to eliminate $\mathcal{H}_2$.

By writing out Eq. (10), we have

$$\mathcal{H}' = \mathcal{H}_0 + \mathcal{H}_1 + \mathcal{H}_2 + i[\mathcal{H}_0 + \mathcal{H}_1, S] + i[\mathcal{H}_2, S] - \tfrac{1}{2}[S, [S, \mathcal{H}]] \tag{11}$$

We can eliminate the third term on the right by choosing

$$\mathcal{H}_2 + i[\mathcal{H}_0 + \mathcal{H}_1, S] = 0 \tag{12}$$

Then we have

$$\mathcal{H}' = \mathcal{H}_0 + \mathcal{H}_1 + i[\mathcal{H}_2, S] + \frac{i^2}{2}[[\mathcal{H}_0 + \mathcal{H}_1, S], S] + \frac{i^2}{2}[[\mathcal{H}_2, S], S] \tag{13}$$

If $\mathcal{H}_2$ were zero, S would vanish. Therefore, we expect S will be of order $\mathcal{H}_2$, and the last term of order $\mathcal{H}_2^3$. Neglecting it, and utilizing Eq. (12), we have

$$\mathcal{H}' = \mathcal{H}_0 + \mathcal{H}_1 + \frac{i}{2}[\mathcal{H}_2, S] \tag{14}$$

Equation (12) may be put in matrix form to obtain an explicit matrix for S. Using the facts that $\mathcal{H}_1$ has no matrix elements between states of different l and that $\mathcal{H}_2$

has none diagonal in l, we have

$$(l\alpha|\mathcal{H}_2|l'\alpha') + i \sum_{l'',\alpha''} (l\alpha|\mathcal{H}_0 + \mathcal{H}_1|l''\alpha'')(l''\alpha''|S|l'\alpha') - (l\alpha|S|l''\alpha'')(l''\alpha''|\mathcal{H}_0 + \mathcal{H}_1|l'\alpha') = 0 \tag{15}$$

Thus

$$(l\alpha|\mathcal{H}_2|l'\alpha') + i(E_l - E_{l'})(l\alpha|S|l'\alpha') + i \sum_{\alpha} (l\alpha|\mathcal{H}_1|l\alpha'')(l\alpha''|S|l'\alpha') - i(l\alpha|S|l'\alpha'')(l'\alpha''|\mathcal{H}_1|l'\alpha') = 0 \tag{16}$$

If $l \neq l'$, we may neglect the terms in $\mathcal{H}_1$, as being small compared with that involving $E_l - E_{l'}$. Then

$$(l\alpha|S|l'\alpha') = \frac{1}{i} \frac{(l\alpha|\mathcal{H}_2|l'\alpha')}{(E_{l'} - E_l)} \tag{17}$$

If $l = l'$, we have, for Eq. (16),

$$\sum_{\alpha''} (l\alpha|\mathcal{H}_1|l\alpha'')(l\alpha''|S|l\alpha') = \sum_{\alpha''} (l\alpha|S|l\alpha'')(l\alpha''|\mathcal{H}_1|l\alpha') \tag{18}$$

This is readily satisfied by choosing Eq. (18a):

$$(l\alpha|S|l\alpha'') = 0 \tag{18a}$$

Therefore S does not join states of the same l. [Equations (17) and (18a) enable one to verify that S is Hermitian; that is, that $(l\alpha|S|l'\alpha') = (l'\alpha'|S|l\alpha)^*$, where the star indicates a complex conjugate.] By using Eq. (17) in Eq. (14), we may find the new matrix elements between $|l\alpha)$ and $|l'\alpha')$. First we note that the states off-diagonal in l are

$$(l\alpha|\mathcal{H}'|l'\alpha') = \frac{i}{2} (l\alpha|[\mathcal{H}_2, S]|l, \alpha') \tag{19}$$

since $\mathcal{H}_0$ and $\mathcal{H}_1$ are diagonal in l. Thus,

$$\begin{aligned}(l\alpha|\mathcal{H}'|l'\alpha') &= \frac{i}{2} \sum_{l'',\alpha''} [(l\alpha|\mathcal{H}_2|l''\alpha'')(l''\alpha''|S|l'\alpha') - (l\alpha|S|l''\alpha'')(l''\alpha''|\mathcal{H}_2|l'\alpha')] \\ &= \tfrac{1}{2} \sum_{l'',\alpha''} (l\alpha|\mathcal{H}_2|l''\alpha'')(l''\alpha''|\mathcal{H}_2|l'\alpha') \times \left[\frac{1}{E_{l'} - E_{l''}} + \frac{1}{E_{l''} - E_l}\right]\end{aligned} \tag{20}$$

The off-diagonal matrix elements are therefore reduced in the ratio of $\mathcal{H}_2$ to the difference between eigenvalues of $\mathcal{H}_0$, and the states of different l are "uncoupled."

The matrix elements diagonal in l are modified, too. They become, using Eqs. (14) and (17),

$$(l\alpha|\mathcal{H}'|l\alpha') = (l\alpha|\mathcal{H}_0 + \mathcal{H}_1 + \frac{i}{2}[\mathcal{H}_2, S]|l\alpha')$$

$$= E_l\,\delta_{\alpha\alpha'} + (l\alpha|\mathcal{H}_1|l\alpha')$$

$$+ \frac{i}{2}\sum_{l'',\alpha''} (l\alpha|\mathcal{H}_2|l''\alpha'')(l''\alpha''|S|l\alpha') - (l\alpha|S|l''\alpha'')(l''\alpha''|\mathcal{H}_2|l\alpha')$$

$$= E_l\,\delta_{\alpha\alpha'} + (l\alpha|\mathcal{H}_1|l\alpha') + \sum_{l'',\alpha''} \frac{(l\alpha|\mathcal{H}_2|l''\alpha'')(l''\alpha''|\mathcal{H}_2|l\alpha')}{E_l - E_l'} \tag{21}$$

If $\alpha = \alpha'$, we recognize that the terms in $\mathcal{H}_2$ give the familiar expression for the energy shift in second-order perturbation theory. However, our expression also includes matrix elements for $\alpha \neq \alpha'$. In this connection we wish to emphasize that in degenerate perturbation theory, ordinarily one must find zero-order functions that have vanishing off-diagonal elements. The method we have described places no such restriction on the basis functions $|l\alpha)$. If the quantum numbers α lead to elements $(l\alpha|\mathcal{H}'|l\alpha')$ between states of different α, it means merely that we must still diagonalize the matrix $(l\alpha|\mathcal{H}'|l\alpha')$ of Eq. (21). We conclude that the presence of a term $\mathcal{H}_2$ is to a good approximation equivalent to adding to the Hamiltonian $\mathcal{H}_0 + \mathcal{H}_1$ matrix elements diagonal in l of

$$\sum_{l'',\alpha''} \frac{(l\alpha|\mathcal{H}_2|l''\alpha'')(l''\alpha''|\mathcal{H}_2|l\alpha')}{E_l - E_{l''}}$$

and neglecting the coupling between states of different l.

APPENDIX E: THE HIGH TEMPERATURE APPROXIMATION

In several places in the text we make use of the high temperature approximation. For example, on page 51 in Chapter 3 we replace the exponentials by unity in the expression for $\chi''(\omega)$:

$$\chi''(\omega) = \frac{\pi\hbar\omega}{kTZ}\sum_{a,b} e^{-E_a/kT}|(a|\mu_x|b)|^2\delta(E_a - E_b - \hbar\omega) \tag{1}$$

where

$$Z = \sum_a e^{-E_a/kT}$$

is the partition function. Since the energies E_a are energies of the N-particle system, they may range from $-N\gamma\hbar H_0 I$ to $+N\gamma\hbar H_0 I$ as a result of the Zeeman energy alone. Of course, the energy $-N\gamma\hbar H_0 I$ would occur only if all N spins were in the state $m = I$, and is thus quite unlikely on a statistical basis. However, we expect to find typical values of $|E_a| \cong \sqrt{N}\,\gamma\hbar H_0 I$ combining the m values of the N spins at random. Since $N \cong 10^{23}$ in a typical sample, how can we approximate $E_a/kT \ll 1$?

It is clear that no one spin interacts with many others, so that in some sense we do not really need to consider 10^{23} spins to get a fair precision in computing χ''. That is, asserting that 10^{23} spins are involved is really a fiction. After all, in an applied field of reasonable strength we can predict the location of the absorption by considering only one spin.

We believe, therefore, that the high temperature approximation will hold if the energy of a *single* spin is small compared to kT. We wish now to demonstrate how that comes about. To do so, we shall consider a simplified case, that of N non-interacting identical spins, and assert that a similar argument should hold for interacting spins provided that the effective interaction between pairs is still small compared to kT so that no drastic phenomena such as ferromagnetism results.

If the spins are non-interacting, we can choose as exact quantum numbers the individual spin quantum numbers $m_1, m_2, \ldots, m_N$. The energy E_a then becomes

$$E_a = -\gamma\hbar H_0 \sum_{j=1}^{N} m_j = -\hbar\omega_0 M \tag{2}$$

where ω_0 is the Larmor frequency, and $M = \sum_j m_j$. The wave function $|a)$ and operator μ_x are

$$|a) = |m_1, m_2, \ldots, m_N) \tag{3}$$

$$\mu_x = \sum_j \mu_{xj} \tag{4}$$

Then

$$|(a|\mu_x|b)|^2 = (a|\sum_j \mu_{xj}|b)(b|\sum_k \mu_{xk}|a)$$

$$= \sum_{j,k} (a|\mu_{xj}|b)(b|\mu_{xk}|a) \tag{5}$$

Since the μ_{xj}'s involve the coordinates of only one nucleus, we see from Eq. (3) that we only get terms in which $j = k$ so that

$$|(a|\mu_x|b)|^2 = \sum_j |(m_1, m_2, \ldots, m_j, \ldots|\mu_{xj}|m_1, m_2, \ldots, m_j', \ldots)|^2 \tag{6}$$

giving us

$$\chi''(\omega) = \frac{\pi\hbar\omega}{kTZ} \sum_{\substack{m_1, m_2, \ldots, m_j, \ldots, m_N \\ m_j'}} e^{\hbar\omega_0 M/kT}$$

$$\times \sum_j |(m_1, m_2, \ldots, m_j, \ldots|\mu_{xj}|m_1, m_2, \ldots, m_j', \ldots)|^2$$

$$\times\ \delta[\hbar\omega_0(m_j - m_j') - \hbar\omega]. \tag{7}$$

If we define $m = M - m_j$, we can write

$$e^{\hbar\omega_0 M/kT} = e^{\hbar\omega_0 m/kT}\, e^{\hbar\omega_0 m_j/kT} \tag{8}$$

Then, using the fact that $(m_1, m_2, \ldots, m_j, \ldots|\mu_{xj}|m_1, m_2, \ldots, m'_j, \ldots) = (m_j|\mu_{xj}|m'_j)$ Eq. (7) becomes

$$\chi''(\omega) = \frac{\pi\hbar\omega}{kTZ} \sum_{m_1, m_2, \ldots m_{j-1}, m_{j+1}, \ldots} e^{m\hbar\omega_0/kT} \times \sum_{\substack{j, m_j \\ m'_j}} |(m_j|\mu_{xj}|m'_j)|^2 \delta[\hbar\omega_0(m_j - m'_j) - \hbar\omega] \tag{9}$$

Here we have used the fact that the sum over the $N - 1$ coordinates omitting m_j is independent of which j we omit since the spins are identical. But

$$Z = \sum_{m_1, m_2, \ldots, m_{j-1}, m_{j+1}, \ldots} e^{m\hbar\omega_0/kT} \sum_{m_j} e^{m_j\hbar\omega_0/kT} \tag{10}$$

If, now, $I\hbar\omega_0 \ll kT$, we can replace the exponentials in the m_j sum by unity, and obtain

$$\sum_{m_j} e^{m_j\hbar\omega_0/kT} = (2I + 1) \tag{11}$$

giving

$$Z = (2I + 1) \sum_{m_1, m_2, \ldots, m_{j-1}, m_{j+1}, \ldots} e^{m\hbar\omega_0/kT} = (2I + 1)Z(N - 1)$$

where $Z(N - 1)$ is the partition function of $N - 1$ particles. The sum

$$\sum e^{+m\hbar\omega_0/kT}$$

now factors out of the numerator of Eq. (9) and out of Z giving

$$\chi''(\omega) = \frac{\pi\hbar\omega}{(2I + 1)kT} \sum_{j=1}^{N} \sum_{m_j, m'_j} |(m_j|\mu_{xj}|m'_j)|^2 \delta[\hbar\omega_0(m_j - m'_j) - \hbar\omega]. \tag{12}$$

We wish to re-express this in terms of the states $|a)$ and $|b)$. To do so we note that

$$\sum_{\substack{m_1, m_2, \ldots, m_j, \ldots, m_N \\ m'_j}} |(m_1, m_2, \ldots, m_j, \ldots|\mu_{xj}|m_1, m_2, \ldots, m'_j, \ldots)|^2 = (2I + 1)^{N-1} \sum_{m_j, m'_j} |(m_j|\mu_{xj}|m'_j)|^2 \tag{13}$$

giving

$$\chi''(\omega) = \frac{\pi\hbar\omega}{(2I + 1)^N kT} \sum_{a,b} |(a|\mu_x|b)|^2 \delta(E_a - E_b - \hbar\omega). \tag{14}$$

But this is just the result we would have had had we replaced all exponentials in Eq. (1) by unity.

We see that we have never asserted that $|E_a| \ll kT$. In fact, we have made no approximation on this score at all. Our only real approximation is that the partition function for N spins shall be $(2I + 1)$ times that for $N - 1$ spins.

A similar situation arises in numerous other places where we use the high temperature approximation. Essentially we are saying that although the energies correspond formally to a large N, in actual fact only a small number of spins is ever really important. Restrictions on the temperature which appear because $N \cong 10^{23}$ must therefore be fictitious, and we need not worry unless the energy of a small number of spins becomes comparable to kT.

SELECTED BIBLIOGRAPHY

The problem of preparing a complete Bibliography of magnetic resonance is hopeless, there have been so many papers. Such a Bibliography would not even be useful for a student, since he would not know where to begin. Therefore, a short list of articles has been selected which touches on a number of the most important ideas in resonance. In some instances, papers were chosen because they are basic references; others because they were representative of a class of papers. In some cases an attempt has been made to augment the treatment of the text. For example, the subjects of cross-relaxation, spin temperature, and nuclear polarization schemes are all important, but none is treated in the book. A few articles were chosen because they have particularly good bibliographies.

Some obvious categories that have been omitted are references to masers and lasers. There are undoubtedly many more. However, even without these, the Bibliography has gotten rather long, but it is hoped that it is long enough to launch a student into the subject of resonance.

Basic Papers

E. M. Purcell, H. C. Torrey, and R. V. Pound, "Resonance Absorption by Nuclear Magnetic Moments in a Solid," *Phys. Rev.*, **69**: 37 (1946).

F. Bloch, W. W. Hansen, and M. Packard, "Nuclear Induction," *Phys. Rev.*, **69**: 127 (1946).

F. Bloch, W. W. Hansen, and M. Packard, "The Nuclear Induction Experiment," *Phys. Rev.*, **70**: 474–485 (1946).

F. Bloch, "Nuclear Induction," *Phys. Rev.*, **70**: 460–474 (1946).

N. Bloembergen, E. M. Purcell, and R. V. Pound, "Relaxation Effects in Nuclear Magnetic Resonance Absorption," *Phys. Rev.*, **73**: 679–712 (1948).

Books, Monographs, and Review Articles

G. E. Pake, "Nuclear Magnetic Resonance," *Solid State Physics*, Vol. 2. Seitz and Turnbull, eds. New York: Academic Press, Inc., 1956, pp. 1–91.

Collected articles, *Nuovo cimento* Suppl., Vol. VI, Ser. X, p. 808 ff. (1957).

G. E. Pake, *Paramagnetic Resonance*. New York: W. A. Benjamin, Inc., 1962 (205 pages).

E. R. Andrew, *Nuclear Magnetic Resonance*. Cambridge, England: Cambridge University Press, 1955 (265 pages).

J. A. Pople, W. G. Schneider, and H. J. Bernstein, *High-Resolution Nuclear Magnetic Resonance*. New York: McGraw-Hill Book Co., Inc., 1959 (501 pages).

C. J. Gorter, *Paramagnetic Relaxation*. New York: Elsevier Publishers, Inc., 1947 (127 pages).

D. J. E. Ingram, *Spectroscopy at Radio and Microwave Frequencies*. London: Butterworth's Scientific Publications, 1955 (332 pages).

A. K. Saha and T. P. Das, *Theory and Applications of Nuclear Induction*. Calcutta, India: Saha Institute of Nuclear Physics, 1957 (516 pages).

M. H. Cohen and F. Reif, "Quadrupole Effects in Nuclear Magnetic Resonance Studies of Solids," *Solid State Physics*, Vol. 5, Seitz and Turnbull, eds. New York: Academic Press, Inc., 1957, pp. 321–438.

T. P. Das and E. L. Hahn, "Nuclear Quadrupole Resonance Spectroscopy," *Solid State Physics*, Supplement 1, Seitz and Turnbull, eds. New York: Academic Press, Inc., 1958 (223 pages).

T. J. Rowland, "Nuclear Magnetic Resonance in Metals," *Progr. in Materials Sci.*, Vol. 9, B. Chalmers, ed. Oxford: Pergamon Press, 1961, pp. 1–91.

R. V. Pound, *Progr. in Nuclear Phys.*, Vol. 2, O. R. Frisch, ed. London: Pergamon Press, 1952, pp. 21–50.

William Low, "Paramagnetic Resonance in Solids," *Solid State Physics*, Supplement 2, Seitz and Turnbull, eds. New York: Academic Press, Inc., 1960 (212 pages).

J. S. Griffith, *The Theory of Transition-Metal Ions*. Cambridge, England: Cambridge University Press, 1961 (455 pages).

N. F. Ramsey, *Nuclear Moments*. New York: John Wiley & Sons, Inc., 1953 (169 pages).

N. F. Ramsey, *Molecular Beams*. Oxford: Clarendon Press, 1956 (466 pages).

A. Abragam, *The Principles of Nuclear Magnetism*. Oxford: Clarendon Press, 1961 (599 pages).

N. Bloembergen, *Nuclear Magnetic Relaxation*. New York: W. A. Benjamin, Inc., 1961 (178 pages).

John D. Roberts, *Nuclear Magnetic Resonance*. New York: McGraw-Hill Book Co., Inc., 1959 (118 pages).

General Theory of Resonance

D. Pines and C. P. Slichter, "Relaxation Times in Magnetic Resonance," *Phys. Rev.*, **100**: 1014–1020 (1955).

H. C. Torrey, "Bloch Equations with Diffusion Terms," *Phys. Rev.*, **104**: 563–565 (1956).

R. Kubo and K. Tomita, "A General Theory of Magnetic Resonance Absorption," *J. Phys. Soc. Japan*, **9**: 888–919 (1954).

P. W. Anderson and P. R. Weiss, "Exchange Narrowing in Paramagnetic Resonance," *Rev. Mod. Phys.*, **25**: 269–276 (1953).

P. W. Anderson, "A Mathematical Model for the Narrowing of Spectral Lines by Exchange or Motion," *J. Phys. Soc. Japan*, **9**: 316–339 (1954).

R. K. Wangness and F. Bloch, "The Dynamical Theory of Nuclear Induction," *Phys. Rev.*, **89**: 728–739 (1953).

F. Bloch, "Dynamical Theory of Nuclear Induction II," *Phys. Rev.*, **102**: 104–135 (1956).

A. G. Redfield, "On the Theory of Relaxation Processes," *IBM Journal*, **1**: 19–31 (1957).

H. C. Torrey, "Nuclear Spin Relaxation by Translational Diffusion," *Phys. Rev.*, **92**: 962–969 (1953).

Nuclear Magnetic Resonance in Metals

C. H. Townes, C. Herring, and W. D. Knight, "The Effect of Electronic Paramagnetism on Nuclear Magnetic Resonance Frequencies in Metals," *Phys. Rev.*, **77**: 852–853 (1950) (letter).

W. D. Knight, "Electron Paramagnetism and Nuclear Magnetic Resonance in Metals," *Solid State Physics*, Vol. 2, Seitz and Turnbull, eds. New York: Academic Press, Inc., 1956, pp. 93–136.

J. Korringa, "Nuclear Magnetic Relaxation and Resonance Line Shift in Metals," *Physica*, **16**: 601–610 (1950).

D. F. Holcomb and R. E. Norberg, "Nuclear Spin Relaxation in Alkali Metals," *Phys. Rev.*, **98**: 1074–1091 (1955).

G. Benedek and T. Kushida, "The Pressure Dependence of the Knight Shift in the Alkali Metals and Copper," *J. Phys. Chem. Solids*, **5**: 241 (1958).

$I_1 \cdot I_2$ Coupling

N. F. Ramsey and E. M. Purcell, "Interactions between Nuclear Spins in Molecules," *Phys. Rev.*, **85**: 143–144 (1952) (letter).

E. L. Hahn and D. E. Maxwell, "Spin Echo Measurements of Nuclear Spin Coupling in Molecules," *Phys. Rev.*, **88**: 1070–1084 (1952).

H. S. Gutowsky, D. W. McCall, and C. P. Slichter, "Nuclear Magnetic Resonance Multiplets in Liquids," *J. Chem. Phys.*, **21**: 279–292 (1953).

N. F. Ramsey, "Electron Coupled Interactions Between Nuclear Spins in Molecules," *Phys. Rev.*, **91**: 303–307 (1953).

N. Bloembergen and T. J. Rowland, "Nuclear Spin Exchange in Solids: Tl^{203} and Tl^{205} Magnetic Resonance in Thallium and Thallic Oxide," *Phys. Rev.*, **97**: 1679–1698 (1955).

M. A. Ruderman and C. Kittel, "Indirect Exchange Coupling of Nuclear Magnetic Moments by Conduction Electrons," *Phys. Rev.*, **96**: 99–102 (1954).

Kei Yosida, "Magnetic Properties of Cu-Mn Alloys," *Phys. Rev.*, **106**: 893–898 (1957).

H. M. McConnell, A. D. McLean, and C. A. Reilly, "Analysis of Spin-Spin Multiplets in Nuclear Magnetic Resonance Spectra," *J. Chem. Phys.*, **23**: 1152–1159 (1955).

H. M. McConnell, "Molecular Orbital Approximation to Electron Coupled Interaction Between Nuclear Spins," *J. Chem. Phys.*, **24**: 460–467 (1956).

W. A. Anderson, "Nuclear Magnetic Resonance Spectra of Some Hydrocarbons," *Phys. Rev.*, **102**: 151–167 (1956).

Pulse Methods

E. L. Hahn, "Spin Echoes," *Phys. Rev.*, **80**: 580–594 (1950).

H. Y. Carr and E. M. Purcell, "Effects of Diffusion on Free Precession in Nuclear Magnetic Resonance Experiments," *Phys. Rev.*, **94**: 630–638 (1954).

Second Moment

L. J. F. Broer, "On the Theory of Paramagnetic Relaxation," *Physica*, **10**: 801–816 (1943).

J. H. Van Vleck, "The Dipolar Broadening of Magnetic Resonance Lines in Crystals," *Phys. Rev.*, **74**: 1168–1183 (1948).

G. E. Pake, "Nuclear Resonance Absorption in Hydrated Crystals: Fine Structure of the Proton Line," *J. Chem. Phys.*, **16**: 327–336 (1948).

H. S. Gutowsky and G. E. Pake, "Nuclear Magnetism in Studies of Molecular Structure and Rotation in Solids: Ammonium Salts," *J. Chem. Phys.*, **16**: 1164–1165 (1948) (letter).

E. R. Andrew and R. G. Eades, "A Nuclear Magnetic Resonance Investigation of Three Solid Benzenes," *Proc. Roy. Soc.*, **A218**: 537–552 (1953).

H. S. Gutowsky and G. E. Pake, "Structural Investigations by Means of Nuclear Magnetism II — Hindered Rotation in Solids," *J. Chem. Phys.*, **18**: 162–170 (1950).

Nuclear Polarization

A. W. Overhauser, "Polarization of Nuclei in Metals," *Phys. Rev.*, **92**: 411–415 (1953).

T. R. Carver and C. P. Slichter, "Experimental Verification of the Overhauser Nuclear Polarization Effect," *Phys. Rev.*, **102**: 975–980 (1956).

A. Abragam, "Overhauser Effect in Nonmetals," *Phys. Rev.*, **98**: 1729–1735 (1955).

C. D. Jeffries, "Polarization of Nuclei by Resonance Saturation in Paramagnetic Crystals," *Phys. Rev.*, **106**: 164–165 (1957) (letter).

J. Uebersfeld, J. L. Motchane, and E. Erb, "Augmentation de la Polarisation Nucléaire dans les Liquides et Gaz Adsorbés Sur Un Charbon. Extension Aux Solides Contenant des Impuretés Paramagnétiques," *J. phys. radium*, **19**: 843–844 (1958).

A. Abragam and W. G. Proctor, "Une nouvelle méthode de polarisation dynamique des noyaux atomique dans les solides," *Compt. rend.*, **246**: 2253–2256 (1958).

C. D. Jeffries, "Dynamic Nuclear Polarization," *Progress in Cryogenics.* London: Heywood & Company, Ltd., 1961.

G. R. Khutsishvili, "The Overhauser Effect and Related Phenomena," *Soviet Physics Uspekhi*, **3**: 285–319 (1960).

Robert H. Webb, "Steady-State Nuclear Polarizations via Electronic Transitions," *Am. J. Phys.*, **29**: 428–444 (1961).

Quadrupole Effects

R. V. Pound, "Nuclear Electric Quadrupole Interactions in Crystals," *Phys. Rev.*, **79**: 685–702 (1950).

N. Bloembergen, "Report of the Conference on Defects in Crystalline Solids," *Phys. Soc.*, (London), 1955, p. 1.

T. J. Rowland, "Nuclear Magnetic Resonance in Copper Alloys. Electron Distribution Around Solute Atoms," *Phys. Rev.*, **119**: 900–912 (1960).

W. Kohn and S. H. Vosko, "Theory of Nuclear Resonance Intensity in Dilute Alloys," *Phys. Rev.*, **119**: 912–918 (1960).

T. P. Das and M. Pomerantz, "Nuclear Quadrupole Interaction in Pure Metals," *Phys. Rev.*, **123**: 2070 (1961).

T. Kushida, G. Benedek, and N. Bloembergen, "Dependence of Pure Quadrupole Resonance Frequency on Pressure and Temperature," *Phys. Rev.*, **104**: 1364 (1956).

Chemical Shifts

W. G. Proctor and F. C. Yu, "The Dependence of a Nuclear Magnetic Resonance Frequency upon Chemical Compound," *Phys. Rev.*, **77**: 717 (1950).

W. C. Dickinson, "Dependence of the F^{19} Nuclear Resonance Position on Chemical Compound," *Phys. Rev.*, **77**: 736 (1950).

H. S. Gutowsky and C. J. Hoffman, "Chemical Shifts in the Magnetic Resonance of F^{19}," *Phys. Rev.*, **80**: 110–111 (1950) (letter).

N. F. Ramsey, "Magnetic Shielding of Nuclei in Molecules," *Phys. Rev.*, **78**: 699–703 (1950).

N. F. Ramsey, "Chemical Effects in Nuclear Magnetic Resonance and in Diamagnetic Susceptibility," *Phys. Rev.*, **86**: 243–246 (1952).

A. Saika and C. P. Slichter, "A Note on the Fluorine Resonance Shifts," *J. Chem. Phys.*, **22**: 26–28 (1954).

J. A. Pople, "The Theory of Chemical Shifts in Nuclear Magnetic Resonance I — Induced Current Densities," *Proc. Roy. Soc.*, **A239**: 541–549 (1957).

J. A. Pople, "The Theory of Chemical Shifts in Nuclear Magnetic Resonance II — Interpretation of Proton Shifts," *Proc. Roy. Soc.* (London), **A239**: 550–556 (1957).

H. M. McConnell, "Theory of Nuclear Magnetic Shielding in Molecules I — Long-range Dipolar Shielding of Protons," *J. Chem. Phys.*, **27**: 226–229 (1957).

R. Freeman, G. Murray, and R. Richards, "Cobalt Nuclear Resonance Spectra," *Proc. Roy. Soc.*, **242A**: 455 (1957).

Spin Temperature

N. Bloembergen, "On the Interaction of Nuclear Spins in a Crystalline Lattice," *Physica*, **15**: 386–426 (1949).

E. M. Purcell and R. V. Pound, "A Nuclear Spin System at Negative Temperature," *Phys. Rev.*, **81**: 279–280 (1951) (letter).

A. Abragam and W. G. Proctor, "Experiments on Spin Temperature," *Phys. Rev.*, **106**: 160–161 (1957) (letter).

A. Abragam and W. G. Proctor, "Spin Temperature," *Phys. Rev.*, **109**: 1441–1458 (1958).

Alfred G. Redfield, "Nuclear Magnetic Resonance Saturation and Rotary Saturation in Solids," *Phys. Rev.*, **98**: 1787–1809 (1955).

Alfred G. Redfield, "Nuclear Spin-Lattice Relaxation Time in Copper and Aluminum," *Phys. Rev.*, **101**: 67–68 (1956).

C. P. Slichter and W. C. Holton, "Adiabatic Demagnetization in a Rotating Reference System," *Phys. Rev.*, **122**: 1701–1708 (1961).

A. G. Anderson and A. G. Redfield, "Nuclear Spin-Lattice Relaxation in Metals," *Phys. Rev.*, **116**: 583–591 (1959).

L. C. Hebel and C. P. Slichter, "Nuclear Spin Relaxation in Normal and Superconducting Aluminum," *Phys. Rev.*, **113**: 1504–1519 (1959).

A. Anderson, "Nonresonant Nuclear Spin Absorption in Li, Na, and Al," *Phys. Rev.*, **115**: 863 (1959).

Rate Effects

H. S. Gutowsky and A. Saika, "Dissociation, Chemical Exchange, and the Proton Magnetic Resonance in Some Aqueous Electrolytes," *J. Chem. Phys.*, **21**: 1688–1694 (1953).

James T. Arnold, "Magnetic Resonances of Protons in Ethyl Alcohol," *Phys. Rev.*, **102**: 136–150 (1956).

R. Kubo, "Note on the Stochastic Theory of Resonance Absorption," *J. Phys. Soc. Japan*, **9**: 935–944 (1954).

H. M. McConnell, "Reaction Rates by Nuclear Magnetic Resonance," *J. Chem. Phys.*, **28**: 430–431 (1958).

S. Meiboom, Z. Luz, and D. Gill, "Proton Relaxation in Water," *J. Chem. Phys.*, **27**: 1411–1412 (1957) (letter).

Cross-Relaxation

N. Bloembergen, S. Shapiro, P. S. Pershan, and J. O. Artman, "Cross-Relaxation in Spin Systems," *Phys. Rev.*, **114**: 445–459 (1959).

P. S. Pershan, "Cross Relaxation in LiF," *Phys. Rev.*, **117**: 109–116 (1960).

Electron Spin Resonance in Paramagnetic Systems

B. Bleaney and K. W. H. Stevens, "Paramagnetic Resonance," *Repts. Prog. in Phys.* **XVI**: 108–159 (1953).

T. G. Castner and W. Känzig, "The Electronic Structure of *V*-Centers," *J. Phys. Chem. Solids*, **3**: 178–195 (1957).

G. D. Watkins, "Electron Spin Resonance of Mn^{++} in Alkali Chlorides: Association with Vacancies and Impurities," *Phys. Rev.*, **113**: 79–90 (1959).

G. D. Watkins, "Motion of Mn^{++}-Cation Vacancy Pairs in NaCl: Study by Electron Spin Resonance and Dielectric Loss," *Phys. Rev.*, **113**: 91–97 (1959).

G. Feher, "Observation of Nuclear Magnetic Resonances via the Electron Spin Resonance Line," *Phys. Rev.*, **103**: 834–835 (1956).

G. Feher, "Electronic Structure of F Centers in KCl by the Electron Spin Double Resonance Technique," *Phys. Rev.*, **105**: 1122–1123 (1957).

G. Feher, "Electron Spin Resonance Experiments on Donors in Silicon I — Electronic Structure of Donors by the Electron Nuclear Double Resonance Technique," *Phys. Rev.*, **114**: 1219–1244 (1959).

H. H. Woodbury and G. W. Ludwig, "Spin Resonance of Transition Metals in Silicon," *Phys. Rev.*, **117**: 102–108 (1960).

A. F. Kip, C. Kittel, R. A. Levy, and A. M. Portis, "Electronic Structure of F Centers: Hyperfine Interactions in Electron Spin Resonance," *Phys. Rev.*, **91**: 1066–1071 (1953).

C. J. Delbecq, B. Smaller, and P. H. Yuster, "Optical Absorption of Cl_2^- Molecule-Ions in Irradiated Potassium Chloride," *Phys. Rev.*, **111**: 1235–1240 (1958).

M. Weger, "Passage Effects in Paramagnetic Resonance Experiments," *Bell System Tech. J.*, **39**: 1013–1112 (1960) (Monograph 3663).

George Feher and A. F. Kip, "Electron Spin Resonance Absorption in Metals I — Experimental," *Phys. Rev.*, **98**: 337–348 (1955).

Nuclear Resonance in Ferromagnets

A. M. Portis and A. C. Gossard, "Nuclear Resonance in Ferromagnetic Cobalt," *J. Appl. Phys.*, **31**: 205S–213S (1960).

W. Marshall, "Orientation of Nuclei in Ferromagnets," *Phys. Rev.*, **110**: 1280–1285 (1958).

R. E. Watson and A. J. Freeman, "Origin of Effective Fields in Magnetic Materials," *Phys. Rev.*, **123**: 2027–2047 (1961).

G. Benedek and J. Armstrong, "The Pressure and Temperature Dependence of the Fe^{57} Nuclear Magnetic Resonance Frequency in Ferromagnetic Iron," *J. Appl. Phys.*, **32**: 1065 (1961).

Nuclear Resonance in Paramagnetic and Antiferromagnetic Substances

N. Bloembergen, "Fine Structure of the Magnetic Resonance Line of Protons in $CuSO_4 \cdot 5H_2O$," *Physica*, **16**: 95 (1950).

N. J. Poulis and G. E. G. Handeman, "The Temperature Dependence of the Spontaneous Magnetization in an Antiferromagnetic Single Crystal," *Physica*, **19**: 391 (1953).

R. G. Shulman and V. Jaccarino, "Nuclear Magnetic Resonance in Paramagnetic MnF_2," *Phys. Rev.*, **108**: 1219 (1957).

N. Jaccarino and R. G. Shulman, "Observation of Nuclear Magnetic Resonance in Antiferromagnetic MnF_2," *Phys. Rev.*, **107**: 1196 (1957).

G. Benedek and T. Kushida, *Phys. Rev.*, **118**: 46 (1960).

W. Marshall and R. N. Stuart, "Theory of Transition Ion Complexes," *Phys. Rev.*, **123**: 2048 (1961).

Ferromagnetic Resonance

B. Lax and K. Button, *Microwave Ferrites and Ferrimagnets*. New York: McGraw-Hill Book Co., Inc., 1962.

INDEX